G000230029

PLANTS FOR BEES

W.D.J. KIRK & F.N. HOWES

PLANTS FOR BEES

W.D.J. KIRK & F.N. HOWES

A Guide to the Plants that Benefit the Bees
of the British Isles

CONTENTS

ACKNOWLEDGEMENTS

We thank John D. Howes for generously granting permission for us to use, edit and update much of the text of his father's enduringly popular book *Plants and Beekeeping*, which was originally published in 1945 and then came out as a second edition in 1979. Beekeepers still ask for the book today, 65 years after it was originally published!

The following photographers kindly donated their work: Jane V. Adams, Janet Craig, Jeremy P. Early, Will George, Leslie Hebdon, Louise A. Hislop, Thomas C. Ings, Nigel P. Jones, Maria A. Kirk, William D. J. Kirk, Marek Kucharczyk, David Magnier, Christopher O'Toole, Nick W. Owens, David R. Skingsley, Carole Stevens, Peter A. Thomas, Robin Williams and John F. Wright. BCP Certis supplied a photograph of a bumblebee hive. All the photographs of pollen grains were taken by William D. J. Kirk. We thank Cambridge University Botanic Garden and Bridgemere Nursery and Garden World for granting permission to photograph plants. We thank the following people for assistance with locating plants: Wally Gampl, Marianne Märkl, Clare Sampson and Peter Thomas.

We gratefully acknowledge help with bee identification from Dr Thomas C. Ings (Queen Mary University of London) and Nigel P. Jones, help with plant identification from Dr Peter A. Thomas (Keele University) and help with hoverfly identification from David W. Emley (Keele University). We thank George Else for allowing us access to his unpublished checklist of bees of the British Isles.

FOREWORD

Bees are not just beautiful and fascinating to watch, they are also vital pollinators of many of our food crops. The recent dramatic decline in bee numbers has highlighted the extent to which our bees are struggling and need our help. Bees are battling with parasites, diseases, changes in farming practices, pesticides, loss of wild flowers and poor summers. Surprisingly, some bees are doing better in cities than in the countryside because the rich variety of flowers that is planted in gardens is providing plenty of year-round food for bees. This shows that we can all help bees, wherever we live.

An easy way to help is by planting a range of the best plants. This can make an enormous difference, not just to honeybees, but to bumblebees and the hundreds of species of solitary bee. There is always room for a bee-friendly plant, even if it is just on a balcony or in a window box.

This book provides detailed and authoritative information to help select the plants that help the different types of bee. Superb photos of bees visiting flowers illustrate what we can hope to see when we create a bee-friendly garden.

Let us all do what we can to ensure that future generations can continue to enjoy and benefit from a rich diversity of bees in our gardens and countryside.

Kate Humble
(television presenter and beekeeper)

CHAPTER ONE

WHY BEES NEED HELP

NORMAN L. CARRECK

International Bee Research Association, Cardiff, UK and University of Sussex, UK

This is a book about plants and their relationships with bees, so we need to begin by considering what bees are. There are about 25,000 species of bee found in the world, and around 270 species have been recorded from the British Isles. Of these, there is one species of honeybee (*Apis mellifera*), 27 species of bumblebee (*Bombus* species) and the remainder are solitary bees. These groups will be covered in more detail in Chapters 2–4.

Left:
*Honeybee visiting blackberry (*Rubus fruticosus*)*
(photo: C. Stevens)

Bees are a group of insects closely related to ants and wasps in the scientific order Hymenoptera and it is thought that the common ancestor of both bees and social wasps was a kind of solitary wasp that was predatory on other small creatures and lived in the Cretaceous Period (146 million to 66 million years ago). In that period, when dinosaurs ruled the earth, flowering plants (angiosperms) began to appear, and it was at this time that some of these common–ancestor wasps became vegetarian and began to exploit the resources provided by this new type of plant. These vegetarian solitary wasps evolved to become bees. To begin with, all of these early bees still led solitary lives, each female bee making an individual nest, which she then provisioned with nectar and pollen collected from flowers as food for her developing young. Many bee species do this to this day, but some bees began to colonise good nesting locations in large numbers, forming aggregations, some then making common burrows (see Chapter 4). Eventually, some species developed a social lifestyle, with a dominant female laying eggs, supported by partially developed 'worker' females in the summer. This social behaviour is characterised by the bumblebees (see Chapter 3). A few species took this sociality even further, developing large colonies, which exist all year round, and produce a surplus of honey. Our honeybee, native to Europe, Asia and Africa, has been exploited by man for many thousands of years, and has been transported to all remaining parts of the world (see Chapter 2).

The Value of Bees

When considering the value of bees, we immediately think of honey, and perhaps other hive products such as beeswax, propolis and royal jelly, but this only applies to honeybees. All bees are, however, of vital importance because of the intimate relationship that they have with flowering plants. Bees need plants, and many plants need bees. Many flowering plants depend on insects for pollination – the process of transfer of pollen from the male to the female parts of the flower in order to effect fertilisation to set seed. In return for this service, many flowers produce excess pollen and/or nectar as a reward.

Many commercially grown agricultural and horticultural crops depend to varying degrees on insect pollination to produce the seeds, fruits and nuts that we eat, and many other crops that we grow for the vegetative parts, such as leaves and roots, also require insect pollination to produce seed. It is often said that the human race would perish without bees. This is not true, as many of the world's staple food crops such as wheat, maize and rice are wind pollinated and therefore do not require insect pollination, but many of the foods that make eating a pleasure, such as fruits and nuts, do require insect pollination, and bees are the most important group of insect pollinators. Without bees, therefore, man would have a very boring diet and, furthermore, our gardens would be very dull since many ornamental plants also require insect pollination to set seed.

It is possible to make estimates of the economic importance of bees in terms of the production of commercial crops. Recent estimates have suggested that the annual contribution of bees worldwide may be US\$217 billion. For the UK, recent estimates suggest the annual value of bee pollination of agricultural crops is approximately £200 million per year at 'farm gate' prices, and nearly £1 billion at the supermarket checkout. For many years honeybees have been deliberately managed for crop pollination, as their large colonies and habit of nesting in convenient wooden boxes makes them very easy to transport. This has been developed as a vast industry in certain countries, notably in the USA, where the multibillion dollar almond industry depends absolutely on bee

Above:
A commercial apple orchard in bloom
(photo: W. D. J. Kirk)

pollination, leading to thousands of honeybee colonies being transported thousands of miles on a regular basis. In economic terms, the most important bee-pollinated crops in the British Isles are (in descending order) apples, oilseed rape, raspberries, strawberries, runner and dwarf beans (*Phaseolus* species), and field beans. Honeybees are not, however, the best pollinators of all crops, and nowadays glasshouse-grown crops such as tomatoes and sweet peppers are pollinated by commercially reared bumblebee colonies, mainly buff-tailed bumblebees (*Bombus terrestris*). The management of solitary bees is less well developed, but in North America the alfalfa leafcutter bee (*Megachile rotundata*) is produced commercially for field pollination, and trials of other solitary bee species for orchard and other crops have taken place in recent years (see Chapter 4).

What cannot be measured in economic terms, however, is the value of bees as pollinators of our wild plants. In many cases the relationships between bees and wild flowers have not been studied in detail, but what is known is that many of our rare and threatened species of wild plants are insect pollinated. It is also known that many wild plant species may be pollinated by only a limited range of bees. If these bees are rare or threatened too, this can lead to a downward spiral. In extreme circumstances, if a rare plant species depends on just one rare bee species, and this were to become extinct, a perennial plant may fail to set seed for many years before anybody noticed the problem, by which time it may be too late to save either the bee or the plant.

Above:
A commercial bumblebee hive for crop pollination, containing the British Isles subspecies of the buff-tailed bumblebee (Bombus terrestris audax) *(photo: BCP Certis)*

The Decline of Bees

In recent years the world's headlines have been full of reports of the decline of bees, particularly the phenomenon of 'Colony Collapse Disorder' of honeybee colonies in the USA. While it is encouraging that governments and the public are becoming more aware of the problem and are willing to take some action, the situation is more complicated than it might at first appear.

Which bees are declining?

It is known that all groups of bees found in the world have suffered declines, but information is often lacking, and some bees have suffered more serious declines than others. Because of their economic importance, honeybees have been relatively well studied, and long-term declines have been documented in many parts of the world. In the British Isles, although honeybees are still common, their population may have declined by as much as 75% over the last century. In the case of our bumblebees, one species has been confirmed as extinct in recent years, and others are seriously threatened. Work carried out in the 1980s established that in the large central area of England, dominated by agricultural crops, only six common bumblebee species are now found, although others were common in these areas earlier in the 20th century. Rare bumblebee species have often become restricted to coastal areas because these are less dominated by intensive agriculture, particularly on the southern English coastline and on small Scottish islands. As discussed in Chapter 3, however, the common bumblebee species remain common, some have expanded their range, and one new species has recently been found in England. In the case of solitary bees, information about many species is lacking, but we do know that a number of species recorded many years ago have not been found recently, and many others are known to have become very scarce or endangered.

Why are they declining?

Bees are insects, and the general public, especially gardeners, are aware that one characteristic of insect populations is that they fluctuate widely from year to year, causing pest problems one year and not the next. Bees are no exception to this fluctuation, but there is good evidence that bee declines have become more severe, sometimes catastrophic, in recent years. The great publicity that the phenomenon of these bee declines has produced has led to many suggestions as to the causes being proposed, and much research work has been carried out throughout the world. Many of these suggestions such as mobile phones, nanotechnology, sunspots or alien abduction can be swiftly dismissed as fanciful or unlikely. Scientific consensus is, however, forming that there is unlikely to be one single universal cause, but there are almost certainly a number of factors working together. Furthermore, the same factors may not apply to all types of bee, and when considering a single species such as the honeybee, the same cause may not apply in all parts of the world, or even within a single country such as the USA.

One factor that can be demonstrated conclusively is the effects of pests and diseases. For many years it has been known that bees suffer from a number of these but they seem to have become more important in recent years. This phenomenon is almost certainly influenced by man-made bee movement, whether accidental or deliberate, exposing isolated bee populations to new pests and diseases, or to foreign strains of commonly occurring diseases. It is also likely that pests and diseases may interact with some of the other factors discussed below, and become more serious than they were formerly.

Pests and diseases of honeybees have been well studied and much is known, although much still remains to be discovered. Interest in the pests and diseases of bumblebees has recently greatly increased, but those of solitary bees, with a few exceptions, are very poorly studied or understood.

Well-documented historic losses of honeybee colonies are thought to have been due to bacterial diseases such as American and European foulbrood, which are now under statutory control in many countries, and in the UK are treated using antibiotics or by the destruction of infected colonies. A parasitic mite (*Acarapis woodi*) that lives in the breathing tubes of bees was blamed for serious losses in the British Isles 100 years ago and in North America more recently, but this is hard to prove. A gut parasite (*Nosema apis*) has been known to be present for many years, but more recently a new species (*Nosema ceranae*) has emerged and has been blamed, especially by researchers in Spain, for extensive colony losses. Viruses are undoubtedly of great importance, and the development of new molecular analytical techniques has recently made their study much easier. 'Colony Collapse Disorder' in the USA is almost certainly associated with viruses, although the picture is far from clear, and other factors must be involved.

The most serious pest of honeybees worldwide is, however, another mite, this time living on the body of the bee, called varroa (*Varroa destructor*). This can live on adult bees, sucking their blood, but enters the brood cells to reproduce, feeding off the developing bee pupae, emerging with the bee to repeat the cycle until a bee colony may contain many thousands of mites. Although the mite itself seems to cause little damage, its feeding on the bees' blood leads it to unwittingly transmit naturally occurring honeybee viruses from bee to bee, and crucially from pupae to adults and vice versa. Viruses that normally exist in the bee population at a very low level, causing little or no harm, can thus be introduced simultaneously throughout the honeybee colony, leading to the often spectacular collapse of an apparently vigorous colony within a matter of days.

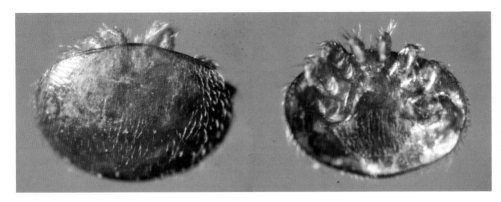

Left:
Upperside and
underside of a
varroa mite, which
is about 2 mm wide
(photo: W. D. J. Kirk)

Varroa has spread in the last 60 years from the far east of Russia and is now found throughout the world apart from Australia. Extensive honeybee colony losses have been reported from all parts of the northern hemisphere where the mite is found. The native honeybees of Africa seem to be naturally resistant to the mite, and these bees were imported into South America in the 1950s to increase honey production, with the result that varroa is much less of a problem in the southern hemisphere. However, these bees also have the disadvantage that they can be very aggressive. Many treatments for varroa have been developed, mainly using chemicals, but the mite has already become resistant to some of the best of these, rendering them useless, and in many parts of the world few reliable treatments are available. It is generally agreed that the ideal solution is to breed resistant bees or develop biological control using, for example, fungi, but progress has been slow. Inadequate control of varroa is almost certainly the major cause of honeybee colony loss in the British Isles.

Climate change is frequently mentioned as a cause of bee decline, and will undoubtedly have some effects on bee populations, but these are difficult to quantify. These effects are likely to be indirect, mainly by changing natural vegetation or the range of crops that can be grown in a given area, but changing weather patterns could also affect the ability of particular species to survive winter weather. As mentioned already, there is evidence that some bumblebee species, such as the tree bumblebee (*Bombus hypnorum*), and solitary bees, such as the violet carpenter bee (*Xylocopa violacea*), have recently expanded their ranges, possibly for this reason, but there could also be adverse effects.

The development of genetically modified (GM) crops throughout the world has proved controversial, and there have been concerns that they could cause harm to bees. Insect-resistant GM crops certainly have the potential to be harmful to bees, but considerable testing takes place before crops are grown commercially, and despite GM crops being grown extensively in all continents except for Europe, there remains no evidence that the varieties currently grown are harmful to bees.

Conventional insecticides on the other hand, being designed to kill insects, and often applied by spraying in an indiscriminate fashion, have caused extensive problems to bees at various times and places. The use of organochlorine and organophosphorus compounds for insect control, particularly on newly-grown crops such as oilseed rape in the British Isles in the 1970s, caused spectacular and well-documented losses of honeybees, leading to much concern by beekeepers and the establishment of monitoring schemes. The replacement of these compounds with more benign chemicals such as the synthetic pyrethroids led to a dramatic decline in poisoning incidents, and there has not been a proven case of honeybee colony poisoning due to the authorised use of an agricultural pesticide in the UK for many years.

This is not, however, the end of the story: the pyrethroids have now become less effective because pests have developed resistance to them, and they have, in turn, been replaced by newer classes of insecticide, in particular, compounds known as neonicotinoids. One particular chemical, imidacloprid, marketed as 'Gaucho', was blamed by French beekeepers for extensive losses of honeybee colonies foraging on sunflowers in the 1990s. Although scientific studies have failed to confirm this, attention was drawn to the different mode of action of these new chemicals. Instead of being sprayed on the plant, these so-called 'systemic' compounds are often used as a seed dressing, being taken up by the plant and being present in the sap and thus particularly effective against sucking insects. This raises the question of whether the compounds could be present in nectar and pollen, and harm bees in this way. Recent work suggests that exposure to these compounds may affect homing in honeybees and queen production in bumblebee colonies. Further studies are under way, and the subject remains controversial, but these compounds may act in subtle ways, possibly interacting with pests and diseases. What is clear is that the testing procedures, intended to test direct toxic effects on bees, may not be appropriate to evaluate long-term sub-lethal effects. Furthermore, the testing procedures considered only honeybees for many years, but bumblebees may not react to individual chemicals in the same way, and solitary bees have been totally ignored. Honeybees and bumblebees tend to forage at different times of the day. For example, the peak of honeybee foraging occurs in the warmest middle part of the day, so for many years the advice to growers has been to spray early in the morning or late in the evening to avoid damage to honeybees, but these are precisely the times when bumblebees will be foraging. Procedures are now being changed to take account of all bees, but it is likely that the use of insecticides has harmed bee populations, although this is difficult to quantify.

Below:
Pastures with flowers in them are now a rare sight
(photo: M. A. Kirk)

Other agricultural chemicals that are not directly toxic to bees, such as herbicides, may nonetheless have adverse effects by removing weeds from arable crops that would normally flower and provide forage. Some of our rarest wild plants such as the corncockle (*Agrostemma githago*) were formerly agricultural weeds. Similarly, the use of large quantities of nitrogen fertilisers applied to grassland, while harmless in itself, causes grasses to crowd out flowering clover (*Trifolium* species), which rapidly disappears.

This has brought us to the most important factor in bee decline, namely changes in land use. These have occurred worldwide, but in the British Isles, the agricultural landscape, which had remained relatively unchanged for centuries, was dramatically changed in the few decades after the Second World War. Food shortages led to a push for agricultural production at all costs, with subsidies for food production and 'improvements' such as hedgerow removal, drainage of wetland, ploughing of ancient pasture, moorland and heathland. Agricultural production became more intensive, with heavily fertilised arable crops treated with agrochemicals, and improved pasture managed with nitrogen for silage production for intensively reared livestock. This had the effect of both reducing the availability of forage for all bees, and removing nesting sites for many bee species, as discussed below.

These land use changes have resulted in a vicious circle. For farmers growing insect-pollinated crops, if managed bees decline, their crops set less seed. They can then switch to growing other crops that do not need pollination, but which provide less forage, exacerbating bee decline and reducing the viability of beekeeping, leading to beekeepers giving up keeping bees. For wild plants, fewer bees means plants setting less seed, which in turn leads to a decline in wild flowers, leading to less forage for bees, leading to a decline of other bee species. It is thus easy to see why bee declines have occurred in this environment.

Fortunately, recent years have seen some reversal of these trends, with growing interest in organic farming systems, and 'extensification', with Countryside Stewardship Schemes promoting the reinstatement of hedgerows and other landscape features, and the introduction of forage nectar and pollen mixtures, sometimes specifically tailored for bees and butterflies. There are, however, questions as to whether these mixtures are suited to all bee species, and whether they truly benefit pollinator populations in the long term.

What Do Bees Need?

All bee species need three fundamental things: nest sites; pollen, for protein food; and nectar for carbohydrate food. They cannot thrive with only one or two of these three things in a given location – all are essential. Nesting requirements vary between species. Honeybees naturally nest in cavities such as hollow trees, but man-made structures such as cavity walls, chimneys and purpose-built hives are all suitable (see Chapter 2). Bumblebees have a range of preferred nest sites, usually just under or just above the earth, and tussocky unmanaged grassland, the base of hedgerows and field and woodland edges provide suitable habitat (see Chapter 3). Solitary bees nest in holes, often in the ground, but also in hollow stems, and in holes bored in wood, soft stone or even the walls of houses. Ground-nesting species tend to require bare soil, preferably well drained, and may be seen nesting in large numbers in sunny flower beds or paths (see Chapter 4).

The Value of Pollen and Nectar to Bees

Pollen is produced by the anthers of flowers (see Figure 2.2 on p.18 and the glossary on p.290). Pollen production may vary considerably at different times of the day and under different weather conditions. Pollen contains about 6–28% protein, but also contains 1–20% fats, together with sterols, sugars, starches, vitamins and minerals in small quantities. The value of the pollen to the plant is that it contains the male gametes, the genetic material necessary for seed setting. To the bee, pollen provides protein for growth of developing larvae. Adult bees themselves require little protein, but need it to feed their brood. Some

solitary bees simply collect pollen and mix it with nectar, but worker honeybees consume pollen and secrete 'brood food', which they feed to larvae. It has been estimated that a single worker honeybee larva may require 125–145 mg of pollen, containing about 30 mg protein, and that a normal size honeybee colony may require 15–55 kg of pollen per year.

Nectar is a solution of various sugars, at a concentration of 5–80% depending on the plant species. It also contains small quantities of proteins, minerals, organic acids, vitamins and other substances. It is generally produced by nectaries inside the flower at the base, but in some plants it is also produced by extrafloral nectaries, which can occur outside the flower at the base or on stipules (small leaf-like structures at the base of leaf stalks) or other locations. Nectar secretion may also vary widely throughout the day, and be affected by such external factors as weather conditions and soil type influencing water availability to the plant. Nectar provides the carbohydrate component of the bee diet, to provide energy. As with pollen, many bee species use nectar directly as it comes from flowers, but honeybees turn it into honey by adding enzymes to alter the sugar composition, and evaporate much of the moisture (see Chapter 2). A honeybee colony may need as much as 120 kg of nectar per year, mainly in order to maintain the colony through the winter when foraging is not possible. In contrast, bumblebee colonies require much less, as the peak of the colony is short-lived, and solitary bees require much less still.

The Value of Different Plant Groups

Chapter 5 discusses individual plant species in detail, but plants can be broken down into a number of basic groups, which affect their value for bees. No single plant will suit all bees. As discussed in Chapter 3, the length of the tongue varies considerably between bee species. Some bumblebees have long tongues, other bumblebees and honeybees have short tongues and solitary bees tend to have even shorter tongues – some very short indeed. In order to provide food for all bees a range of flower types is therefore needed. Long-tongued bees are suited to the pea family (Fabaceae) with their complex flowers, while in contrast solitary bees require simple open flowers such as those found in the daisy family (Asteraceae).

Top left:
Complex flowers in the pea family (Fabaceae) are suited to long-tongued bees

Bottom left:
Simple open flowers in the daisy family (Asteraceae) are suited to solitary bees
(photos: W. D. J. Kirk)

Annuals

Annual plants may produce considerable quantities of both nectar and pollen, but due to their life cycle will not flower early in the season, so cannot contribute much to the early build up of bee colonies. On the other hand, bee species which undergo their entire life cycle in a short summer period may particularly benefit from annual species.

Perennials

Perennial herbaceous plants, in contrast, often have storage structures such as bulbs, corms and tubers that enable them to grow and flower very early in the season and provide spring food for honeybee colonies and for bumblebee queens emerging from hibernation. Trees are also often overlooked as bee forage plants, but due to their extensive root systems can produce enormous quantities of nectar. The vogue for planting large flowering trees such as lime (*Tilia* species) in towns and cities has led to the success of suburban and urban beekeeping. Sadly, magnificent mature trees are often nowadays felled for 'health and safety' reasons and replaced with unsuitable smaller species, which provide little food for bees.

Wild flowers

Prior to the development of agriculture by man, wild flowers would have provided the only food source for bees, and they remain important today. Beekeepers tend to dismiss them as food sources because an individual plant species rarely occurs in sufficient quantity to produce a recognisable honey surplus, but many honey crops will contain nectar from many wild flower sources. Plants such as heather (*Calluna vulgaris*) and heath (*Erica* species) are exceptions and are prized for honey production.

Arable and horticultural crops

As mentioned above, many crops depend on insects for pollination, but they differ in their usefulness for bees. For example, orchard crops such as apples and pears are totally dependent on insect pollination – without insects they will not set fruit. The reward to the bee is less clear, however, as these trees tend to produce nectar with a very low sugar concentration, so if bees have to travel a long distance to an orchard, they will expend more energy in flight than they can bring back in nectar. For this reason, growers of tree fruit crops usually pay beekeepers to bring their honeybee colonies directly into the orchard, to ensure adequate pollination, but the beekeeper may gain little if any honey. In contrast,

Below:
An oilseed rape
crop in bloom
(photo: M. A. Kirk)

oilseed rape produces nectar with a high sugar concentration, and honeybees will fly several kilometres to reach it. The crop itself has little reliance on insect pollination, since it will eventually set seed itself, but insect pollination results in more even ripening and higher yields to the farmer. Because a beekeeper placing his or her hives close to an oilseed rape crop will obtain a significant yield of honey, money rarely changes hands in such situations. The land use changes mentioned above have been reflected in the most important nectar sources reported by beekeepers. Prior to the Second World War, beekeeping books listed white clover (*Trifolium repens*) as the most important honey plant; now it is oilseed rape.

Ornamental plants

Ornamental plants have been deliberately bred for visual characteristics, scent or husbandry factors such as cold or drought tolerance. Pollen production and nectar secretion are rarely, if ever, considered as selection criteria, and sadly many highly-bred ornamental plants are of little value to bees. Some may yield no pollen or nectar, even if their wild relatives do so in profusion, and structural changes, such as the presence of additional petals in 'double' flowers may render any nectar or pollen entirely inaccessible to bees. This is discussed in more detail in relation to individual species in Chapter 5.

Top left:
*A double-flowered
dahlia offering no
nectar or pollen for
bees*

Bottom left:
*A single-flowered
dahlia with
plentiful nectar and
pollen for bees*
(photos: W. D. J. Kirk)

CHAPTER TWO

PLANTS FOR HONEYBEES

DAVID ASTON[1] AND SALLY BUCKNALL[2]

[1] *Master Beekeeper, holder of the National Diploma in Beekeeping and Chair of the British Beekeepers' Association*
[2] *Biologist, author and Trustee of Garden Organic*

This chapter describes the complex interaction between plants and honeybees, how honeybees live and why honeybees need plants and plants need bees. It also discusses the relationship that humans have with honeybees, how important they are in our lives and how we can help them to survive and thrive.

What is a Honeybee?

Left:
*Honeybee on anise hyssop (*Agastache foeniculum*)*
(photo: W. D. J. Kirk)

Most people will have seen honeybees flying among summer flowers but many will not notice that among these bees there are many different kinds. Honeybees look much like other bees and can be confused with the 24 species of bumblebee and 230 or so species of solitary bee living in the British Isles, but as there is only one honeybee species throughout Europe, America and Australasia, identification is easy (although the colour of the bands on their body does vary from dark yellow to black). Honeybees are thought to have originated in Southern Asia and a few other species are found there. All honeybee species belong to the genus *Apis* and the one familiar to us in the British Isles has the scientific Latin name *Apis mellifera* (*Apis* = bee, *mellifera* = honey-producing). It is also sometimes called the 'western honeybee' to distinguish it from the other honeybee species found in Asia.

Honeybees have some unique features. Unlike other kinds of bee they use beeswax to build long-lasting nests of honeycomb in which they can store enough honey to enable them to survive through summers when forage is short and hard winters when the weather is too cold for them to fly and forage for nectar. They also have an advantage over other bees through their ability to conserve heat and survive long periods of cold weather by forming tight clusters of interlocking bees around the frames containing their winter stores. During the middle of winter a healthy colony may contain around 10–12,000 bees. They are quiescent, i.e. not very active and they cluster over the frames, only moving to access their food stores or seek warmth by moving from the outside of the cluster into its warmer centre.

Bees continue to need energy in the winter months to keep them alive and to prevent the bees on the outside of the cluster and in the outer layers of the cluster becoming too cold to hold on. If they fall from the cluster they will die of cold and starvation. During the summer, colonies may contain as many as 50–60,000 bees. Figure 2.1 shows the number of adult bees and brood, i.e. eggs and larvae found in a colony that has not swarmed during the current year.

Figure 2.1. Number of adult bees and brood in the colony population through the year in the British Isles

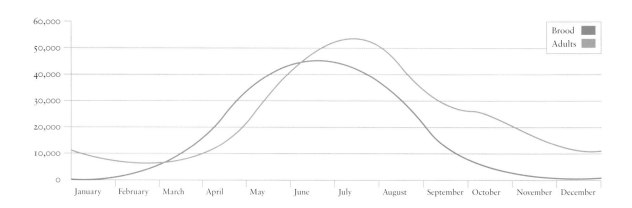

Our Relationship with Honeybees

The relationship between humans and honeybees is thousands of years old. The earliest known hunters and gatherers of wild honey lived in the Middle Stone Age between around 280,000 and 50–25,000 years BP when wild colonies lived in rock crevices and tree cavities often difficult to access by predators including humans. From around 10,000 BP, hunter-gatherers in some areas had begun to establish settled communities and, if a swarm of wild honeybees chose homes in the baskets and pots of the community, it could only have been a short step to 'managing' them and this may be how the skill of beekeeping developed. However, it was only in the middle of the 19th century that wooden beehives with moveable frames, similar to those we use today, were invented.

How Honeybees Live

Honeybees live in complex social groups called colonies. Wild or feral colonies will make their nests in hollow trees or rock cavities, but in the British Isles there are now very few wild honeybees. The principal cause of this is the previously mentioned parasitic varroa mite (*Varroa destructor*) and the damaging bee viruses it can transmit. Once these mites access a wild colony it is not likely to survive more than 2–3 years. Today, most honeybees are kept in wooden or plastic hives and managed by beekeepers who monitor the colonies for various diseases and conditions and, through a mixture of husbandry and medication, help them to survive and stay healthy. However, despite this care it is important to remember that they are wild creatures and the beekeeper needs to understand their requirements and work with them for successful beekeeping.

Above:
A beekeeper
inspecting a colony
(photo: D. Magnier)

For most of the year the colony consists of a single queen who specialises in egg production, laying her eggs in hexagonal cells made of beeswax. In the British Isles, she lays eggs from January until late autumn, which develop into female worker bees. During the spring and early summer months she will also lay eggs that develop into male bees called drones. Their main function is to mate in flight with young queens produced by the colonies usually as a result of swarming. This is the natural method of honeybee colony reproduction as the first swarm of the season will establish itself as a new colony containing the old queen away from the parent site, while in the original colony a new mated queen will become established. The original colony may produce several virgin queens each of which, if not killed by the worker bees or the strongest virgin queen, will leave the colony with small swarms of bees called casts. If conditions are right these will establish new colonies.

The worker bees are beautifully adapted to perform the wide range of tasks needed for the colony to survive, these include cleaning the hive, feeding young, tending the queen, producing wax, processing nectar to store as honey, processing pollen for protein reserves, guarding the hive and, in the last quarter of their lives, foraging for nectar, pollen and propolis (resinous material collected by bees from plants with a variety of uses, including as an antiseptic) and collecting water. As the worker bee gets older she changes her role in the colony and often the periods during which she does certain jobs overlap.

Left:
A queen bee
(marked with a spot
of blue paint) and
worker bees.
Capped honeycomb
is top left and
capped brood comb
is bottom right
(photo: D. Magnier)

Table 2.1. Changes in worker honeybee activities in the hive during her adult life

Age	Activities of the worker honeybee
0–6 days	Cell cleaning, general hive cleaning
3–9 days	Producing brood food and feeding the brood
3–15 days	Attending the queen
6–18 days	Nectar and honey processing
12–20 days	Production of wax and comb building
15–25 days	Hive ventilation
18–35 days	Guard duty – defending the colony
20 days–death	Collection of nectar
20 days–death	Collection of pollen
20 days–death	Collection of water and propolis

Below:
Empty worker comb with brown staining from propolis
(photo: W. D. J. Kirk)

Beeswax contains more than 300 different chemical components. It is produced as flakes of wax from glands arranged in pairs on the underside of the worker bee abdomen. The individual wax flakes are manipulated by the bees into tubes, which become hexagonal cells linked together to form comb. These cells are of two different sizes, small diameter ones in which the workers develop and larger diameter ones for the drones. Each hive contains between 100,000 to 200,000 cells. Honeybee combs fulfil many functions including providing places to:

- Rear brood
- Process nectar to convert it into honey
- Store honey
- Store pollen in the form of 'bee bread'.

Why Plants Need Honeybees

Flowering plants and their insect pollinators have co-evolved and are dependent on each other. Many plants contain flowers with both male parts (stamens), which produce pollen, and female parts (pistils), which receive pollen and produce seeds (see Figure 2.2). These flowers usually require pollen from a different plant to fertilise the female parts of the flower and honeybees will transfer the pollen between plants. This is called cross-pollination and also occurs when the male and female parts are on separate plants, as occurs in holly. Cross-pollination has an advantage for the plant as it maximises the amount of genetic variation in the seeds. This enables the species to respond to the process of natural selection and cope with a changing environment. Some plants use their own pollen and this is called self-pollination. In both cases once pollen has been transferred to the female parts of a plant the pollen grains will fertilise the ovules, which subsequently develop into fruits, seeds and nuts. These are then dispersed and give the plant species an increased chance of survival through colonising new areas.

Flowers need to attract bees and other plant pollinators in order to carry out pollination. Plants use a variety of interesting ways to entice pollinators to their flowers and the usual reason why bees visit flowers is to obtain nectar and pollen to eat. The flowers advertise this with large colourful petals, scent and structural modifications to help the bee to find the reward. The plant needs a bee carrying the pollen from another flower of the same species to come into contact with its stigma (see Figure 2.2), so the structure of the flower has to ensure that a bee seeking nectar will brush against the stigma, so that pollen from a previously visited flower will be dislodged onto it and there are various ways of achieving this. If pollen is being released at the same time, the visiting bee will be dusted by it and carry it to the next flower she visits.

Why Honeybees Need Plants

Flowering plants provide nectar and pollen, which are the key nutritional requirements of the honeybee. They also provide propolis, which is used by bees as an antiseptic in hive hygiene, as a water repellent, to patch up holes in the hive, and to 'mummify' other insects and small animals that are too large for the bees to remove from the hive. Honeybee colonies require pollen and nectar throughout the brood-rearing season, which, depending on the geographical location and the weather, can be January to October.

Traditionally beekeepers referred to the 'June gap', a period when spring and early summer flowers were over and main summer flowers were not yet producing nectar and pollen. This was observed throughout the British Isles and the plant species varied according to geographical location. Today the June gap is less obvious, probably because of climate change affecting the flowering period of many plants, nevertheless, honeybees may experience periods when forage availability is limited and this may be exacerbated by intensive agriculture and urban development.

Typically a colony requires about 120 kg of nectar per year to fuel growth and development during the active season, and to forage, process the nectar and store it as honey. At least 16 kg of honey stores are required to survive the winter when the bees are clustered and not producing brood.

Nectar contains many different substances, and the proportions of these vary from one flower species to another. It is a complex mixture of water and sugars, mainly sucrose (table sugar), glucose and fructose together with small quantities of nitrogenous substances, minerals, organic acids, vitamins, lipids, pigments and other aromatic substances. Honeybee colonies forage from a wide range of flowers and this will inevitably mean they collect nectar of varying composition, but the concentration of sugars in the nectar is probably a key factor in the selection and exploitation of nectar sources.

Below:
A honeybee using its tongue to feed on honey

(photo: W. D. J. Kirk)

Foraging for nectar

Nectar is produced by specialised structures called nectaries, which are located on different parts of the flower depending on the plant species. Some are found on non-floral parts of the plant and these are called extrafloral nectaries. A foraging bee learns to find the nectaries in each plant species in order to access the nectar. She collects nectar from flowers using her tongue, which is also known as a proboscis. This is a tube formed from an intricate arrangement of her complex mouthparts.

The length of the honeybee proboscis is in the range 5.7–6.8 mm (varying slightly between strains of honeybees), which facilitates access to a wide range of flowers. The honeybee will also exploit larger flowers by ignoring the front access to the flowers and utilising holes previously cut by short-tongued bumblebees to access the nectar. In some flowers such as lavender, very warm weather is necessary to stimulate nectar secretion to fill the flower tube to a high enough level for the honeybee to reach it.

Figure 2.2. A diagram of a typical flower showing the male parts (stamens) where pollen is produced and the female parts (pistil)

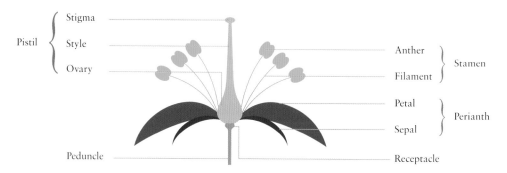

Table 2.2. Examples of the location of nectaries in different plants

The location of the nectaries	Some examples
Sepals	Lime tree
Petals	Buttercup and hellebore
Base of stamens	Runner bean
Pistil	Ivy
Base of the ovary	Dead-nettle
Extrafloral nectaries on the stipules	Broad bean and field bean

Not all nectars are the same; the type of nectar is often typical of the plant family. For example, sucrose-dominated nectars are found in the buttercup family (Ranunculaceae), glucose and fructose with small amounts of sucrose are found in the cabbage family (Brassicaceae) and the daisy family (Asteraceae) while fructose, glucose and sucrose are found in equal proportions in the pea family (Fabaceae).

Finding the forage

Some worker bees act as scouts and will explore a large area of their surroundings and return to the colonies with samples of the pollen and nectar they have obtained. The scout bees then try to interest other forager bees to investigate what they have found and its location. They communicate with interested bees through a variety of bee dances. A round dance is the simplest of dances indicating that there is a useful source of forage within 15 m of the hive and a waggle dance will communicate the direction and distance of forage further away. To date about 20 other communication signals have been reported, such as trembling, buzzing, jostling, vibrating and shaking interested bees to recruit them to go out to forage, and it is thought that there is a particular dance used to alert the workers to prepare for work in the morning. The roles of communication dances and signals in the hive are still the subject of study.

The honeybee colony is very adept at optimising, locating and exploiting forage resources. It is this ability of honeybees to be able to locate and quickly recruit additional foragers to exploit the resource that makes them so useful in terms of pollinating early crops such as apples, pears and plums when other pollinating species of insect are few in number compared to the numbers in a honeybee colony.

Foraging bees make 5–15 trips per day, the duration of which depends on many factors – the most important being the weather, forage availability and distance from the hive to the forage.

On the flight back to the hive the nectar is held in the bee's honey stomach. During the journey she secretes an enzyme called sucrase (the -ase ending denotes an enzyme), which splits the complex sucrose into the simpler sugars glucose and fructose. Back in the hive the foraging bee transfers her nectar load of between 25–40 mg to another worker who continues the process of sucrose conversion and the evaporation of water from the nectar. When all the chemical and physical changes have taken place and the processed nectar has a sugar content of about 80% it becomes honey. It is then stored in clean cells and capped with wax to prevent it deteriorating. When required, some of the bees will uncap the cells, add water to make a 50:50 honey to water mix and distribute it to others in the colony to provide the energy they need.

Honeybees are vegetarian

They obtain proteins derived from the pollen of plants to enable them to grow, develop and mature.

The typical composition of pollen includes:

- Proteins
- Lipids – essential for brood food production
- Carbohydrates and related compounds
- Major minerals, including potassium, sodium, calcium, and magnesium
- Organic acids
- Free amino acids
- Nucleic acids
- Terpenes (constituents of essential oils that give flowers their fragrance)
- Enzymes
- Vitamins B2 (riboflavin), B6 (niacin), B5 (pantothenic acid), B7 (biotin), C (ascorbic acid) and E
- Nucleosides (building blocks in the synthesis of DNA and RNA)
- Pigments such as carotenoids and flavonoids
- Plant growth regulators.

A colony's annual pollen requirement has been estimated as being between 15–55 kg. In colonies managed for honey production, around 30 kg of pollen for each colony every year is needed to provide enough protein and other important constituents of pollen to produce sufficient brood, feed adult bees and help ensure the health of the colony. A further amount of several kilograms is also needed to provide substances essential in the production of beeswax to produce new comb.

Foraging for pollen

Bees engaged in collecting pollen are recognised by the presence of pollen loads on their hind legs, often called pollen baskets. These baskets are actually masses of pollen packed around a central bristle and associated hairs that hold the grains together. While working some flowers bees can become covered in pollen and when they fly away from the flower and move to another you may see them brushing the pollen down their bodies towards their hind legs. Here the pollen is compacted and pressed into the pollen load. The typical pollen load of a foraging worker bee is between 10–30 mg, which means about 1.5 million loads are needed to collect the 30 kg of pollen a colony needs per year.

Not all pollens have the same quality or are produced by flowers in the same quantities

Right:
Pollen loads on the hind legs of a honeybee
(photo: C. Stevens)

(see Chapter 5). Little is known about the bee's assessment of pollen quality or quantity but there is evidence to indicate that they can detect different levels of available pollen. Bees learn by trial and error how to work the flowers to obtain the pollen. Anthers split and expose the pollen at different times of day and the honeybee learns to use visual and olfactory cues from the flowers that indicate that dehiscence (the spontaneous opening at maturity of an anther) has taken place and the pollen will therefore be available and accessible and can be collected. Individual bees sometimes work only one species of flower, particularly if the source is extensive and in flower for the whole of the bee's foraging lifetime, which, in the summer months, can be as short as three weeks.

Different types of flowers require the foraging bees to adopt different strategies to obtain nectar and pollen. Some examples are:

- Open flowers – the bee will bite the anthers and use her forelegs to pull them towards her, e.g. bramble
- Tubular flowers – she inserts her tongue for nectar, pollen is incidentally caught on her legs and mouthparts, e.g. heather
- Closed flowers – she uses her forelegs to force the petals apart and gathers pollen on her mouthparts and forelegs, e.g. field bean
- Spike and catkin flowers – she runs along the spike or catkin shaking the pollen onto her body hairs, e.g. hazel
- Presentation flowers – she presses her abdomen against the flower forcing the pollen mass out, e.g. salvia and sage.

Above:
Pollen loads collected by honeybees in April, mainly from willow and flowering cherry
(photo: W. D. J. Kirk)

On returning to the hive the foraging bee goes to the frames where the young brood is developing and kicks off the pollen loads into cells dedicated to pollen storage, which are usually found in an arc around the brood area. Here the receiving bees add various secretions that protect the pollen from deterioration, together with some honey, before pressing the pollen into the cells and covering them with a little more honey to be stored until required. This is known as 'bee bread'. Honeybee colonies do not store large amounts of pollen and must have access to it all through the active brood-rearing season. This is why it is so important that sufficient quantities of flowers and their pollen are available throughout this period.

Loss of forage for honeybees and its implications

Before the use of herbicides and inorganic fertilisers, fields of cereal crops in the British Isles contained herbaceous species, generally called arable weeds, many of which were used by honeybees. Because of the spread of monocultures and cleaning to remove weed seeds this wide range of forage plants has been lost. Even temporary grass fields lack wild plants and usually consist mainly of rye grass. Traditional hay meadows and other flower-rich grasslands are very scarce except in protected areas and designated wildlife areas. The legacy of species-rich hedgerows has also been lost in recent years, not only by bad management but also by grubbing out, especially in intensively farmed arable areas where they have no useful economic value for the farmer. We know that an average colony of honeybees needs a minimum of 120 kg of nectar and 30 kg of pollen to be healthy and in some largely arable areas it is becoming harder to keep bees in good health unless there are headlands and field margins where a diversity of flowers are growing.

Some pollens have a low protein content and are of less nutritive value, for example sunflowers (viper's bugloss is nearly three times higher). Some pollens contain proteins which are deficient in certain essential amino acids, for example oilseed rape is low in valine. The effect of protein and amino acid deficiencies and malnutrition (inability to obtain enough forage and also be unable to fully utilise the protein in the pollen) will compromise the immune systems of honeybees, resulting in an increased risk of poor colony development, ill health and honeybees more vulnerable to disease. Honeybees need adequate quantities of protein and a range of different proteins and the amino acids they contain. They need this range throughout the 9–10 months they are active and rearing brood. The importance of flower diversity and its availability throughout the active season is now seen to be a key factor in honeybee nutrition and health.

Why We Need Honeybees

Honeybee products are used in the human diet and for pharmaceutical, cosmetic and industrial uses, but of greater importance is their value in the amount of pollination they carry out in agricultural and horticultural crops and for the pollination of wild flowers, shrubs and trees. Pollination is necessary for the development of fruits, seeds and nuts, which are a key part of food chains and so are vital to support ecosystems and maintain biodiversity. The value of the pollination services provided by British Isles honeybees alone is hard to estimate because of the lack of a common agreed valuation method for quantifying pollination services, but it is generally accepted to be hundreds of millions of pounds sterling. The approach of using the commercial value of crops pollinated by bees (p.2) is just one of many possible methods.

What Can We Do to Help Honeybees?

The public interest in both honeybees and bumblebees increased considerably in the first decade of the 21st century and many people now want to try and help them. Farmers, land managers, gardeners and other members of the public can all help to increase the range and quantity of forage for honeybees in the following ways:

- Watch which plants honeybees are visiting in private or public and open gardens and cultivate them.
- Plant the right flower species in combinations that will provide sources of nectar and pollen through the honeybee's active season from January to end of October. Include some very early-flowering plants such as crocus, aconite, snowdrop and viburnum because honeybees will leave the hive and forage in warm bright weather at the beginning of the year.
- Manage hedgerows in ways that enable wild plants and hedgerow trees to produce flowers to provide forage for bees and other pollinators, and allow them to set fruits, seeds and nuts which can be used by birds and mammals.
- Plant new hedges of mixed species and allow them to flower. A good forage hedge with hedgerow trees would include hawthorn, hazel, dog rose, blackthorn, honeysuckle, holly, ivy, crab apple, willow, wild cherry and wild pear.
- Leave plants and weeds until they stop flowering before pulling them up. Be especially

careful not to cut back nectar plants, like ivy, that flower in late autumn into winter and holly, which often starts to flower while it is still bearing berries.
- Make use of government grants to manage field margins and plant nectar- and pollen-yielding flower mixes.
- Reduce the frequency of lawn mowing to allow white clover to flower, cutting it down once the flower heads have turned brown. It will re-grow to provide a second or third flowering.
- Create a wild flower area including nectar-rich flowers in gardens, fields or school premises.
- Become a beekeeper or invite a beekeeper to keep bees on your land.

Table 2.3. Top 10 plants for honeybees (in alphabetical order)

Plant name	Value to honeybees
Borage (*Borago officinalis*)	Good source of nectar and pollen. Flowers April to October.
Bramble (*Rubus fruticosus*)	Good source of nectar and pollen. Flowers May to September.
Cherry (*Prunus* species) including Morello cherry, bird cherry, and gean	Nectar and pollen. Flowers mid-April to mid-May.
Dandelion (*Taraxacum officinale*)	Nectar and pollen in abundance. Flowers March to October.
Lime (*Tilia* x *europaea* and *Tilia platyphyllos*)	Good source of nectar. Flowers June to July.
Michaelmas daisy (*Aster* species)	Good useful source of pollen and nectar. Late flowering, July to late October.
Orchard fruit (*Prunus* species) including damson, plum, pear and apple	Mainly pollen but also some nectar. Damson and plum will flower first followed by pear and apple early April to late May, depending on geographical location.
Rosebay willowherb (*Chamerion angustifolium*)	Good source of nectar and pollen. Flowers over a long period from July to September
White clover (*Trifolium repens*)	Good source of nectar. Flowers June to September.
Willow, e.g. goat willow (*Salix caprea*)	Good early source of pollen and some species also produce nectar. Flowers February to May.

Honeybees need nectar and pollen sources throughout the brood-rearing season, therefore a succession of plant species which flower at different times throughout the year is needed to provide the continuity of forage. For gardeners there is a range of plants that will provide this continuity, but many horticultural varieties of flowers, for example double flowers and hybrid roses, are of little or no use to honeybees because they are bred for show and colour, often the flowers are sterile and do not produce pollen or nectar. Also, when planting or sowing, note that honeybees visit clumps or expanses of flowers rather than solitary blooms as this is more energy efficient for them.

Table 2.4. A calendar of some useful plants for honeybees. Precise flowering times will vary depending on geographical location and weather.

January and February	Snowdrop, Bodnant viburnum, winter aconite, sweet box, crocus, mahonia and hellebore, including green hellebore, Christmas rose and lenten rose.
March	Celandine, blackthorn, cherry plum, marsh marigold, goat willow and stinking hellebore.
April and May	Blackthorn, arabis, damson, pear, apple, grape hyacinth, glory of the snow, violet, gorse, firethorn, hawthorn, cotoneaster, forget-me-not and the early rose 'Canary Bird'.
June and July	Lime, butterfly bush, Portugal laurel, barberry, white clover, thyme, oregano, sage, catnip, mint, lavender, single and semi-double rose, false acacia, borage, phacelia, broom and veronica.
August	Many of the July flowers will continue to bloom together with heather, heath, hebe, stonecrop, fuchsia, rosebay willowherb and mallow.
September and October	Michaelmas daisy, knapweed, aster, late stonecrop, sneezeweed, bellflower, goldenrod and ivy.
November and December	Ivy, stonecrop, laurustinus, Farrer's viburnum (*Viburnum farreri*) and Bodnant viburnum.

Plants Harmful to Honeybees

There are very few plants in the British Isles known to be harmful to honeybees. Harm can occur due to toxic substances that occur in the nectar or pollen. Periodically in the British Isles, especially in dry years, honeybees may be found paralysed or dying under flowering lime trees, especially *Tilia* 'Petiolaris', *Tilia tomentosa* and *Tilia* 'Orbicularis'. In the 1970s, research on these bee deaths suggested that the nectar was unusually high in a sugar called mannose. However, research in Germany in the 1990s and 2000s by Thomas Baal and others has contradicted this. No evidence was found for mannose in the nectar from trees with dead bees beneath them. Bees were most affected at the end of the lime flowering period or in dry years when there was very little nectar in the flowers; this would not be expected if nectar was the problem. When incapacitated bees below a tree were fed with nectar from the same tree they were able to recover, implying there was no evidence for toxic nectar. Instead, the evidence indicated that bees were starving or running out of the nectar they needed as fuel to be able to fly back to their nest.

Honeybees have also been reportedly affected by rhododendron; however, they rarely visit the flowers of rhododendron in the British Isles. This cannot be due to difficulty in reaching the nectar because short-tongued bumblebees can access the nectar and the pollen is easily available at the front of the flower. The nectar and pollen of rhododendron contain a toxin called grayanotoxin and this is toxic to honeybees, but not bumblebees, in the British Isles. Honeybees may well avoid the flowers for this reason.

How Beekeeping Can Help Honeybees

Beekeeping is an enjoyable and fascinating way to help bees. The discovery of the varroa parasite in England in 1992 and its subsequent spread across the British Isles significantly changed beekeeping. Today most honeybee colonies, with the exception of a few feral colonies, only exist because of the craft of beekeeping. The varroa mite and associated bee viruses are a potent combination and our honeybees have yet to develop ways of dealing with them. Beekeepers endeavour to control the level of varroa mites and to keep their bees in conditions where they are well fed and not stressed. The availability of good quality forage throughout the active season appears vital to helping honeybees resist disease. There are other factors that contribute to helping honeybee survival and these include good beekeeping husbandry by trained and competent beekeepers, the ability to recognise problems including diseases in colonies, the skill to decide on strategies to help them recover and where appropriate to make proper use of the available medications to control disease, all of which contribute to an Integrated Bee Health Management Strategy (IBHMS).

Above:
Beekeepers being trained in disease recognition
(photo: D. Magnier)

In the last few years, the increased difficulties facing both honeybees and beekeepers have been recognised by the UK and Irish governments and this has resulted in an increase in both public and private funding for research aimed at finding ways to help and support honeybees. However, the main responsibility for ensuring that honeybees are healthy is the individual beekeeper.

Training courses and study programmes run by local, county and national beekeeping associations and government agencies are available to beekeepers to learn more about modern threats to their bees and increase their skills in order to meet existing and future challenges.

CHAPTER THREE

PLANTS FOR BUMBLEBEES

JANE STOUT

Trinity Centre for Biodiversity Research, School of Natural Sciences, Trinity College Dublin, Ireland

Bumblebees are familiar and much-loved bees, commonly seen visiting flowers in suburban parks and gardens as well as in more rural settings. They visit a wide range of plant species, collecting both nectar and pollen for themselves and their colonies. This chapter describes the diversity of bumblebee species in the British Isles and discusses how plants can be used to help them and influence their foraging behaviour.

Bumblebee Diversity

Left:
*Male early bumblebee (*Bombus pratorum*) on hen and chicks* (Echeveria *'Painted Lady')*
(photo: C. Stevens)

Although we are all familiar with the amiable buzzing of bumblebees during the summer months, it often comes as a surprise to people when they find out that there is more than one species of bumblebee. In fact, there are nearly 250 bumblebee (*Bombus*) species worldwide, and 24 species living in the British Isles. These species vary from one another in terms of their body size, tongue lengths, colour patterns, physiology, nesting requirements, activity during the year, relative abundance and the flowers they visit for food. We need to understand these differences between the bumblebee species in order to help them in any meaningful way. While there has been a lot of study into the more common species in terms of their ecology and floral preferences, this is more challenging for the rarer species, especially those that are difficult to identify reliably in the field – some of the rarer species look very similar to the common ones and can be easily overlooked.

Tongue Length

One of the factors affecting a bumblebee's choice of flower is the length of its tongue. Among the most common bumblebee species in the British Isles, there is a quite a lot of variation in tongue length. The garden bumblebee (*Bombus hortorum*) has the longest

Left:
Worker garden
bumblebee
(Bombus hortorum)
showing its long
tongue
(photo: M. A. Kirk)

tongue, measuring a massive 13 mm – quite remarkable for a bee whose body length is only 11–16 mm. This means that garden bumblebees can access nectar even when hidden at the base of flowers with long floral tubes, such as red clover (*Trifolium pratense*), foxglove (*Digitalis purpurea*) and honeysuckle (*Lonicera periclymenum*). With a similar body-length, buff- and white-tailed species (*Bombus terrestris* and *Bombus lucorum*) are relatively short-tongued (approximately 7.5 mm). This means they are better suited to collecting nectar from flowers with shorter floral tubes. However, this does not stop these shorter-tongued bumblebees from getting to the rewards hidden deep inside the longer-tubed flowers. With their strong jaws, they are able to bite holes into floral tubes and steal nectar from deep inside. These 'nectar robbing' holes are then used by other short-tongued species such as the early bumblebee (*Bombus pratorum*) as well as honeybees, who act as secondary robbers.

Common, Rare and Recently Arrived Species

Unfortunately, many of our bumblebee species are in decline, mainly due to agricultural intensification and associated loss of wild plants and nesting and hibernating sites and the increasing use of pesticides. Three species of 'true' bumblebee (the other species are 'cuckoos' – see below) that used to occur in Britain and Ireland are no longer found here, and a further eight have undergone serious decline in the last 50 years. Five of these rarer species have become the focus of detailed studies as a result of being listed as part of an internationally recognised programme addressing threatened species in the UK in the 1990s, and the other three have been studied as part of English Nature's Species Recovery Programme. Despite this, our knowledge of the ecology of the declining species is still limited. Many of the declining species are long-tongued and it is thought that the reduction in long-tubed flowers, particularly red clover (*Trifolium pratense*), in the wider countryside has contributed to this decline. Although there are six species that can still be commonly seen in our gardens and are often referred to as the 'big six' (see opposite and Table 3.1), the real abundance even of these species throughout the British Isles is difficult to quantify. In fact, the 'big six' may actually incorporate eight species, given recent discoveries of species which look almost identical and may have previously been overlooked (Table 3.1).

The 'big six' widespread and common species of bumblebee

Far left:
White-tailed
*bumblebee (*Bombus
lucorum*) queen*

Left:
Buff-tailed
*bumblebee (*Bombus
terrestris*) queen*
(photos: T. C. Ings)

Far left:
Early bumblebee
*(*Bombus pratorum*)*
queen

Left:
Red-tailed
*bumblebee (*Bombus
lapidarius*) queen*
(photos: T. C. Ings)

Far left:
Garden bumblebee
*(*Bombus hortorum*)*
worker
(photo: W. D. J. Kirk)

Left:
Common carder bee
*(*Bombus pascuorum*)*
queen
(photo: L. A. Hislop)

At the same time, some species have expanded their range: the early bumblebee (*Bombus pratorum*), common throughout Britain, was absent from Ireland until 1947 and has since spread throughout the island. The mountain or bilberry bumblebee (*Bombus monticola*) was also a late arrival to Ireland, being first recorded there in 1974. This species is interesting as it is a declining BAP (Biodiversity Action Plan) species in Britain, but is expanding its range in Ireland. Finally, the tree bumblebee (*Bombus hypnorum*) is the most recent arrival to these islands, having been first sighted in 2000 in southern England. It has spread across England and Wales, and is now one of the most commonly seen species in some parts of England. However, it is not yet known in Ireland.

Right:
Tree bumblebee
(Bombus
hypnorum) *queen*
(photo: N. W. Owens)

Table 3.1. British and Irish true bumblebee species arranged by colour group.
Common species, the 'big six', are in bold.

A: Short-tongued species

Colour group	Common name	Distribution and abundance	Queen emergence	Favourite flowers
2-banded white tails	**White-tailed bumblebee (Bombus lucorum)**	**Widespread and common**	**February–April**	**Wide range, can rob nectar from longer-tubed flowers**
	Buff-tailed bumblebee (Bombus terrestris)	**Widespread and common**	**February–April**	**Wide range, can rob nectar from longer-tubed flowers**
	Cryptic bumblebee (Bombus cryptarum)	Unknown – only recently recognised in the UK & Ireland – part of the 'lucorum complex'		
	Northern white-tailed bumblebee (Bombus magnus)	Unknown – only recently recognised in the UK & Ireland – part of the 'lucorum complex'		
	Broken-belted bumblebee (Bombus soroeensis)	Widespread but localised, absent from Ireland	June	Melilot and other small-flowered pea family flowers, harebell, other bellflower species, devil's bit scabious
3-banded white tails	Heath bumblebee (Bombus jonellus)	Widespread but most common in heathy habitats	March–June	Sallow, heath, heather and a range of flowers
Banded red tails	**Early bumblebee (Bombus pratorum)**	**Widespread and common**	**March–April**	**Often visits shrubs and wide range of other plants, able to visit upside-down and drooping flowers**
	Bilberry bumblebee (Bombus monticola)	Restricted to upland/heathy habitats in north and west, declining in Britain, spreading in Ireland	April	White clover, bird's-foot trefoil, raspberry, bell heath, bilberry, rhododendron
Black-bodied red tails	**Red-tailed bumblebee (Bombus lapidarius)**	**Widespread and common**	**March–June**	**Bird's-foot trefoil and other yellow flowers, scabious and knapweed, visits flowers with landing platforms**
Browns	Tree bumblebee (Bombus hypnorum)	Expanding from first sighting in UK in south in 2000, not yet known in Ireland, urban and woodland habitats	February–March	Wide range, including fruit trees and bramble

Far left:
*Early bumblebee (*Bombus pratorum*) characteristically visiting an upside-down flower*
(photo: T. C. Ings)

Left:
*Red-tailed bumblebee (*Bombus lapidarius*) characteristically visiting a flower with a landing platform*
(photo: C. Stevens)

B: Long-tongued species

Colour group	Common name	Distribution and abundance	Queen emergence	Favourite flowers
3-banded white tails	**Garden bumblebee** (***Bombus hortorum***)	**Widespread and common, especially in gardens**	March–May	**Foxglove, red clover, dead-nettle, flowers with long flower tube**
	Ruderal bumblebee (*Bombus ruderatus*)	Scarce and declining, in wet heaths – difficult to distinguish from *Bombus hortorum*, absent from Ireland	April–May	Clover and dead-nettle, flowers with long flower tube
Banded red tails	Shrill carder bee (*Bombus sylvarum*)	Declining, restricted to south	May	Long flowers, including red clover, red bartsia, knapweed and woundwort
Black-bodied red tails	Red-shanked carder bee (*Bombus ruderarius*)	Declining	April–May	Clover and other pea family, mint family, knapweed and red bartsia
Browns	**Common carder bee** (***Bombus pascuorum***)	**Widespread and common**	March–May	**Wide range, but especially pea family, dead-nettle, foxglove**
	Great yellow bumblebee (*Bombus distinguendus*)	Very restricted and declining	May–July	Red clover and other pea family, including bird's-foot trefoil, white clover, marsh woundwort, marsh thistle and knapweed
	Brown-banded carder bee (*Bombus humilis*)	Declining, restricted to tall open grasslands in south, absent from Ireland	April–May	Clover and other pea family, mint family, knapweed, red bartsia
	Moss carder bee (*Bombus muscorum*)	Declining, in taller grasslands, more frequent in north and west	May–June	Clover and other pea family, mint family, knapweed, red bartsia

Life Cycle

Bumblebees have an annual life cycle that begins when large queen bumblebees emerge from hibernation in the spring, as early as February or as late as May, depending on the species and the weather. Often the first queens to be seen in the spring are the large yellow-and-black banded, white- and buff-tailed species (*Bombus lucorum* and *Bombus terrestris*). These queens can often be seen slowly flying low to the ground, exploring holes as they search for an appropriate place to nest. Once a suitable home has been found, the queen lays the first eggs, which she incubates with her body. The eggs hatch after a few days and the queen then feeds the larvae on pollen over the following 4–5 weeks as they develop. The larvae then spin a cocoon and after 1–2 weeks of pupating, the adult bees emerge, all of whom are females. They take over from the queen in rearing the new larvae and are thus named the 'workers'. Several batches of workers are produced, and the colony grows in size. Some species produce up to 300 workers, although others produce considerably fewer. Once the colony is big enough, it starts producing males and new queens, which leave the nest to find other bees to mate with. Neither the males nor the new queens contribute to the 'work' of the colony, but they do visit flowers to collect food for themselves. Outside the nest, the male bumblebees often leave scent-marks on twigs, leaves and other objects in their surroundings. They then patrol this area in a systematic way, revisiting the scented objects routinely and in a fixed order. The scents attract the new queens with whom they mate. In most bumblebee species,

Right:
Inside a buff-tailed
bumblebee nest
(Bombus terrestris*)*
(photo: T. C. Ings)

queens mate with only one male. Once the males and new queens leave the nest, the rest of the colony starts to die out, so that by the end of summer, the old queen, all the workers and the males have died. Only the newly mated queens survive. By this time the nest can be quite a jumble of old pupal cocoons, nectar and pollen stores, droppings and detritus, and can be full of wax moths, mites and other invertebrates. Therefore it is no longer habitable, and bumblebees tend not to reuse nest holes in subsequent years. The newly mated queens find a suitable hole in the ground in which to hibernate, where they survive for the winter on their fat reserves, before founding a new nest themselves the following spring.

There are differences among bumblebee species in how quickly they complete their life cycle. Those that do it rapidly, such as the early bumblebee (*Bombus pratorum*), can abandon the over-winter hibernation period and new queens can found new colonies within the same summer, resulting in two generations being produced in a single year. Other departures from the annual cycle have been seen in the buff-tailed bumblebee (*Bombus terrestris*), which has forsaken the winter hibernation in some parts of southern England, and new queens have founded colonies that have survived with workers right through the winter months.

Cuckoo Bumblebees

Some bumblebee species, the 'cuckoo' bumblebees (Table 3.2), dispense with the production of their own workers and, in a manner akin to the more familiar cuckoo birds, take over a nest of 'true' bumblebees. Female cuckoo bumblebees emerge from hibernation and find a colony already initiated by a true bumblebee, kill the queen and lay their own eggs. The true bumblebee workers then rear the cuckoo larvae, which develop either into new breeding females, or into males. Since cuckoo bumblebees do not produce their own workers and rely on the food brought to the nest by the true bumblebee workers, they are much less often seen foraging on flowers.

Left:
Male southern
cuckoo bee
(Bombus vestalis*)*
(photo: T. C. Ings)

Table 3.2. British and Irish cuckoo bumblebee species arranged by colour group. All visit a wide range of flowers.

Colour group	Common name	Distribution and abundance	Queen emergence
2-banded white tails	Barbut's cuckoo bee (*Bombus barbutellus*)	Widespread	April–May
	Gypsy cuckoo bee (*Bombus bohemicus*)	Widespread, more common in north	April–May
	Southern cuckoo bee (*Bombus vestalis*)	Widespread, absent from Ireland	From end of March
3-banded white tails	Forest cuckoo bee (*Bombus sylvestris*)	Widespread	April–June
Black-bodied red tails	Red-tailed cuckoo bee (*Bombus rupestris*)	Widespread in south UK	April–May
Browns	Field cuckoo bee (*Bombus campestris*)	Widespread	April–May

Nectar and Pollen Collection by Bumblebees

When bumblebee queens emerge from hibernation, their internal fat resources are depleted and their ovaries underdeveloped: they need food. They get this in the form of nectar and pollen from flowers. Nectar provides the queens with energy with which to search for a nest and then lay and incubate the first eggs. Pollen provides protein for the queens to develop their ovaries and lay eggs. Thus the first bumblebees seen foraging in the spring are the queens. Larvae feed on pollen which is either provided for them in 'pockets' adjacent to the wax brood chamber in which they grow, or in other species, kept in a wax 'store' and fed to the larvae mixed with nectar. Initially, the queens provision the nest with nectar and pollen, but once the first workers are produced, they take over. As worker bumblebees are collecting food not only for themselves, but for their colony, they are tireless foragers. They leave the nest to gather nectar and pollen, and are less likely to specialise on collecting one or the other as honeybees tend to do. Once they have filled their honey stomachs and pollen sacs, they return and deposit nectar and pollen in the nest, and head out again. Nectar and pollen are stored within the nest in wax cups or in empty pupal cocoons, and so bumblebees do produce a sort of honey, but not to the extent that honeybees do. Most of the bumblebees seen foraging on flowers during the summer months are workers. Since males and cuckoo bees do not collect pollen and nectar to provision the nest, they only visit flowers to fuel their own activities and maintain their own bodies. Thus males and cuckoo bees are less frequently seen visiting flowers.

Because of their relatively large, hairy bodies, and their ability to generate some internal heat, bumblebees are able to forage earlier in the season and in more adverse weather conditions than other bees. This means that they can access nectar and pollen in plants both earlier in the season, and earlier and later during a single day, allowing them to feed on a wide range of plant species. Thus bumblebees are ecological 'generalists' – feeding from a range of plants, and not restricted to a single specialised host plant. Since different species come into flower and stop flowering throughout the season, bumblebees have to learn which plants offer the best food at any given time.

Learning and Choosing the Best Food Source

Although bumblebees do not have the honeybee's ability to perform complex dances within the colony to inform nest mates of the location of especially good patches of forage, workers do communicate the general availability of suitable flowers using scent. Returning foragers who have located a good food source bring back with them the odour of the flowers on which they have been foraging. In addition, returning foragers release pheromones, which are chemical odours, and actively spread them through the hive. These chemical odours increase the activity of the other bees in the nest, causing them to leave to go foraging.

Above:
Worker garden bumblebee (Bombus hortorum) *accessing the concealed nectar of snapdragon* (Antirrhinum majus)
(photo: T. C. Ings)

Once out of the nest, foragers can locate suitable flowers not only by smell, but also using visual cues. The size, shape and colour of flowers affect how attractive they are to bumblebees, and once naive foragers have had some practice, they can learn which flowers are particularly good to visit. They also learn how to extract the nectar and pollen from flowers with complicated floral structures or hidden nectar. For example, in snapdragons (*Antirrhinum majus*) nectar is concealed within the flower and the bumblebee has to learn how to open the flower, crawl inside and find the nectar. Once an individual has learned how to do this, and become adept at quickly extracting nectar and pollen, it will tend to visit these flowers repeatedly, at least during a single foraging bout. In this way, individual bumblebees may bypass equally rewarding flowers, simply because they are unfamiliar, or more time-consuming to handle. This phenomenon is known as 'floral constancy' and has benefits for the plants too – their pollen is moved between flowers of the same species and not wasted on other species as the bee switches between flower types.

Even within a single plant species, bumblebees can maximise their foraging efficiency by avoiding individual flowers that have been recently depleted of their nectar by another bee. They do this by interpreting the smell of the previous visitor's 'footprint' – this indicates to them whether the visitor was recent or some time ago. Thus they can avoid flowers that have just been emptied of nectar and visit flowers that were visited long enough ago that the nectar has re-accumulated.

Buzz Pollination

Bumblebees also have the ability to extract pollen that is held firmly in tubular anthers (see glossary on p.290) with an opening at one end. Bumblebees do this by grasping these anthers, or another part of the flower, and vibrating their flight muscles rapidly, causing the pollen to be dislodged. This is known as 'buzz pollination' since the vibration of the flight muscles is accompanied by a characteristic buzzing sound. Since honeybees are not able to collect pollen in this way, this means the bumblebees have the advantage with respect to access to these resources. Many flowers of the nightshade family (Solanaceae), including tomatoes, have anthers of this form and require buzz pollination.

How Can Plants be Used to Help Bumblebees?

Bumblebees require large quantities of nectar and pollen to supply their colony throughout the season in order to complete their colony growth. Since different species have different preferences, and these change according to the time of year, it is extremely difficult to generalise about which plants are best for bumblebees. In addition, we are yet to fully understand which plants provide not only the most nectar and pollen, but the best quality nectar and pollen for bumblebees. However, perennial and biennial herbaceous plants tend to be preferred by bumblebees and it is clear that several species stand out as bumblebee favourites in the countryside. Some of these are given in Table 3.3 along with an explanation of why they are included in this Top 10.

Table 3.3. Top 10 plants for bumblebees (in alphabetical order)

Plant name	Value to bumblebees
Bird's-foot trefoil (*Lotus corniculatus*)	A favourite of both common species such as the red-tailed bumblebee (*Bombus lapidarius*) and rare species such as the great yellow bumblebee (*Bombus distinguendus*), reflowers after mowing, visited for both nectar and pollen.
Bramble (*Rubus fruticosus*)	Abundant, lots of nectar and relatively long flowering season.
Clover (*Trifolium* species)	Considered an important species in the diet of many of our rarer and declining bumblebee species; especially red clover (*Trifolium pratense*).
Foxglove (*Digitalis purpurea*)	With its long tubular flowers, the flowers of this species are an exclusive bumblebee banquet.
Knapweed (*Centaurea* species)	Produce a lot of nectar, particularly in late summer; a favourite of both common and rare bumblebee species.
Rhododendron (*Rhododendron ponticum*)	A non-native, but plants of this species produce a vast number of flowers which contain lots of nectar and pollen early in the season, and bumblebees appear to be the only insects that can tolerate the toxins they contain, making it a great bumblebee-only resource.
Thistle (*Cirsium* species)	Produce a lot of nectar, particularly in late summer; a favourite of both common and rare bumblebee species.
Vetch (*Vicia* species)	Pea-family flowers are thought to be of particularly high quality for bumblebees and many vetches are favourites of the medium- and longer-tongued species.
Willow (*Salix* species)	Important as an early-season pollen and nectar source for queens.

Suggested Combinations of Plants

Bumblebees need nectar and pollen sources throughout the season, from early spring when the first queens emerge, right through to autumn when the last workers die out and new queens go into hibernation. Therefore, a succession of plant species that flower at different times of the year is needed. In addition, like many other animals, bumblebees tend to collect as much food as they can while spending as little energy as possible collecting it. This means that it is more efficient for them to visit patches of flowers, rather than single isolated ones, because this saves them energy. Thus clumps of plants that are useful to bees are better than single specimens. Furthermore, a range of flower shapes and sizes are required to suit both long- and short-tongued bumblebee species, and both nectar and pollen sources are necessary. Many horticultural varieties of plants commonly available for gardens are of little or no use to bumblebees: this is because often they are selectively bred for their unusual traits such as 'double' petals, but this can mean that nectar and pollen are no longer accessible to the bees.

Although bumblebees visit a range of flower species for nectar, they may be more fussy when it comes to pollen. Studies of the pollen collected by the great yellow bumblebee (*Bombus distinguendus*) among others, has suggested that pollen from three plant families: the pea family (Fabaceae), the mint family (Lamiaceae) and the figwort family (Scrophulariaceae) is particularly important. Research on honeybees has suggested that diversity in pollen in their diet benefits their immune system. Thus, a diverse mix of flowering plants is better as a food source than extensive areas with only a single species. Since bumblebees, like all animals, need particular proteins and sugars in their diets, and these are seldom available from a single source, it is likely that a diversity of flowers is also beneficial for bumblebees.

Plants Harmful to Bumblebees

Although nectar is produced by flowers as food for pollinating animals, nectar from some species contains chemicals which may be toxic to bees. Several explanations have been offered for the apparent paradox, including the idea that toxic nectar may deter flower visitors that do not pollinate. Over 20 plant families have toxins in their nectar, including wild tobacco (*Nicotiana attenuata*) whose nectar contains nicotine. Bumblebees appear to be remarkably adept at coping with the toxic nectar of many species. For example, monk's hood (*Aconitum* species) nectar contains aconitine, an alkaloid that can be highly toxic to humans, but this species is exclusively pollinated by bumblebees who readily consume the nectar and appear to suffer no adverse effects. Similarly, invasive non-native rhododendron (*Rhododendron ponticum*) nectar and pollen contains grayanotoxins, which are toxic to humans as well as honeybees and other insects, but again are tolerated by worker bumblebees.

Left:
*Monk's hood flowers (*Aconitum napellus) *contain aconitine*
(photo: W. D. J. Kirk)

Nectar (and pollen) may contain chemicals that do not kill bumblebees but do affect their behaviour. For example, yellow jessamine (*Gelsemium sempervirens*), the state flower for South Carolina in the USA, secretes nectar that contains toxic alkaloids: the higher the concentration of alkaloids in the nectar, the further bumblebees fly after visiting flowers, presumably in an attempt to escape from the flowers with unpleasant-tasting nectar. Although the nectar does not appear to harm the worker bumblebees, the alkaloids may affect the bee larvae once the nectar has been taken back to the nest. Or they may affect parasites of the bees and hence the bees are to some extent 'self-medicating' by drinking this nectar. These possibilities are currently the focus of ongoing research.

Nest Sites

Right:
Early bumblebee
(Bombus pratorum)
characteristically
visiting an upside-
down flower of
columbine
(Aquilegia
vulgaris).
See p.31 and p.104.
(photo: T. C. Ings)

Bumblebees tend to nest under or on the surface of the ground, often using old mammal nests. The common buff- and white-tailed species generally nest underground with a narrow tunnel linking their nest cavity with the surface. These tunnels can be quite long – up to several metres – or very short. The cavities are often old rodent burrows and can be found in suburban areas under garden sheds and patios. If the entrance hole is blocked up, the bees will dig out a new one. Nesting materials include whatever is present in the hole when it is discovered, as well as dead leaves, grasses, fine roots or moss.

The carder bees are named so because of the way they create their nests. Carding is the process by which fibres are broken up and aligned, and different fibres are combined into a homogenous mix. The carder bees tend to nest on or above ground level, and form their nests out of leaf litter and moss. Common carder bee nests are often found in compost heaps, piles of grass clippings and under undisturbed foliage in suburban gardens.

Some of the other species are more adaptable and nest either above or below ground, making use of a variety of cavities, including bird boxes, hollow spaces in fascia boards on houses and ivy-covered walls. Since the bees are relatively docile, and their nests not long-lived, people discovering nests in their gardens are usually content to watch the bees come and go, and they do not present a problem. Indeed, some people actively encourage bumblebees to nest in their gardens by providing artificial nesting sites for them, either in the form of holes excavated underground connected to the surface with a length of piping, or in the form of artificial nest boxes. The success rate of these artificial nest sites is debatable and usually only a low proportion of artificial nests will be colonised. Carder bees can be encouraged to nest in the garden if grass clippings or moss are left in undisturbed piles.

CHAPTER FOUR

PLANTS FOR SOLITARY BEES

CHRISTOPHER O'TOOLE

Honorary Research Associate, Hope Entomological Collections, Oxford University Museum of Natural History, UK

Of the 271 species of bee that have been recorded from the British Isles (including the Channel Islands), 90% are non-social or solitary. Along with bumblebees, the little-known solitary bees have suffered the depredations of modern intensive agriculture, which has produced a landscape that is no longer bee-friendly. By growing a suitable diversity of plants, and making nest sites available, there is much we can do in our gardens for bee conservation and the enhancement of our pollinator resource.

Solitary Bees? The Unsuspected Diversity

Left:
Mining bee
(Andrena
hattorfiana) *on field*
scabious (Knautia
arvensis)
(photo: N. W. Owens)

We normally think of bees as social insects such as honeybees and bumblebees, but more than 90% of the planet's 20,000 or so bee species are solitary. That is, each nest is the work of a single female working alone; there is no caste of sterile females called workers. Although solitary bees collect nectar, they do not convert it into honey. Instead, they mix it with the pollen they collect and deposit it in their brood cells.

There are 243 such species that have been recorded in the British Isles and they can be divided into three broad groups on the basis of their nesting habits – mining bees, cavity nesters and carpenter bees. Unfortunately, very few have common names.

As the name suggests, mining bees excavate their nests in the ground. There is a wide diversity of nest architecture, according to species. Typically, a nest comprises a main tunnel, with one or more side branches, each culminating in a brood cell. Females of almost all mining bees line brood cells with a waterproof lining secreted by a large abdominal gland. This waterproof lining is resistant to fungi and bacteria. Nest sites include earth banks, well-drained lawns and compacted, well-trodden paths. Some species, such as Davies's mining bee (*Colletes daviesanus*) and the hairy-footed flower bee (*Anthophora plumipes*) nest in the soft mortar of old walls, which mimics their natural nest sites, which are either sandy banks or vertical clay banks and cliffs.

The cavity nesters comprise stem nesters, mason bees, leafcutter bees and carder bees.

Above:
*Brood cell with the larva of a red mason bee (*Osmia rufa*) in an artificial nest made from a glass tube*
(photo: L. A. Hislop)

They nest in pre-existing cavities such as hollow plant stems and beetle borings in dead wood. Instead of producing glandular secretions to line their brood cells, they collect a range of materials. According to species, mason bees use mud, resin or a mastic of chewed leaves to partition cells and seal nests. Leafcutter bees use their powerful jaws to excise pieces from the margins of leaves, which they use to line and seal their nest cells. Females of the wool-carder bee (*Anthidium manicatum*) strip or card dense velvety hairs from the leaves of certain plants and use these to line and seal their nests. This is the only solitary carder bee (*Anthidium* species) found in the British Isles.

The two species of carpenter bee excavate nests in solid materials. The blue carpenter bee (*Ceratina cyanea*) excavates tubular nests in the soft pith of broken plant stems such as bramble and elder, while the much larger and more robust violet carpenter bee (*Xylocopa violacea*) bores into solid wood.

Solitary bees differ from the honeybee and bumblebees in the way they transport pollen. Instead of a pollen basket on the outer face of the hind legs, female solitary bees have a brush of specialised hairs called the scopa. In mining bees and carpenter bees, the scopa is on the hind leg; in the leafcutter, mason and carder bees, it is on the underside of the abdomen (see opposite).

Stem-nesting bees in the genus *Hylaeus* do not have a scopa. Instead, they carry their pollen internally, mixed with ingested nectar. Another 65 of the species occurring in the British Isles also have no scopa for the simple reason that they do not collect pollen. These are the cuckoo bees, which lay their eggs in the nests of other species, just like the cuckoo bumblebees – see Chapter 3. Although they have no interest in collecting pollen, they still visit flowers to meet their own energetic needs by feeding on nectar.

Table 4.1. An outline of the solitary and primitively social bees that have been recorded from the British Isles (including the Channel Islands)

Type of bee	Families: constituent genera [number of species]
Mining bees	Melittidae: *Melitta* [4], *Macropis* [1], *Dasypoda* [1]. Colletidae: *Colletes* [9]. Andrenidae: *Andrena* [67][1], *Panurgus* [2]. Halictidae: *Halictus* [8][1], *Lasioglossum* [33][1,2], *Dufourea* [2], *Rophites* [1]. Apidae: *Eucera* [2], *Anthophora* [5].
Stem nesters	Colletidae: *Hylaeus* [12].
Mason bees	Megachilidae: *Chelostoma* [2], *Heriades* [2], *Hoplitis* [2], *Osmia* [12].
Leafcutter bees	Megachilidae: *Megachile* [9].
Carder bees	Megachilidae: *Anthidium* [1].
Carpenter bees	Apidae: *Ceratina* [1], *Xylocopa* [1].
Cuckoo bees	Halictidae: *Sphecodes* [17]. Megachilidae: *Stelis* [4], *Coelioxys* [8]. Apidae: *Nomada* [33], *Epeolus* [2], *Melecta* [2].

[1] *Contains some species that are communal, with two or more females sharing a single nest entrance.*
[2] *Contains some species that are primitively social; that is, colonies in which some dominant females are the principal egg-layers, with the majority of females functioning as workers, which lay few eggs and do almost all of the work in terms of foraging and nest excavation.*

A range of female bees showing the position of the scopa used to transport pollen

Far left:
Mining bee (Melitta leporina) with scopa on hind leg

Left:
Mining bee (Dasypoda hirtipes) with scopa on hind leg
(photos: J. P. Early)

Far left:
Mining bee (Colletes succinctus) with scopa on hind leg
(photo: T. C. Ings)

Left:
Mining bee (Andrena nitida) with scopa on hind leg
(photo: J. P. Early)

Far left:
Mining bee (Lasioglossum species) with scopa on hind leg

Left:
Mining bee (Anthophora plumipes) with scopa on hind leg
(photos: J. P. Early)

Far left:
Mason bee (Osmia rufa) with scopa on the underside of the abdomen
(photo: T. C. Ings)

Left:
Leafcutter bee (Megachile ligniseca) with scopa on the underside of the abdomen
(photo: J. P. Early)

Life cycles and mating

Almost all species of solitary bee have a single generation per year. The offspring of species active in spring complete their development in summer or early autumn and remain over winter as adults in their natal cells. Species active in summer and early autumn overwinter as full-grown larvae and complete their development the following spring.

The males of solitary bees are usually smaller than females and appear up to a week or 10 days before the females. During this time they feed at flowers and seek nest sites where they may eventually encounter virgin females as they emerge.

Above:
*A mating ball of mining bees (*Colletes *species) containing two males and one female*
(photo: L. A. Hislop)

Females of many solitary mining bees often nest in dense aggregations of up to several thousand nests. The males of such species patrol these nest sites in search of mates. There is intense competition between them because, with few exceptions, the females mate only once, storing sperm in a special sac, the spermatheca. Often 10–15 males will cluster around a single female in a distinctive 'mating ball', which disperses as soon as a male has successfully started to mate. This mating strategy is termed 'scramble competition'. By contrast, the males of species in which the females nest sparsely rather than in dense aggregations patrol patches of flowering plants in search of mates.

Males of the wool-carder bee (*Anthidium manicatum*) are unusual in two ways. Firstly, most individuals are much larger than the females and secondly, they are aggressively territorial. Each male establishes a territory at a clump of the females' favourite forage plant in gardens: lamb's ears (*Stachys byzantina*, formerly called *Stachys lanata*). The males have a rapid, darting flight and hover frequently, often darting at bumblebees, honeybees and other flower visitors and driving them away. The females are also unusual: they mate more than once and it is thought that, in terms of time and energy, multiple mating is the price females pay in return for a protected food resource.

Right:
*Male wool-carder bee (*Anthidium manicatum*) patrolling a territory. This was photographed in France where the males have more extensive yellow markings than in Britain.*
(photo: J. V. Adams)

Bee Guilds

Ecologists often divide bees into different 'guilds', which are categories based on tongue length and seasonality. The guilds described below are convenient divisions and relate broadly to bee–plant associations.

Short-tongued guild

Most solitary bee species are short-tongued (1–7 mm), which means they forage from relatively open or short-tubed, low-reward, easy-access flowers. These are relatively slow-flying, 'low energy bees' and do not forage for more than a few hundred metres from their nest sites. Members of this guild belong to the families Melittidae, Colletidae, Andrenidae and Halictidae (see Table 4.1).

Long-tongued guild

By contrast, the long-tongued bees forage at deeper-tubed, restricted-access flowers with high nectar rewards. These bees are fast-flying, 'high energy bees' and long distance foragers. The mason bees and leafcutter bees (Megachilidae) are in this guild, at the lower end of the long tongue length scale and forage up to 1.5 km from the nest. The solitary bees with the longest tongue lengths are the hairy-footed flower bee (*Anthophora plumipes*) and the fork-tailed flower bee (*Anthophora furcata*). With tongues of 14 and 12 mm respectively, these two bees rival the longest of the long-tongued bumblebees. The hairy-footed flower bee can forage up to 4 km from the nest site.

Above:
Fork-tailed flower bee (Anthophora furcata)
(photo: L. A. Hislop)

Seasonal guilds

The earliest of spring-flying species, often called vernal bees, forage at the earliest of flowering plants. This is the most distinctive of seasonally-based bee guilds and they forage at plants such as willow (*Salix* species), lesser celandine (*Ficaria verna*), mahonia (*Mahonia aquifolium*), winter heath (*Erica carnea*), lungwort (*Pulmonaria* species) and comfrey (*Symphytum* species). Vernal bees include several mining bees, especially *Andrena* species, the red mason bee (*Osmia rufa*) and the hairy-footed flower bee (*Anthophora plumipes*). We can also include in this guild the queens of bumblebees such as the buff-tailed bumblebee (*Bombus terrestris*), the early bumblebee (*Bombus pratorum*) and the red-tailed bumblebee (*Bombus lapidarius*) freshly emerged from hibernation, and using spring flowers as refuelling stations while searching for nest sites.

Some spring bees overlap with the earliest of the summer bees, as do summer bees with the earliest of the autumn bees. The primitively social mining bees (species of *Halictus* and *Lasioglossum*), with several generations per year, occupy several seasonal guilds and the long nesting season of the recently established violet carpenter bee (*Xylocopa violacea*) means that it too does not fit easily into a guild concept based on seasonality.

Plants for Solitary Bees

The easiest way to support our solitary bee fauna and increase its diversity in domestic gardens is to maximise the diversity of the flowering plants we grow. The mix of flowers grown in the typical cottage garden is an excellent starting point. Visits to gardens open to the public, such as those managed by the National Trust or owned by the Royal Horticultural Society in the UK can be excellent sources of ideas for bee-friendly plantings in our own gardens.

The plants outlined below are mostly native species, including cultivars (cultivated varieties of wild species), which are easily obtainable from garden centres or on the web from seed merchants. Some are non-native species, which are now commonly grown in gardens in the British Isles.

Most garden centres now sell 'bee mixtures' of seeds specially chosen to be attractive to bees. You can try these mixtures and see which species do best in your garden and then go on to specialise in later seasons.

Double-flowered varieties should be avoided. In these triumphs of the plant breeder's art the nectaries, if any, may be inaccessible to bees and the pollen-bearing stamens may be entirely converted to extra whorls of petals, rendering the flowers themselves sterile and thus not a pollen resource for bees. Floribunda roses and many dahlia and chrysanthemum cultivars are among the commonest forms with double flowers. I appeal to anyone who finds the aesthetic attraction of such flowers irresistible to make a point of growing a single-flowered variety for each double-flowered one.

Solitary and primitively social bees active in spring

Although the typical fauna of solitary spring bees in gardens is dominated by mining bees in the genus *Andrena* (Table 4.2), in most gardens the gingery males of the hairy-footed flower bee (*Anthophora plumipes*) are the first harbingers of spring, along with the first of the nest-seeking queen bumblebees.

The hairy-footed flower bee, though, does not bumble about: both sexes have a rapid, darting flight and they are common at patches of comfrey (*Symphytum* species) and lungwort (*Pulmonaria* species). If the males of this bee resemble the ginger species of bumblebee, the females resemble no other bee found in the British Isles; they are entirely black, except for the bright orange hairs forming the pollen scopa on their hind legs.

The tawny mining bee (*Andrena fulva*) frequently nests in lawns in dense aggregations. This is sometimes a matter of concern to gardeners, whose attention is drawn to the bees by small mounds of excavated soil. The bees seem not to be perturbed by mowing activities, are active for only a few weeks and do no lasting harm to the lawn. Females of the mining bee *Andrena carantonica* often nest in the narrow bands of soil between the base of walls and concrete paths and along the edges of paths through lawns.

Below:
Entrance to the nest of a tawny mining bee (Andrena fulva) *(photo: C. O'Toole)*

The females of some mining bees (*Halictus rubicundus, Lasioglossum albicans* and *Lasioglossum calceatum*) often nest in small aggregations in well-trodden paths.

Spring mining bees (*Andrena* species) are valuable pollinators of apples, pears, plums and cherries; this is particularly true of the tawny mining bee and also the red mason bee (*Osmia rufa*). The latter has great potential as an alternative to the honeybee as a managed pollinator of orchard crops, especially apples, pears, plums and cherries. Apple farmers in southeast Poland manage it commercially as a pollinator. I have shown that it can be used to pollinate strawberries in enclosed situations such as poly-tunnels and that it is an excellent pollinator of blueberries.

Table 4.2. Some common solitary and primitively social bees active in spring

Species	Type of bee	Flight period	Distribution
Andrena bicolor	Mining bee	*March–May; June–August	Widespread
Andrena carantonica [1]	Mining bee	March–mid-August	Common
Andrena chrysosceles	Mining bee	March–June	Widespread
Andrena cineraria	Mining bee	March–June or July	Locally common
Andrena flavipes	Mining bee	*March–May; May–September	Widespread
Andrena fulva	Mining bee	March–late June	Widespread
Andrena haemorrhoa	Mining bee	March–May, some females to August	Common
Andrena nigroaenea	Mining bee	March–June	Widespread
Halictus rubicundus [2]	Mining bee	Females March–late September; males June–October	Widespread
Lasioglossum albipes [2]	Mining bee	Females April–September; males June–September	Widespread
Lasioglossum calceatum [2]	Mining bee	Females March–September; males July–September	Widespread
Lasioglossum morio [2]	Mining bee	Females late March–October; males May–October	Widespread
Lasioglossum smeathmanellum	Mining bee	Females March–April to late September; males June–September	Widespread
Anthophora plumipes	Mining bee	March–May	Widespread
Osmia rufa	Mason bee	March–May, sometimes June	Widespread
Osmia caerulescens	Mason bee	*April–August	Widespread
Xylocopa violacea	Carpenter bee	Late March–August	A spreading recent arrival

[1] *A communal species in which several females share a common nest entrance.*
[2] *Females only in spring: only adult females overwinter in these primitively social species; males appear only in mid–late summer.* Lasioglossum smeathmanellum *is a solitary species.*
A double-brooded species.

Plants for spring bees

Time is an important but little-considered resource for solitary bees. This is especially true for spring species because the weather is often changeable and the number of consecutive days when foraging is possible can be scarce, especially in bad years. Nectar-rich flowers are therefore important for spring bees – a crop full of this energy-rich food will enable a bee to survive periods when she is confined to her nest.

Table 4.3 is a selection of spring plants that are valuable to solitary bees. It is important to remember that these plants are not only a source of protein-rich pollen for the offspring of foraging females, but also important re-fuelling stations for the females themselves and their males. However, poppy species, including the Welsh poppy (*Meconopsis cambrica*), produce no nectar. Poppies make up for this with their prodigious production of pollen and the Welsh poppy additionally compensates by having a long flowering period: from mid-spring to mid-autumn. It is a prolific self-seeder and once established, it will look after itself for years in flowerbeds. It makes a good companion to cranesbills (*Geranium* species), which are rich sources of nectar.

The flower spikes of cherry laurel (*Prunus laurocerasus*) attract males of spring mining bees, especially *Andrena bicolor*, *Andrena carantonica* and *Andrena chrysosceles*. They may assemble in large numbers, waiting for the arrival of females, which are attracted to the pungent-smelling flowers.

Right:
The centre of a Welsh poppy flower (Meconopsis cambrica)
(photo: M. A. Kirk)

Far right:
Female mining bee (Andrena carantonica) *on cherry laurel* (Prunus laurocerasus)
(photo: L. A. Hislop)

Table 4.3. Spring-flowering plants for solitary and primitively social bees

Common name	Scientific name	Family
Apple	*Malus pumila* [+C]	Rosaceae
Bugle	*Ajuga reptans, Ajuga genevensis* [+C]	Lamiaceae
Cherry	*Prunus avium* [+C]	Rosaceae
Cherry laurel	*Prunus laurocerasus* [+C]	Rosaceae
Comfrey**	*Symphytum* species [+C]	Boraginaceae
Dandelion	*Taraxacum officinalis*	Asteraceae
Dead-nettle	*Lamium album, Lamium purpureum*	Lamiaceae
Dusky cranesbill*	*Geranium phaeum* [+C]	Geraniaceae
Firethorn	*Pyracantha rogersiana* [+C]	Rosaceae
Green alkanet**	*Pentaglottis sempervirens*	Boraginaceae
Hedgerow cranesbill*	*Geranium pyrenaicum* [+C]	Geraniaceae
Herb Robert*	*Geranium robertianum* [+C]	Geraniaceae
Lesser celandine	*Ficaria verna* [+C]	Ranunculaceae
Lungwort**	*Pulmonaria* species [+C]	Boraginaceae
Pear	*Pyrus communis* [+C]	Rosaceae
Plum	*Prunus domestica* [+C]	Rosaceae
Wallflower	*Erysimum cheiri* [+C]	Brassicaceae
Welsh poppy	*Meconopsis cambrica* [+C]	Papaveraceae
Willow	*Salix* species [+C]	Salicaceae
Wood cranesbill*	*Geranium sylvaticum* [+C]	Geraniaceae

*   *Flowering period can be considerably extended by assiduous dead-heading.*
** *The leaves of these plants make excellent green compost.*
[+C] *including cultivars.*

Solitary and primitively social bees active in summer and autumn

I know summer has arrived when the last red mason bees have become a sun-bleached grey and the first leafcutter bees (*Megachile* species) betray their presence by leaving beautifully neat excisions in the leaf margins of rose and snowberry shrubs. Species of *Andrena* no longer dominate the mining bee scene and, depending where you live, are replaced by species of *Melitta* and *Colletes* and even more *Lasioglossum* (Table 4.4). There are new mason bees to look out for and females of the wool-carder bee (*Anthidium manicatum*) can be found flitting about between the flowering spikes of lamb's ears (*Stachys byzantina*) and stripping small balls of the cottony down which covers the leaves and stems of this plant. They line and seal their nests with this home-grown cotton wool.

Top left:
Excisions where a leafcutter bee (Megachile *species) has removed discs from rose leaves*
(photo: C. O'Toole)

Bottom left:
Leaf of lamb's ears (Stachys byzantina) *with a patch of the hairy surface removed by a female wool-carder bee* (Anthidium manicatum)
(photo: C. O'Toole)

Table 4.4. Some solitary and primitively social bees active in summer and autumn

Species	Type of bee	Flight period	Distribution
Melitta haemorrhoidalis	Mining bee	Mid-July–late August, sometimes to mid-October	Widespread, but patchy
Melitta leporina	Mining bee	Late June–August	Southern England to Yorkshire, but patchy
Colletes daviesanus	Mining bee	Mid-June–mid-September	Widespread
Colletes hederae	Mining bee	Early September–late October, or early December	Southern and central England, but spreading
Andrena bicolor	Mining bee	*March–May; June–August	Widespread
Andrena flavipes	Mining bee	*March–May; May–September	Widespread
Andrena subopaca	Mining bee	April–late July	Ubiquitous
Halictus rubicundus	Mining bee	Females March–late September; males June–October	Widespread
Halictus tumulorum	Mining bee	Females April–mid-October; males early June–September	Widespread, commonest in south
Lasioglossum albipes	Mining bee	Females April–September; males June–September	Widespread
Lasioglossum calceatum	Mining bee	Females March–September; males July–September	Widespread
Lasioglossum morio	Mining bee	Females late March–October; males May–October	Widespread
Lasioglossum smeathmanellum	Mining bee	Females March–April to late September; males June–September	Widespread
Anthophora bimaculata	Mining bee	Late June–mid-September	Southern England, north to Buckinghamshire
Anthophora furcata	Wood-nesting mining bee**	Late May–August, sometimes September	Widespread
Anthophora quadrimaculata	Mining bee	Early June–late August	Southern England, north to Buckinghamshire and Cambridgeshire
Hylaeus communis	Stem nester	Late May, early June–mid-September	Ubiquitous
Chelostoma florisomne	Mason bee	Mid-May–mid-July	Widespread, north to Yorkshire
Chelostoma campanularum	Mason bee	Mid-June–late August	Southern England – Midlands
Osmia caerulescens	Mason bee	*April–August	Widespread
Osmia leaiana	Mason bee	Mid-March–August	Widespread
Megachile centuncularis	Leafcutter bee	June–August	Widespread, common
Megachile willughbiella	Leafcutter bee	Late June–end of August	Widespread
Anthidium manicatum	Carder bee	Late May–early August	Widespread
Xylocopa violacea	Carpenter bee	Late March–August	A spreading recent arrival

*   *A double-brooded species.*
** *Females excavate their nest tunnels in soft, semi-rotten wood.*

Plants for summer and autumn bees

The most attractive plants for summer and autumn bees are long-flowering species, such as members of the daisy family (Asteraceae), which serve the needs of short-tongued bees, while the mint family (Lamiaceae) and pea family (Fabaceae) meet the needs of longer-tongued bees (Table 4.5).

This is the time of year when the males of many species can be found at thistle-type flowers and at cornflowers and knapweeds (*Centaurea* species). Males of the metallic green

Halictus tumulorum and the even more metallic *Lasioglossum smeathmanellum* often congregate in large numbers at these flowers, their heads buried deeply, with their long antennae extending backwards. These flowers are important fuelling stations while the males are on the hunt for prospective mates.

Left:
Female mining bee (Halictus tumulorum) *on ragwort (Senecio species)*
(photo: L. A. Hislop)

Table 4.5. Summer- and autumn-flowering plants for solitary and primitively social bees

Common name	Scientific name	Family
Bellflower	*Campanula* species [+C]	Campanulaceae
Bird's-foot trefoil	*Lotus corniculatus*	Fabaceae
Blue cornflower	*Centaurea cyanus* [+C]	Asteraceae
Coneflower	*Echinacea* species [+C; NN] *Rudbeckia* species [+C; NN]	Asteraceae
Cotoneaster	*Cotoneaster* species [+C]	Rosaceae
Cross-leaved heath	*Erica tetralix* [+C]	Ericaceae
Firethorn	*Pyracantha coccinea* [+C]	Rosaceae
Great mullein	*Verbascum thapsus*	Scrophulariaceae
Hawksbeard	*Crepis* species	Asteraceae
Heather	*Calluna vulgaris* [+C]	Ericaceae
Ivy	*Hedera helix* [+C]	Araliaceae
Lamb's ears	*Stachys byzantina* [+C]	Lamiaceae
Lavender	*Lavandula* species [+C]	Lamiaceae
Meadow clary	*Salvia pratensis* [+C]	Lamiaceae
Oxeye daisy	*Leucanthemum vulgare* [+C]	Asteraceae
Poppy	*Papaver* species [+C]	Papaveraceae
Rosemary	*Rosmarinus officinalis* [+C]	Lamiaceae
Sage	*Salvia officinalis* [+C]	Lamiaceae
Shrubby germander	*Teucrium fruticans* [+C]	Lamiaceae
Spotted dead-nettle	*Lamium maculatum* [+C]	Lamiaceae
Thistle	*Cirsium* species [+C]	Asteraceae
Thyme	*Thymus* species [+C]	Lamiaceae
Viper's bugloss	*Echium vulgare*	Boraginaceae
Wild marjoram	*Origanum vulgare* [+C]	Lamiaceae
Yellow archangel	*Lamiastrum galeobdolon* [+C]	Lamiaceae

[+C] *Including cultivated varieties.*
[NN] *Not native, but these North American prairie plants are highly attractive to a wide range of bees.*

Catering for specialists

Females of many species of solitary bee specialise in their sources of pollen. Such bees are said to be oligolectic and they usually restrict their pollen-gathering to a particular family or genus of flowering plants (Table 4.6). Very few actually restrict themselves to a single plant species and all oligolectic bees will visit a wider range of plants for nectar; many will also collect some pollen from species they do not normally use as a pollen source.

It can be a rewarding experience to choose to grow plants on which bees specialise. Bees are very good at finding their special flowers and it is interesting to see how long they take to arrive in the garden.

Table 4.6. Some British Isles solitary bees that specialise in their sources of pollen

Species	Type of bee	Pollen sources
Melitta haemorrhoidalis	Mining bee	Bellflower (*Campanula* species)
Melitta leporina	Mining bee	Pea family (Fabaceae)
Colletes daviesanus	Mining bee	Daisy family (Asteraceae)
Colletes succinctus	Mining bee	Heather (*Calluna vulgaris*) and heath (*Erica* species)
Colletes hederae	Mining bee	Ivy (*Hedera helix*)
Chelostoma campanularum	Mason bee	Bellflower (*Campanula* species)
Chelostoma florisomne	Mason bee	Daisy family (Asteraceae)
Osmia leaiana	Mason bee	Daisy family (Asteraceae)

Top 10 Plants for Solitary Bees

Although a diversity of plants is best, a Top 10 list of plants is given in Table 4.7 for those who are short of space in their garden. This selection supports a range of solitary bee species through the season and would attract interesting species to a garden.

Table 4.7. Top 10 plants for solitary bees (in alphabetical order)

Plant name	Value to solitary bees
Apple (*Malus pumila*) or other fruit trees	A spring source of pollen and nectar
Bellflower (*Campanula* species)	Supports several specialist species
Comfrey (*Symphytum* species)	Particularly for hairy-footed flower bees (*Anthophora plumipes*)
Cornflower and knapweed (*Centaurea* species)	A summer source of pollen and nectar
Cranesbill, for example dusky cranesbill (*Geranium phaeum*)	A source of nectar over a long period
Firethorn (*Pyracantha coccinea*)	A summer source of pollen and nectar
Hawksbeard (*Crepis* species)	Attracts a wide range of species
Lamb's ears (*Stachys byzantina*)	Particularly for the wool-carder bee (*Anthidium manicatum*)
Welsh poppy (*Meconopsis cambrica*)	A source of pollen over a long period
Willow (*Salix* species)	A spring source of pollen and nectar

A little tolerance, please

Dandelions (*Taraxacum officinale*) and green alkanet (*Pentaglottis sempervirens*) may be regarded by many as weeds, but they are, however, very valuable resources for spring and early summer bees. I appeal here for some tolerance for these plants. My wife used to regard them with some hostility until I asked her to take a close look at them. They are, she finally agreed, rather beautiful.

Solitary Bees on the Move

The tree bumblebee (*Bombus hypnorum*) is not the only bee on the move in the British Isles. The ashy mining bee (*Andrena cineraria*) has been known as a widespread, but only locally common species. In recent years, though, it has broadened its range and in 2011 made its first appearance in my Leicestershire garden.

The violet carpenter bee (*Xylocopa violacea*) is a relative newcomer to the British Isles and seems to be spreading, having been recorded from southern coastal areas, Wiltshire, Ceredigion, Northamptonshire, Leicestershire and Cheshire. It is the size of a queen bumblebee, black, with dark, metallic violet wings.

The most spectacular newcomer is the ivy bee (*Colletes hederae*). It was recognised as a new species as recently as 1993 from southern European specimens and was first recorded in Britain in 2001. It has since spread along much of the south coast of England in both directions from its original Dorset locality and has spread north to localities in the Bristol and Oxford areas. The bee nests in dense aggregations in well-drained, sandy banks and has been recorded from gardens. It should be looked for wherever there is a profusion of ivy in flower.

The website of the Bees, Wasps and Ants Recording Society (see list of further reading and information at the back of this book) gives detailed distribution maps of nearly all bees found in the British Isles. These maps are updated at intervals and the website contains a wealth of information on bees, with many excellent photographs, which reflect the diversity of our bee fauna.

Top:
Violet carpenter bee (Xylocopa violacea) *photographed in France*
(photo: J. V. Adams)
Above:
Ivy bee (Colletes hederae) *photographed in France*
(photo: N. W. Owens)

Providing artificial nests

It is easy to get cavity-nesting species – masons, leafcutters and the wool-carder bee – to nest in artificial nests. You can make your own by packing hollow lengths of bamboo into suitable containers and placing them in a sheltered, south- or southwest-facing situation. A dry log pile or wooden shed are good positions because nest-seeking females explore wooden features of their environment when they search for their natural nest sites, which include beetle borings in dead wood. The red mason bee (*Osmia rufa*) is the most frequent user of artificial nests.

Right:
Heaven at the bottom of the garden for cavity-nesting bees, such as the red mason bee (Osmia rufa)
(photo: C. O'Toole)

The optimal length is 15 cm, with a diameter of 7–8 mm. Many garden centres now stock 'bee houses' based on bundles of bamboo in wooden boxes, sometime made to look like old fashioned beehives. These are expensive and lose much of their effectiveness by having the tubes too short and a large proportion of them too narrow. Bees that nest in such tubes produce offspring in which the sex ratio is biased too much in favour of males.

Right:
Brood cells of red mason bees (Osmia rufa) *in artificial nests made from glass tubes*
(photo: L. A. Hislop)

Far right:
Male blue carpenter bee (Ceratina cyanea) *on dry stems of blackberry* (Rubus fruticosus)*, which are nested in by the females. See blackberry on p.78.*
(photo: J. P. Early)

In my experience, the most effective design is that produced by CJ WildBird Foods of Shropshire. This comprises cardboard tubes of the correct length and diameter, each with an inner liner; these are deployed in a plastic container with a frontal grid to prevent access by magpies and other birds, which sometimes remove tubes to get at larvae.

CHAPTER FIVE

THE BEST PLANTS FOR BEES

WILLIAM D. J. KIRK[1] AND F. NORMAN HOWES[2]

[1] *School of Life Sciences, Keele University, Staffordshire, UK*
[2] *Formerly Royal Botanic Gardens, Kew, Surrey, UK*

The plants described in this chapter can be grown to help bees. Detailed information is provided about them and their value to honeybees, short-tongued bumblebees, long-tongued bumblebees and solitary bees. A quick reference guide on p.281 shows the best plants at a glance.

Left:
*Worker buff-tailed bumblebee (*Bombus terrestris*) collecting pollen from the anthers of flannel bush (*Fremontodendron *'Californian Glory')*
(photo: C. Stevens)

The aim of this chapter is to provide detailed information about the plants that help bees. In it we hope to encourage those who can, to grow these plants in their gardens and conserve them in the wild in order to increase the number and diversity of bee species. This is not a practical gardening book; rather, we aim to give the keen gardener the information he or she needs to plan a bee-friendly garden. However, a useful and comprehensive guide to garden plants is included in the list of further reading and information (p.287). Similarly, this is not a bee identification book and useful guides to help identify bees are also included in the list of further reading and information (p.287). The common bumblebee species are illustrated together in Chapter 3 (p.29) and some common types of solitary bee are illustrated together in Chapter 4 (p.43).

Bees visit a vast range of plants, but there is only space in this book to cover a few hundred, so we have selected the best from those that are cultivated or grow wild in the British Isles. Inevitably, this choice is rather subjective and some good bee plants have had to be omitted, but we have endeavoured to include those that are of value to honeybees, bumblebees and solitary bees throughout the season. Nearly all the plants are of value for the nectar or pollen in the flowers, but a few provide other resources too. For example, the leaves of lamb's ears (see stachys) and rose provide nesting materials for some solitary bees and the stems of blackberry provide nest sites. The best plants are often those that are visited by many types of bee but there are also plants that are of particular value to restricted groups of bees, such as long-tongued bumblebees or certain specialist solitary bees – many of these plants have also been included. Some of the plants may not be suitable for well-tended gardens and may be better in wild gardens, and for the wilder gardens still we have included some common weeds, such as dandelion and white clover, because they are excellent for bees.

The scientific names of plants and the families to which they belong are provided. Some of them may seem unfamiliar because they incorporate recent changes, following the classification in Stace's *New Flora of the British Isles* 3rd edition (see the list of further reading and information on p.287).

Each plant has an information box next to it, such as the example below.

The following abbreviations are used:

Cultivation: This describes the type of growth of the plant. The categories are: annual herb, biennial herb, perennial herb, shrub or tree. These terms are explained in the glossary on p.290. Shrubs are categorised as dwarf (0–1 m), small (1–2 m), medium (2–3 m) or large (over 3 m) and similarly for trees: small (3–10 m), medium (10–18 m) or large (over 18 m).

Honey: This indicates whether or not the plant is a major source of honey from honeybees in the British Isles (yes/no). This takes account of not just the nectar production of the plant but also the amount that is grown.

Honeybees: The number of squares indicates the value to honeybees.

ST Bumblebees: The number of squares indicates the value to short-tongued bumblebees.

LT Bumblebees: The number of squares indicates the value to long-tongued bumblebees.

Solitary Bees: The number of squares indicates the value to solitary bees.

These ratings are intended only as a very rough guide. The number of visits by different bees will vary considerably with place, aspect, season and year. A high rating does not guarantee visits and a zero rating does not mean that the relevant bees will never visit. Our knowledge of which flowers are visited by honeybees is fairly detailed because of the observations of many beekeepers over many years, but since bumblebees and solitary bees do not tend to be observed in this way we have far less information to draw on for these species.

Many of the plants in this chapter are illustrated with a picture of the flower, often with a bee visiting. When known, the species of plant and bee are given in the caption. In some cases, the plant or bee was not fully identified when the photograph was taken and the genus is known but not the species or hybrid. For example, 'Erysimum species' means that the plant is in the genus Erysimum but the exact species or hybrid is not known.

Some plant species are illustrated with a photograph of a pollen grain taken down a microscope. The photographs show the enormous variety of pollen shape and size that normally goes unnoticed. The diameter of the pollen grain, in micrometres, is given in brackets below the photograph (1000 μm = 1 mm). Although the grains are all reproduced at about the same size in the photographs, the actual sizes range from forget-me-not at 7 μm to evening primrose at 127 μm. The pollen has been stained purple so that it shows up well, but it is brightly coloured in real life and this can be seen particularly well in the lumps of pollen, known as pollen loads, on the hind legs of foraging bees. Although pollen is often yellow, it can be almost any other colour, including red, orange, green, violet, brown, black or white, depending on the plant species.

Left:
Stem-nesting bees (Hylaeus hyalinatus) *mating on sheep's bit* (Jasione montana) *with a second male watching. See bellflower on p.75.*
(photo: J. P. Early)

A

Achillea — Allium

Achillea — *Achillea* species

Family:	**Asteraceae**
Flowering:	**July to September**
Cultivation:	**perennial herb**
Honey:	**no**
Honeybees:	‖‖‖ ‖‖‖
ST Bumblebees:	‖‖‖ ‖‖‖
LT Bumblebees:	‖‖‖
Solitary Bees:	‖‖‖ ‖‖‖ ‖‖‖

The achilleas of the herbaceous border or rock garden are often worked by bees, particularly the stronger-growing kinds like the fern-leaf yarrow (*Achillea filipendulina*), which are best grown in large groups in mixed borders or shrubberies. The flowering period of these perennials is usually from July to September.

The wool-carder bee (*Anthidium manicatum*) lines its nest with plant hairs gathered from plants with hairy leaves and stems. The hairy leaves and stems of yarrow (*Achillea millefolium*) are often visited for this purpose. The females can be observed collecting their little balls of wool before flying off to the nest. The bees can be recognised by the rows of distinctive yellow spots down the body.

Mining bees (*Colletes* species), such as Davies's mining bee (*Colletes daviesanus*), particularly visit the flowers of yarrow and other daisy-like flowers. They can be recognised by the pale whitish stripes across the body.

Right:
Honeybee on yarrow (Achillea millefolium)
(photo: W. D. J. Kirk)
Far right:
A stem-nesting bee (Hylaeus *species*) *on achillea* (Achillea *species*)
(photo: J. P. Early)

Agrimony — *Agrimonia eupatoria*

Family:	**Rosaceae**
Flowering:	**June to July**
Cultivation:	**perennial herb**
Honey:	**no**
Honeybees:	‖‖‖
ST Bumblebees:	‖‖‖
LT Bumblebees:	‖‖‖
Solitary Bees:	‖‖‖

This wild plant is visited by bees for pollen, but does not yield nectar. Its familiar yellow flowers have a faint odour of lemon and appear in June and July, a time when there is an abundance of pollen available from other plants. If the plant flowered early or late in the season it would doubtless be more freely visited for pollen.

Right:
Flowers of agrimony (Agrimonia eupatoria)
(photo: W. D. J. Kirk)

Ajuga, see bugle

Alder — *Alnus glutinosa*

Alder is one of the early-flowering woodland trees bearing catkins, like willow and hazel, which may be a useful source of fresh pollen for early brood rearing by honeybees, provided the weather is warm enough for flight and trees are fairly near the hives. The catkins usually open in February or March. In very mild seasons, they may even open at the end of January. The tree is widely distributed in the British Isles, especially near streams and in damp situations. In the wetter parts of the region it is often abundant in oak woods. Other European and American alders are also useful for pollen.

Family:	Betulaceae
Flowering:	January to March
Cultivation:	deciduous medium tree
Honey:	no
Honeybees:	‖‖‖
ST Bumblebees:	—
LT Bumblebees:	—
Solitary Bees:	‖‖‖

Left:
*Catkins of alder (*Alnus glutinosa*)*
(photo: M. Kucharczyk)

Alfalfa, see lucerne

Alkanet, see anchusa

Allium — *Allium* species

The alliums of the flower garden, which may have purple, crimson, red, yellow or white flowers are visited by bees mainly for nectar. Were it not for the strong onion-like odour when crushed they would probably be more popular and generally grown. The genus *Allium* also includes important vegetable crops such as the onion (*Allium cepa*), leek (*Allium porrum*) and chive (*Allium schoenoprasum*), which are all good nectar plants. The many wild species, such as ramsons (*Allium ursinum*), which starts flowering earlier in April and is sometimes common in meadows and woods, is freely visited by honeybees and bumblebees. In the last century, their presence in herbage for cows sometimes caused tainting in milk.

Crops like onion and leek are of course normally harvested before they flower, but when they are grown on a field scale for seed, honey may be obtained during the blossoming period. Onion honey, which has been obtained on seed farms in California and elsewhere, has been described as amber in colour with an onion flavour that disappears as soon as the honey is fully ripened. It is likely that the honey of other allium plants would be similar. The handsome mauve flowers of chives, which are borne in such profusion in early summer, are worked most assiduously by honeybees and bumblebees both for nectar and pollen. In the case of the leek, the large flower-heads may contain from 2000 to 3000 flowers and each head must therefore contribute an appreciable amount of

Family:	Alliaceae
Flowering:	June to August
Cultivation:	perennial herb, grown from a bulb
Honey:	no
Honeybees:	‖‖‖ ‖‖‖
ST Bumblebees:	‖‖‖ ‖‖‖
LT Bumblebees:	‖‖‖ ‖‖‖
Solitary Bees:	‖‖‖

Above:
*Pollen grain of Canadian garlic (*Allium canadense*) (35 µm)*

nectar. Nectar is produced very freely under favourable conditions.

It should be noted that the few-flowered leek (*Allium paradoxum*) and the three-cornered garlic (*Allium triquetrum*) are invasive non-native species in the UK. The Wildlife and Countryside Act 1981 (Variation of Schedule 9) (England and Wales) Order 2010 prohibits planting or causing them to grow in the wild.

Right:
Red-tailed bumblebee (Bombus lapidarius) *on chive* (Allium schoenoprasum*)*
(photo: T. C. Ings)
Far right:
Flower of garden allium (Allium giganteum*)*
(photo: W. D. J. Kirk)

Almond — *Prunus dulcis*

Family:	**Rosaceae**
Flowering:	**February to April**
Cultivation:	**deciduous small tree**
Honey:	**no**
Honeybees:	‖‖‖ ‖‖‖
ST Bumblebees:	‖‖‖
LT Bumblebees:	‖‖‖
Solitary Bees:	‖‖‖

In the British Isles, the almond is grown almost exclusively as an ornamental or flowering tree and not for nuts as in warmer climates. The masses of pink blossoms that appear so early in the spring are always a pleasing sight to the beekeeper who knows their value to his bees for nectar and pollen after the long winter months of confinement. At this early season, much will depend on weather conditions and whether day temperatures are high enough for bees to fly. The flowers appear too early to be of much value to other bees. Fortunately, there are marked differences in the times when flowering commences between the different trees, usually to be found in streets and gardens, and this extends the total flowering period. Blossoms may be available for three weeks to a month. Usually a number of fine or warm days occur during this period, allowing bees to visit them. In some years the flowers may be severely damaged by frost.

In the south of England, flowering may take place any time from mid-February to early April, depending on the conditions and the variety of almond grown, 'Praecox' being one of the earliest. The flowering almonds belong to the bitter almond group for the most part and have darker coloured flowers than the sweet almonds, which are grown for nuts. In these the flowers are generally pale pink or almost white.

Nectar secretion in the almond flower is very profuse under suitably warm conditions. This may be demonstrated by placing a twig of almond blossom in a warm room overnight with the cut end in water and a bell jar or inverted vessel of some sort over it to maintain a still humid atmosphere. The next day the base of the flower will be observed to be swimming in nectar. The nectar is first secreted in small droplets on the brown inner surface of the cup-shaped 'receptacle' at the base of the flower. These increase in size if not sipped away by bees or other insects and eventually coalesce so that the base of the flower is flooded with nectar. Large almond orchards in warmer climates can produce large honey yields, but not in the British Isles where the climate precludes this. The almond also possesses extrafloral nectaries on the leaves, like the cherry and cherry laurel, and these are visited mainly by ants and wasps.

Alsike clover — *Trifolium hybridum*

Alsike or Swedish clover derives its name from the village or district of Alsike in Sweden where it originated. It was introduced to the British Isles over a hundred years ago and is sometimes used in seed mixtures for pastures, especially short leys. It can be used as a hay plant and is generally grown with grasses for support, being somewhat prone to lodge. This clover has the advantage of being able to thrive under soil conditions that are too wet and acid or too deficient in lime for white or red clover. It is also more resistant than red clover to 'clover sickness', which is a condition that arises when clover is grown too frequently. Unlike red clover, it makes little or no second growth after cutting.

The flower-heads are very like those of white clover, but more pinkish. The plant is of erect growth, 30–90 cm, and intermediate in general characteristics between red and white clover. Its flowering period is equally long.

The mechanism of the flower in alsike clover is the same as that in white clover and it is of about the same value as a honey plant. In some areas in fact it is considered to yield nectar more freely than white clover. The flowers are of value to a wide range of bees. Honey obtained from alsike clover is so similar to that from white clover that it is doubtful whether it is distinguishable at all.

Family:	Fabaceae
Flowering:	June to September
Cultivation:	perennial herb
Honey:	no
Honeybees:	||||| ||||| |||||
ST Bumblebees:	||||| ||||| |||||
LT Bumblebees:	||||| ||||| |||||
Solitary Bees:	||||| ||||| |||||

Alyssum, see sweet Alison

Anchusa — *Anchusa* species

Family:	Boraginaceae
Flowering:	June to September
Cultivation:	annual, biennial or perennial herb
Honey:	no
Honeybees:	||||| |||||
ST Bumblebees:	||||| |||||
LT Bumblebees:	||||| |||||
Solitary Bees:	|||||

Far left:
*Flower bee (*Anthophora *species) on anchusa (*Anchusa *species)*
(*photo: T. C. Ings*)
Left:
*Flower of anchusa (*Anchusa *'Loddon Royalist')*
(*photo: M. A. Kirk*)

Some good bee plants exist among the anchusas, both wild and cultivated. Their blue or purple flowers are worked predominantly for nectar. The garden anchusa or Italian bugloss (*Anchusa azurea*) is perhaps the commonest and best garden species, reaching 1–1.5 m. If

A

Almond — Anchusa

not allowed to seed, this perennial will flower continuously from June to September. Several named varieties are available. The Cape bugloss (*Anchusa capensis*), a much smaller plant but equally favoured by bees, may be grown as an annual or biennial. Alkanet (*Anchusa officinalis*) and green alkanet (*Pentaglottis sempervirens*), both natives of southern Europe, are found wild or naturalised in many parts of Britain. They are good nectar plants and are recommended for the wild garden. The latter has sky-blue flowers appearing in spring.

In alkanet and other anchusas, the nectar is secreted by the four-lobed base of the flower and is concealed in the flower-tube by hairs near the entrance. This protects it from rain and from short-tongued insects. As the tube is about 7 mm long in alkanet, the nectar is just within reach of the honeybee and is easily reached by long-tongued bumblebees.

Anise hyssop — *Agastache foeniculum*

This is a North American plant in the mint family (Lamiaceae). It bears heads of pretty mauve flowers and dark green leaves. The plant was first grown in the British Isles in 1826, but failed to take on as a garden plant at that time. It is said to have been widely distributed at one time from Lake Superior and Manitoba to Nebraska westward, and to have been used as a beverage plant and for seasoning by American Indian tribes, in the same way that we might use sage. Some of the earlier settlers reported fine crops of honey from the plant, the honey possessing in some slight degree the same fragrance. The flowers are undoubtedly very attractive to honeybees and bumblebees for nectar. It ranks high as a bee plant in North America and has the advantage of a long flowering season – from June until frosts arrive. Being a perennial and easy to grow and propagate, it is worth a place in the bee garden. As a general garden plant, however, its apparently straggling habit under British Isles conditions may be against it. Several named varieties are now available. Other closely-related species are known to be good nectar plants, especially the nettle-leaf giant hyssop (*Agastache urticifolia*), which in California yields crops of a light-coloured, minty-flavoured honey, and is slow to granulate.

Anthericum — *Anthericum* species

These tuberous-rooted plants are sometimes seen in gardens and are visited by bees for nectar and pollen. The Saint Bernard lily (*Anthericum liliago*) bears white flowers in May and June, whereas the branched Saint Bernard lily (*Anthericum ramosum*), which differs in having a branched flower spike, blooms in June and July.

A

Anise hyssop — Apple

Family:	**Lamiaceae**
Flowering:	**June to October**
Cultivation:	**perennial herb**
Honey:	**no**
Honeybees:	|||||
ST Bumblebees:	|||||
LT Bumblebees:	|||||
Solitary Bees:	|||||

Above:
Honeybee on anise hyssop (Agastache foeniculum)
(*photo: W. D. J. Kirk*)

Family:	*Asparagaceae*
Flowering:	**May to August**
Cultivation:	**perennial herb, grown from tubers**
Honey:	**no**
Honeybees:	|||||
ST Bumblebees:	|||||
LT Bumblebees:	—
Solitary Bees:	|||||

Apple — *Malus pumila*

Apple blossom provides an excellent source of pollen and nectar early in the season, when it is in short supply, and the open, bowl-shaped flowers allow a wide range of bees to access the nectar. Honeybees are well-known visitors because beehives have traditionally been brought to apple orchards for pollination. However, the flowers are also visited by bumblebees and by many solitary bees, such as the red mason bee (*Osmia rufa*), the tawny mining bee (*Andrena fulva*) and the ashy mining bee (*Andrena cineraria*). Red mason bees are increasingly used as alternative pollinators or to supplement honeybee pollination in apple orchards, where it is claimed they are over a hundred times as effective as honeybees.

The flowers of all the tree fruits grown in the British Isles are useful to honeybees for brood rearing if not for surplus honey. Sometimes honey is obtained from them in good districts in favourable seasons. These tree fruits include apple, pear, cherry, plum, quince, medlar, peach and nectarine. The only two fruit trees of no value to the honeybee are the mulberry and the fig.

It has long been held by beekeepers in the British Isles that the apple is the best of the tree fruits as a source of nectar and honey; superior to pear, plum and cherry. It is the last of these fruits to flower, and is therefore more likely to meet the warmer weather as the season advances. Flowering commences some time in April or May, according to season and district, and when stocks are sufficiently strong and weather favourable surplus honey may be obtained. The honey is generally light amber in colour and of good density and flavour. Colour varies with season and locality and may be quite dark. The flavour is inclined to be strong at first, but this passes off with age and it remains pleasantly aromatic. It granulates in time, but not rapidly. The great value of the apple flow is to the bees themselves, because it helps brood rearing and allows them to raise plenty of bees ready to take advantage of the main nectar flow later in the season.

Fortunately, there is a good deal of difference in the times when the various varieties of apple commence to flower – as much as three or even four weeks. In most seasons individual trees are in blossom for only about a fortnight, but the fact that several varieties of apple are to be found in most districts ensures a fairly long total flowering period. Although spells of cold or wet weather are not uncommon at this early period of the year, honeybees are generally able to collect appreciable quantities of nectar for their own use if not for the beekeeper. A honey yield generally does not come round more often than about one year in every five. Beekeepers in fruit districts may do better. In some seasons apples may be in flower at the end of March, but in the case of a late spring there may not be any blossom until the end of April or early May in the same district. Weather conditions in early March, whether warm or cold, have an important bearing on speeding up or retarding flowering. Apple varieties are fairly constant in their flowering periods relative to one another. Among the first varieties to flower are Red Astrachan, St. Edmund's Pippin, Irish Peach, Golden Spire, Reverend W. Wilks, Ribston Pippin and Adam's Pearmain. Varieties with mid-season flowering include Stirling Castle, Bramley's

Family:	Rosaceae
Flowering:	April to May
Cultivation:	deciduous small tree
Honey:	yes
Honeybees:	‖‖‖ ‖‖‖ ‖‖‖
ST Bumblebees:	‖‖‖ ‖‖‖
LT Bumblebees:	‖‖‖ ‖‖‖
Solitary Bees:	‖‖‖ ‖‖‖ ‖‖‖

Top:
Pollen grain of apple (Malus pumila) *(33 μm)*
Above:
Male red mason bee (Osmia rufa) *on apple*
(Malus pumila)
(photo: N. W. Owens)

Top:
*Female tawny mining bee (*Andrena fulva*) on crab apple (*Malus *species)*
Above:
*Female mining bee (*Andrena haemorrhoa*) on crab apple (*Malus *species)*
(photos: L. A. Hislop)

Family:	**Rosaceae**
Flowering:	**February to April**
Cultivation:	**deciduous small tree**
Honey:	**no**
Honeybees:	‖‖‖
ST Bumblebees:	—
LT Bumblebees:	—
Solitary Bees:	‖‖‖

Family:	**Brassicaceae**
Flowering:	**March to May**
Cultivation:	**biennial to perennial herb**
Honey:	**no**
Honeybees:	‖‖‖ ‖‖‖
ST Bumblebees:	‖‖‖ ‖‖‖
LT Bumblebees:	‖‖‖
Solitary Bees:	‖‖‖

Seedling, Peasgood's Nonsuch, Allington Pippin, Charles Ross, Lane's Prince Albert and Worcester Pearmain. Among the last varieties to flower are Royal Jubilee, Mother and King's Acre Pippin. The kind of stock used is known to influence the time of flowering to some extent.

Apple blossoms vary a good deal in colouring and in size. In some varieties the flowers are pure white, as in Christmas Pearmain, Claygate Pearmain, and Worcester Pearmain; in others pinkish, such as Lord Suffield, Brownlees Russet, Orleans Reinette, and Crawley Beauty; while not a few are richly marked with red or crimson as in Bramley's Seedling, James Grieve, Grenadier, King's Acre Pippin, and Lord Derby.

The apple flower, like that of many other tree fruits, is of the open type and the nectar very liable to be washed out by rain or severely diluted by dew. When dilution reaches a certain point the nectar ceases to be attractive to the honeybee. This may be the reason why honeybees are sometimes to be seen in the earlier part of the day working apple blossom for pollen only. Later, when the nectar has had time for its sugar concentration to be increased through evaporation and further secretion from the nectary, bees may again be seen working, this time for nectar. Apple pollen is produced abundantly and is pale yellow in colour with a slight greenish tinge when packed in the pollen baskets of the worker bee.

Crab apples and flowering crabs (of the single type) are probably of about the same value as bee plants as the culinary sorts. They are well worked for both nectar and pollen. The wild crab apple is often to be seen in oak woods in the south of England.

Apricot — *Prunus armeniaca*

As this fruit is best suited for cultivation under glass or against a south wall in the British Isles, it is nowhere near sufficiently abundant to be of importance to honeybee colonies. It flowers early and is visited for nectar and pollen. Early *Andrena* mining bees will also visit. In warmer climates where orchards of the trees exist the apricot is considered to be a valuable bee plant and a heavy nectar yielder in suitable weather.

Aquilegia, see columbine

Arabis — *Arabis* species

Among the several species of arabis or rock-cress found in gardens, the alpine rock-cress (*Arabis alpina*) is probably the most useful to the beekeeper, flowering as early in the year as March and yielding an abundance of pollen and nectar. It is common in gardens and rockeries everywhere although sometimes misnamed white alyssum or alison. Few plants yield nectar so freely so early in the year and so are much appreciated by honeybees. The Dutch name 'honigschub' (honey bush) illustrates the importance of these plants. The flower of alpine rock-cress has two pairs of nectaries at its base and the nectar collects in dilations of the sepals immediately beneath them. Various species and cultivars are available for gardens. These, apart from the double-flowered forms, should all be useful for bees.

Among the wild species of arabis, the hairy rock cress (*Arabis hirsuta*), which is sometimes common in dry rocky places, is also worked for nectar and pollen.

Left:
Flowers of arabis (Arabis '*Spring Charm*')
(photo: M. A. Kirk)

Aralia — *Aralia* species

The two aralias sometimes grown for their ornamental foliage and the oddity of their thick club-like branches appear to be good bee plants. They are the Japanese angelica tree (*Aralia elata*), a prickly shrub or small tree originating in Japan, and the Hercules club (*Aralia spinosa*), a native of the south-eastern USA, and very similar. The masses of small white flowers arranged in huge bunches or panicles up to 50 cm in length have been observed to be covered with honeybees in August and September in southern England. The flowers are very fragrant and the nectar, which must be secreted abundantly, is clearly visible.

Family:	**Araliaceae**
Flowering:	**August to September**
Cultivation:	**deciduous large shrub or small tree**
Honey:	**no**
Honeybees:	||||| |||||
ST Bumblebees:	||||| |||||
LT Bumblebees:	|||||
Solitary Bees:	|||||

Left:
Honeybee on Japanese angelica tree
(Aralia elata)
(photo: W. D. J. Kirk)

Arnica — *Arnica* species

These are hardy, dwarf, herbaceous perennials, allied to senecio (see separate entry) but not often cultivated. The yellow flowers of mountain arnica (*Arnica montana*), a good rock-garden plant, are visited by bees. Both the flowers and root or creeping rhizome of this central European plant have medicinal uses, and so are sometimes grown in herb gardens.

Family:	Asteraceae
Flowering:	June to August
Cultivation:	perennial herb
Honey:	no
Honeybees:	||||| |||||
ST Bumblebees:	||||| |||||
LT Bumblebees:	||||| |||||
Solitary Bees:	|||||

Right:
*Flowers of mountain arnica (*Arnica montana*)*
(photo: J. F. Wright)

Ash — *Fraxinus excelsior*

The small and inconspicuous flowers of this well-known tree, which are devoid of both sepals and petals, are borne in small clusters on the branches. They appear early in the spring and are known to be visited by honeybees for pollen, but are probably not of major importance.

Family:	Oleaceae
Flowering:	April to May
Cultivation:	deciduous large tree
Honey:	no
Honeybees:	|||||
ST Bumblebees:	—
LT Bumblebees:	—
Solitary Bees:	—

Asparagus — *Asparagus officinalis*

The flowers of the common asparagus of the vegetable garden or the asparagus fern of the flowerbed, are much sought after by both bumblebees and honeybees for nectar and pollen. They are pendulous and bell-shaped with a characteristic odour, the male flowers being conspicuously larger than the female. It has become naturalised in many parts of the world, seeds being widely distributed by birds. The wild asparagus (*Asparagus prostratus*) occurs in a few coastal districts of Britain and Ireland. Honey has been obtained from cultivated asparagus in other countries, which in France has been described as greenish and of mediocre quality and in California as amber or dark coloured, of lower market value than many other honeys.

Family:	Asparagaceae
Flowering:	June to August
Cultivation:	perennial herb, grown from rhizomes
Honey:	no
Honeybees:	||||| |||||
ST Bumblebees:	||||| |||||
LT Bumblebees:	||||| |||||
Solitary Bees:	|||||

Right:
*Male flower of asparagus (*Asparagus officinalis*)*
(photo: W. D. J. Kirk)
Far right:
*Pollen grain of asparagus (*Asparagus officinalis*) (23 μm)*

 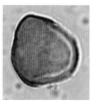

Aster — *Aster* species

A number of popular garden plants belong to the genus *Aster*, including the perennial asters or Michaelmas daisies. The genus contains over 400 species and most are probably useful to the honeybee, having a suitable flower structure. At Kew Gardens, numerous species of aster not in general cultivation have been observed to be freely worked. Most of the cultivated asters and Michaelmas daisies are native to North America where they often occur in large masses in their natural environment. Along with the wild goldenrods (*Solidago* species) (see separate entry), they afford good bee pasturage, especially in the autumn months. The honey obtained has been variously described, but whatever its flavour it affords useful winter stores. The Michaelmas daisies, now so much cultivated for late summer or autumn flowering, and largely of garden or hybrid origin, all appear to be freely worked for both nectar and pollen. They are undoubtedly very useful to urban and suburban beekeepers as late minor food sources, especially pollen, in areas where they are freely grown. Some of the North American asters are now naturalised in the British Isles.

The common annual garden aster so much used for bedding is not a true *Aster* in the botanical sense, the many varieties being derived from a Chinese plant, the China aster (*Callistephus chinensis*). The single forms are visited by bees, but not so freely as the Michaelmas daisies.

The name Michaelmas daisy is, confusingly, sometimes used for the sea aster (*Aster tripolium*), a wild plant found around the coasts of the British Isles and often brightening the salt marshes from July to September with its yellow-centred blue flowers. Beehives are sometimes moved to the coast to benefit from this late nectar source and a honey crop can be obtained, which is of good flavour. The sea aster is particularly visited by a species of mining bee (*Colletes halophilus*), which occurs along southern and eastern coasts of England.

Family:	Asteraceae
Flowering:	July to October
Cultivation:	perennial herb
Honey:	yes
Honeybees:	||||| ||||| |||||
ST Bumblebees:	||||| |||||
LT Bumblebees:	||||| |||||
Solitary Bees:	||||| ||||| |||||

Top:
*Common carder bee (*Bombus pascuorum*) on aster (*Aster *species*)*
Above:
*Male mining bee (*Lasioglossum calceatum*) on aster (*Aster *species*)*
(photos: J. V. Adams)

Aubrieta — *Aubrieta deltoidea*

Aubrietas are useful to many bees because they are among the first of our common garden plants to flower in the early spring and because they produce such masses of blossom. They supply their visitors with both nectar and pollen, the nectar being freely produced at the base of the flower and collecting in large drops in the cup-shaped bases of the sepals. The original plants were native to the mountainous regions of southern Europe, but there are now numerous garden forms and colour varieties in cultivation.

Family:	Brassicaceae
Flowering:	April to May
Cultivation:	perennial herb
Honey:	no
Honeybees:	||||| |||||
ST Bumblebees:	||||| |||||
LT Bumblebees:	||||| |||||
Solitary Bees:	|||||

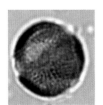

Far left:
*Pollen grain of aubrieta (*Aubrieta deltoidea*) (24 μm)*
Left:
*Aubrieta flower (*Aubrieta deltoidea*)*
(photo: W. D. J. Kirk)

A

Arnica — Aubrieta

Autumn crocus, see meadow saffron

Autumn hawkbit — *Scorzoneroides autumnalis*

Family:	**Asteraceae**
Flowering:	**June to October**
Cultivation:	**perennial herb**
Honey:	**no**
Honeybees:	||||| |||||
ST Bumblebees:	|||||
LT Bumblebees:	|||||
Solitary Bees:	||||| |||||

Right:
*Honeybee on rough hawkbit (*Leontodon hispidus*)*
(photo: W. D. J. Kirk)

Like the hawksbeard and dandelion, the yellow flowers of this plant are visited by honeybees and bumblebees, particularly the red-tailed bumblebee (*Bombus lapidarius*). The plant is closely related to the other hawkbits, such as the rough hawkbit (*Leontodon hispidus*), and was formerly classified with them, so it is also commonly listed under the scientific name *Leontodon autumnalis*. Yellow dandelion-like flowers of this type are visited by a wide range of solitary bees, such as species of mining bee (*Andrena* species) and small, black stem-nesting bees (*Hylaeus* species).

Avens — *Geum* species

Family:	**Rosaceae**
Flowering:	**May to September**
Cultivation:	**perennial herb**
Honey:	**no**
Honeybees:	||||| |||||
ST Bumblebees:	||||| |||||
LT Bumblebees:	||||| |||||
Solitary Bees:	|||||

Right:
*Honeybee on avens (*Geum *species)*
(photo: T. C. Ings)

The avens or geum of the rock garden and flower border is visited by bees mainly for its pollen. The same applies to the wild species. In the water avens (*Geum rivale*), large drops of nectar may be secreted on the base of the flower, which honeybees procure from outside the flower.

Azalea — *Rhododendron* species

Azaleas, like the closely-related rhododendrons, are popular with long- and short-tongued bumblebees. They can also be visited by solitary bees such as hairy-footed flower bees (*Anthophora plumipes*). However, they are rarely visited by the honeybee. This is possibly because in most cases the nectar is too deep-seated to be readily available, or perhaps grayanotoxins play a role (see rhododendron). However, in the case of the dwarf small-flowered azaleas, flowering in early spring, the blossoms can be freely worked for nectar by honeybees when the weather has been favourable.

It should be noted that the yellow azalea (*Rhododendron luteum*) is an invasive non-native species in the UK. The Wildlife and Countryside Act 1981 (Variation of Schedule 9) (England and Wales) Order 2010 prohibits planting or causing it to grow in the wild.

Family:	**Ericaceae**
Flowering:	**April to June**
Cultivation:	**deciduous or evergreen small shrub**
Honey:	**no**
Honeybees:	‖‖‖
ST Bumblebees:	‖‖‖ ‖‖‖
LT Bumblebees:	‖‖‖ ‖‖‖
Solitary Bees:	‖‖‖

Left:
*Flower of azalea (*Rhododendron occidentale *'Irene Koster')*
(photo: M. A. Kirk)

A

Autumn crocus — Azalea

Baby's breath — *Gypsophila paniculata*

Family:	**Caryophyllaceae**
Flowering:	**July to August**
Cultivation:	**perennial herb**
Honey:	**no**
Honeybees:	|||||
ST Bumblebees:	|||||
LT Bumblebees:	—
Solitary Bees:	|||||

Right:
Flowers of baby's breath (Gypsophila paniculata)
(photo: W. D. J. Kirk)

The myriad of tiny white flowers of this well-known perennial are visited by honeybees for nectar in July and August. This applies only to the single form and not to those with double flowers. The flowers of the alpine gypsophila (*Gypsophila repens*), a small perennial of the rock garden, also attract honeybees, as may those of other gypsophilas.

Balsam — *Impatiens* species

Family:	**Balsaminaceae**
Flowering:	**July to October**
Cultivation:	**annual herb**
Honey:	**yes**
Honeybees:	||||| ||||| |||||
ST Bumblebees:	||||| ||||| |||||
LT Bumblebees:	||||| ||||| |||||
Solitary Bees:	|||||

Above:
Worker bumblebee inside a Himalayan balsam flower (Impatiens glandulifera)
Right:
Honeybee dusted with pollen on Himalayan balsam (Impatiens glandulifera)
(photos: W. D. J. Kirk)
Far right:
Pollen grain of Himalayan balsam (Impatiens glandulifera) *(31 μm)*

The cultivated garden balsams (*Impatiens balsamina*) grown as hardy and half-hardy annuals are mostly double-flowered and of no use to bees. The Himalayan balsam or Indian balsam (*Impatiens glandulifera*), which is naturalised across much of the British Isles, is an excellent bee plant. It reaches 2 m in height and has large pink or white flowers with a wide mouth. Bees walk into the flower, disappearing out of sight, and draw the nectar from the narrow curved spur at the base of the flower. As this is only some 5 mm in length all the nectar is available to honeybees and short-tongued bumblebees, not just long-tongued bumblebees. In some areas, with the right weather conditions, a honey crop can be obtained. In entering and leaving a flower the bee's back is dusted white with the pollen from the overhead stamens. The common sight of the rear end of bumblebees sticking out of the flowers has given the plant the popular name of bee bums. The common carder bee (*Bombus pascuorum*) and the buff-tailed bumblebee (*Bombus terrestris*) are very frequent visitors. Another balsam favoured by bees and usually in flower in August and September is the amphora balsam (*Impatiens bicolor*).

It should be noted that the Himalayan balsam or Indian balsam (*Impatiens glandulifera*) is an invasive non-native species in the UK. The Wildlife and Countryside Act 1981 (Variation of Schedule 9) (England and Wales) Order 2010 prohibits planting or causing it to grow in the wild.

Baptisia — *Baptisia* species

This is a group of vigorous perennials from North America, not unlike lupins. Blue false indigo (*Baptisia australis*), which has stunning indigo blue flowers, is sometimes seen in cultivation and attracts honeybees and bumblebees.

Family:	**Fabaceae**
Flowering:	**June to August**
Cultivation:	**perennial herb**
Honey:	**no**
Honeybees:	||||| |||||
ST Bumblebees:	||||| |||||
LT Bumblebees:	||||| |||||
Solitary Bees:	—

Barberry — *Berberis* species

Far left:
Hedge barberry flowers (Berberis x stenophylla)
Left:
Worker buff-tailed bumblebee (Bombus terrestris) *on barberry* (Berberis *species*)
(photos: M. A. Kirk)

The wild barberry (*Berberis vulgaris*) occurs in some parts of the British Isles, especially on chalk. This prickly deciduous shrub bears clusters of small yellow flowers in May, which are attractive to bumblebees and honeybees. The nectar is secreted by nectaries at the base of each petal and collects between the bases of the stamens. The pale yellow pollen is discharged by the interesting movements that the stamens exhibit on being touched. Many other species of barberry are cultivated as ornamental shrubs and are worked by bees for nectar or pollen. The two best known are the hedge barberry (*Berberis* x *stenophylla*) and Darwin's barberry (*Berberis darwinii*). Both of these are evergreen and the former is much grown as a hedge plant, producing an abundance of blossom.

Family:	**Berberidaceae**
Flowering:	**April to May**
Cultivation:	**deciduous or evergreen medium shrub**
Honey:	**no**
Honeybees:	|||||
ST Bumblebees:	||||| ||||| |||||
LT Bumblebees:	|||||
Solitary Bees:	|||||

Basil — *Ocimum* species

The spikes of white, pink or purple flowers of both sweet basil (*Ocimum basilicum*) and bush basil (*Ocimum basilicum* variety *minimum*) are much visited by bees. These aromatic culinary herbs are much less cultivated or used in the British Isles than they are in some other parts of Europe, but are worth a place in the herb garden. There are many varieties, differing mainly in the size, shape and colour of the leaves. You can encourage flowering by not picking the leaves and stems.

Family:	**Lamiaceae**
Flowering:	**July to September**
Cultivation:	**annual to perennial herb**
Honey:	**no**
Honeybees:	||||| |||||
ST Bumblebees:	||||| |||||
LT Bumblebees:	||||| |||||
Solitary Bees:	||||| |||||

Left:
*Honeybee on sweet basil (*Ocimum basilicum*)*
(photo: W. D. J. Kirk)

Bay laurel, see cherry laurel

Bean, see field bean

Bearberry — *Arctostaphylos uva-ursi*

Family:	**Ericaceae**
Flowering:	**May to June**
Cultivation:	**evergreen small shrub**
Honey:	**no**
Honeybees:	‖‖‖
ST Bumblebees:	‖‖‖ ‖‖‖
LT Bumblebees:	‖‖‖ ‖‖‖
Solitary Bees:	‖‖‖

This small trailing shrub, which is locally abundant on heaths in Scotland, the north of England and northern and western Ireland, as well as in the colder parts of North America and continental Europe, is sometimes cultivated. It is especially useful for covering unsightly objects and as a ground cover. Clusters of rose-coloured flowers are produced in May and June. These contain nectar and are visited by bumblebees and honeybees, the nectar being secreted by a fleshy ring surrounding the ovary. Dense hairs protect and hold it at the base of the flower.

Bee balm — *Monarda* species

Family:	**Lamiaceae**
Flowering:	**July to September**
Cultivation:	**annual or perennial herb**
Honey:	**no**
Honeybees:	‖‖‖
ST Bumblebees:	‖‖‖
LT Bumblebees:	‖‖‖ ‖‖‖
Solitary Bees:	‖‖‖

The name bee balm or wild bergamot is used for species of this North American genus, on account of the aromatic sweet-smelling leaves. The main garden species are bee balm (*Monarda fistulosa*) with purple flowers, and scarlet bee balm (*Monarda didyma*) with scarlet flowers. There are also many different named varieties. The brightly coloured flowers are visited for nectar by long-tongued bumblebees, such as the common carder bee (*Bombus pascuorum*), but are generally too long for short-tongued bumblebees and honeybees, although occasionally the nectar can reach far enough up the flower-tube to be within reach. Short-tongued bumblebees can obtain nectar more reliably by making holes at the base of the flower and honeybees also use these holes. Other species with shorter flower tubes, especially spotted bee balm or horse mint (*Monarda punctata*), are better plants for honeybees and short-tongued bumblebees. Early last century, this species was sometimes grown in the USA as a crop for production of thymol. It was considered to be a good source of honey, which was light amber with a minty flavour.

Right:
*Worker garden bumblebee (*Bombus hortorum*) on bee balm (*Monarda *species)*
(photo: W. D. J. Kirk)

Begonia — *Begonia semperflorens*

The single-flowered dwarf begonias often used as bedding plants may be visited by honeybees for their pollen, which is yielded freely.

Family:	**Begoniaceae**
Flowering:	**June to October**
Cultivation:	**perennial herb**
Honey:	**no**
Honeybees:	‖‖‖
ST Bumblebees:	—
LT Bumblebees:	—
Solitary Bees:	—

Far left:
Pollen grain of begonia (Begonia cucullata) *(22 μm)*
Left:
Begonia flower (Begonia 'Green Leaf Rose') *(photo: W. D. J. Kirk)*

Bellflower — *Campanula* species

Bellflowers or campanulas are invariably popular bee plants and are visited for nectar and pollen by honeybees, bumblebees and solitary bees. The harebell mason bee (*Chelostoma campanularum*) is small (4–6 mm), thin, dark and almost hairless and collects pollen almost exclusively from bellflowers. The males fly around the flowers looking for mates and also feed at the flowers and rest inside them. It is not uncommon in gardens in southern and central England. The mining bee *Melitta haemorrhoidalis*, collects pollen exclusively from bellflowers and can be found sheltering in the flowers overnight. It has brownish hairs on the head and thorax and is mainly found in the southeast of England with a few records from Scotland and Wales and none from Ireland. The flowers are also visited by other solitary bees, such as some species of mining bee (*Andrena* species).

Family:	**Campanulaceae**
Flowering:	**June to September**
Cultivation:	**perennial herb**
Honey:	**no**
Honeybees:	‖‖‖ ‖‖‖
ST Bumblebees:	‖‖‖ ‖‖‖ ‖‖‖
LT Bumblebees:	‖‖‖ ‖‖‖
Solitary Bees:	‖‖‖ ‖‖‖ ‖‖‖

Many kinds of bellflower are cultivated ranging from tiny alpine plants (harebells), a few centimetres in height, to tall, vigorous-growing perennials like the chimney bellflower (*Campanula pyramidalis*), which is 1–2 m high. Canterbury bells (*Campanula medium*), in their many and richly-coloured forms, are included with them.

Among the better-known garden bellflowers, the Carpathian harebell (*Campanula carpatica*), popular for rock gardens, has been observed to be freely worked by honeybees on occasions, as has the peach-leaved bellflower (*Campanula persicifolia*). Many campanulas are good edging plants, and when grown in this way provide a greater quantity of blossom for bees to visit.

The wild campanulas of the woods and downs are also visited, but some of the species are comparatively rare plants. The clustered bellflower (*Campanula glomerata*) may appear in good numbers in dry hilly pastures and attracts bees. The harebell or bluebell of Scotland (*Campanula rotundifolia*) is also a common species. Bellflower pollen is often found in heather honey where plants occur together on the moors.

The sheep's bit or sheep's bit scabious (*Jasione montana*) is not, despite

Above:
Harebell mason bee (Chelostoma campanularum) *collecting pollen on peach-leaved bellflower* (Campanula persicifolia) *(photo: L. Hebdon)*

the name, closely related to the other scabious species (see scabious), but is in the same family as the bellflower. It is also very popular with a range of solitary bees, including stem-nesting bees (*Hylaeus* species).

Right:
*Mining bee (*Melitta haemorrhoidalis*) on bellflower (*Campanula *species)*
(photo: T. C. Ings)
Far right:
*Harebell mason bee (*Chelostoma campanularum*) on 2 mm grid squares*
(photo: L. Hebdon)

Bilberry — *Vaccinium myrtillus*

Family:	**Ericaceae**
Flowering:	**April to June**
Cultivation:	**deciduous small shrub**
Honey:	**no**
Honeybees:	‖‖
ST Bumblebees:	‖‖ ‖‖
LT Bumblebees:	‖‖ ‖‖
Solitary Bees:	‖‖ ‖‖

Above:
*Mining bee (*Andrena lapponica*) on cowberry (*Vaccinium vitis-idaea*)*
(photo: T. C. Ings)

The bilberry, also called blaeberry, huckleberry, whortleberry or whinberry, is often abundant on moors and in heathy mountainous areas. It is best known for its edible fruits and rarely exceeds 60 cm in height, with wax-like drooping flowers that appear from April to June. These secrete nectar freely and are relished by bees. Generally the plants are in out of the way places and not many honeybees are on the moors when they are in flower. The flowers of the less common bog bilberry (*Vaccinium uliginosum*) and cowberry (*Vaccinium vitis-idaea*), which appear later, are also worked for nectar. Some of the North American species in the genus *Vaccinium* are known to be good bee plants, especially the sparkleberry (*Vaccinium arboreum*). This small tree will grow in the British Isles, but is slow growing.

Bumblebees are closely associated with *Vaccinium* species and are common native pollinators of blueberry in North America. In the British Isles, several species visit the flowers, but the bilberry bumblebee (*Bombus monticola*) has a close association with bilberry, as the name suggests. It can be recognised fairly easily by the two yellow stripes on the thorax and the large red tail. It collects nectar and pollen from the flowers and often nests at the base of the plant. The distribution across northern and western Britain is declining rapidly, but it is expanding in Ireland.

The bilberry mining bee (*Andrena lapponica*) collects pollen almost exclusively from bilberry and cowberry and so is dependent on them. It occurs locally throughout the British Isles where these plants occur.

Birch — *Betula* species

Family:	**Betulaceae**
Flowering:	**April to May**
Cultivation:	**deciduous medium tree**
Honey:	**no**
Honeybees:	‖
ST Bumblebees:	—
LT Bumblebees:	—
Solitary Bees:	—

The birches are wind-pollinated and do not produce nectar, but they yield an abundance of pale yellow pollen early in the year, which is sometimes collected by honeybees. The silver birch (*Betula pendula*) is more common in the south, especially in the sandy soil of heathland. In the north and west the downy birch (*Betula pubescens*) is the more common species.

Left:
Catkins of silver birch (Betula pendula)
(photo: M. A. Kirk)

Bird's-foot trefoil — *Lotus corniculatus*

This small, clover-like plant is common in grassy places, old pastures and roadsides, often in association with white clover. It has heads of yellow flowers, which are conspicuous from June onwards and are followed by pods arranged like a bird's foot – hence the name. It is included in seed mixtures for permanent pasture, being particularly suitable for soils that are unsuitable for red clover. Possessing a deep tap-root, it is able to thrive in poor dry soils and is very drought-resistant. It is frequently to be seen in great abundance in chalk soils and pastures near the sea, where it is usually in flower about a fortnight before white clover. At some of the higher altitudes it may be the only plant of the clover family in pastures. The double-flowered varieties found in gardens are of no value to bees.

The single-flowered wild plant is a valuable source of nectar for honeybees and, being deep-rooted, the yield may well be less fickle than with white clover. Several bumblebees visit the flowers, particularly the red-tailed bumblebee (*Bombus lapidarius*) and the common carder bee (*Bombus pascuorum*).

The plant is of value to a range of solitary bees. The pollen is used by mason bees (*Osmia* species), including some that are rare within the British Isles. Two rare mason bees with a reddish brown thorax and black abdomen (*Osmia inermis* and *Osmia uncinata*) collect pollen from bird's-foot trefoil and are only found in parts of northern Scotland. At the other end of Britain, another mason bee (*Osmia xanthomelana*) collects pollen from bird's-foot trefoil and horseshoe vetch (*Hippocrepis comosa*) and is restricted to the Isle of Wight. It is endangered and is one of the rarest bees in the British Isles. Leafcutter bees (*Megachile* species) and mining bees (*Colletes* species) also frequent the flowers.

Family:	**Fabaceae**
Flowering:	**June to September**
Cultivation:	**perennial herb**
Honey:	**no**
Honeybees:	||||| |||||
ST Bumblebees:	||||| ||||| |||||
LT Bumblebees:	||||| ||||| |||||
Solitary Bees:	||||| ||||| |||||

Top:
Two-coloured mason bee (Osmia bicolor)
on bird's foot trefoil (Lotus corniculatus)
(photo: T. C. Ings)

Above:
Bird's foot trefoil flowers (Lotus corniculatus)
(photo: W. D. J. Kirk)

Bistort, see persicary

B

Bilberry — Bistort

Blackberry — *Rubus fruticosus*

Family:	**Rosaceae**
Flowering:	**May to September**
Cultivation:	**perennial root with biennial stems**
Honey:	**yes**
Honeybees:	‖‖‖ ‖‖‖ ‖‖‖
ST Bumblebees:	‖‖‖ ‖‖‖ ‖‖‖
LT Bumblebees:	‖‖‖ ‖‖‖ ‖‖‖
Solitary Bees:	‖‖‖ ‖‖‖ ‖‖‖

Top:
*Honeybee on blackberry (*Rubus fruticosus*)*
(photo: J. Craig)
Middle:
*Tree bumblebee (*Bombus hypnorum*) on blackberry (*Rubus fruticosus*)*
(photo: L. A. Hislop)
Bottom:
*Mining bee (*Andrena dorsata*) on blackberry (*Rubus fruticosus*)*
(photo: N. W. Owens)

The common blackberry or bramble of the hedgerow and field and the cultivated varieties grown for fruit in the garden or fruit farm are all extremely valuable to a wide range of bees. Flowering takes place late into the summer and provides nectar and pollen at a time when this is becoming scarce in many areas. Wild blackberries generally commence flowering in June or July, reaching a peak in August, but continue until cold weather and frosts arrive. In the case of the cultivated kinds, which may be grown extensively in fruit districts, the time of flowering depends upon the variety grown – whether early or late.

The wild blackberry grows and flowers freely in almost any soil, including chalk, poor acid sand, rich silt or clay soils, and never fails to be a source of attraction to bees. It is one of the commonest of wild plants and is to be found in all parts of the British Isles. It is very abundant in hedges, often in company with the dog rose (*Rosa canina*), along roadsides and in fields and meadows. In the scrub of commons and heaths and on wasteland it may be very prevalent and form dense clumps up to 3 m high and more across. It also occurs in the undergrowth of woods but is not so happy in shade and does not flower so freely as when growing in the open.

The common blackberry has a wide distribution. It occurs over nearly the whole of Europe and in central Asia and North Africa but not at high altitudes. In the British Isles it is particularly abundant. It has become naturalised in many other countries, even to the extent of becoming a troublesome weed, as in parts of New Zealand.

The flowers of the blackberry are produced on the long main shoots or short lateral ones, generally very freely and over a long period. It is common to see flower buds, flowers and all stages of fruit present at the same time, which adds greatly to the plant's attractiveness. This long flowering period, which may extend over several months, is largely what makes the plant of such value to bees.

There are many different forms or varieties of the wild blackberry throughout the British Isles and various classifications have been put forward for them. It is thought to consist of about three hundred micro-species that are very hard to separate. However, this is of no consequence for bees as they all appear to be useful as bee plants. Several wild forms or varieties with especially good fruits have been introduced to cultivation from time to time and grown as a crop. The flower colour of the wild plants varies, often from district to district, although white is the predominant colour. In some plants the flowers are light pink or tinged with pink, in others they may be pale mauve or lavender. The flowers also vary in their size and in their grouping. However, all are conspicuous by reason of their outspread character. The stamens also spread outwards as they ripen their pollen. Nectar is produced by a circular or disc-like nectary and is easily reached by short-tongued bees. Other visitors to the flowers include butterflies, wasps, beetles and flies.

In some heathland areas in the south of England where blackberries are a prominent feature of the scrub vegetation and there is no other important honey flow until the heather is out, beekeepers have obtained honey that is mainly blackberry. Such honey is usually of fair quality, although pure blackberry honey is considered to be not of the best and to be somewhat coarse in flavour. Pure blackberry honey is uncommon in the British Isles, except in the case of hives near extensive blackberry plantations. It is dense and slow to granulate. Whatever the flavour may be does not detract from its value to the bees as winter stores and it is here that the usefulness of the blackberry to the beekeeper mainly lies, although in the earlier days of beekeeping, the tough wiry stems of the blackberry, with the thorns removed, were frequently used in binding the straw when making skeps. As a honey plant, however, the blackberry is inferior to its close ally the raspberry, which yields a finer honey.

The flowers are excellent for bumblebees and are much visited by short-tongued bumblebees, such as the buff-tailed bumblebee (*Bombus terrestris*), the white-tailed bumblebee (*Bombus lucorum*) and the rapidly spreading tree bumblebee (*Bombus hypnorum*). A wide variety of solitary bees, such as species of mining bee (*Andrena*, *Colletes* and *Lasioglossum* species) and leafcutter bee (*Megachile* species) visit the flowers. The dry stems are nested in by small solitary bees, such as species of stem-nesting bee (*Hylaeus* species) and the blue carpenter bee (*Ceratina cyanea*), which occurs in southeast England.

Above:
*Violet carpenter bee (*Xylocopa violacea*) on blackberry (*Rubus fruticosus*) in France. This large bee appears to have established recently in England and Wales* (photo: J. V. Adams)

Blackcurrant, see currant

Black horehound — *Ballota nigra*

Black horehound and white horehound (see separate entry) are both good bee plants, but the former is better for bumblebees. It is found in hedges and along roadsides and has wrinkled leaves and clusters of purple flowers. The flower tube is rather long (7 mm) and so the flower is very popular with long-tongued bumblebees, such as the common carder bee (*Bombus pascuorum*) and the garden bumblebee (*Bombus hortorum*). Honeybees visit the flowers, but not nearly so freely as with white horehound. The mouth of the flower is wide enough for a honeybee's head to be partly inserted so they can still reach some of the nectar. Flower bees (*Anthophora* species) sometimes visit the flowers. The plant is common in England and Wales, but rare in Scotland and Ireland.

Family:	**Lamiaceae**
Flowering:	**June to September**
Cultivation:	**perennial herb**
Honey:	**no**
Honeybees:	|||||
ST Bumblebees:	|||||
LT Bumblebees:	||||| |||||
Solitary Bees:	|||||

Blackthorn — *Prunus spinosa*

All lovers of wild flowers welcome the snowy-white blossoms of the blackthorn or sloe, which contrast so well with its black, leafless boughs. Appearing as early as March or even February in some years, they are among the first harbingers of spring. The shrub is common in woods, coppices and hedges throughout the British Isles, but not in northern Scotland, and it flourishes in a variety of soils. It often forms extensive local patches, which arise from its free-suckering habit. The flowers are good sources of nectar and pollen in country districts, when weather

Family:	**Rosaceae**
Flowering:	**February to May**
Cultivation:	**deciduous small shrub**
Honey:	**no**
Honeybees:	||||| |||||
ST Bumblebees:	|||||
LT Bumblebees:	—
Solitary Bees:	||||| |||||

B

Blackberry — Blackthorn

conditions allow honeybees to fly. The flowering season is generally too early to be of much benefit to many bees, although it can be visited by short-tongued bumblebees and some solitary bees, such as mining bees (*Andrena* and *Lasioglossum* species). The tawny mining bee (*Andrena fulva*) is a frequent visitor and is widespread in England and Wales, but is rarely recorded from Scotland or Ireland. The females are about 8–10 mm long and their upper surface is covered in bright reddish brown hairs, which makes them easy to recognise on the flowers. Another species of mining bee (*Andrena varians*) is particularly associated with blackthorn and is uncommon, occurring in scattered sites across much of England and Wales, but not Scotland or Ireland. The bullace or damson (*Prunus domestica* subspecies *insititia*) and the wild plum (*Prunus domestica* subspecies *domestica*), so similar to the blackthorn, are also similar in their flowering characters and value as bee plants.

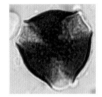

Above:
*Pollen grain of blackthorn (*Prunus spinosa*) (43 μm)*
Right:
*Female tawny mining bee (*Andrena fulva*) on blackthorn (*Prunus spinosa*)*
(photo: J. V. Adams)
Far right:
*Male mining bee (*Andrena chrysosceles*) on blackthorn (*Prunus spinosa*)*
(photo: T. C. Ings)

Bloodroot — *Sanguinaria canadensis*

The reddish-yellow juice of this pretty Canadian plant is what accounts for its name. It is sometimes grown in gardens for its white flowers, which appear in early spring. Like other members of the poppy family it is much visited by bees for pollen. It is a hardy plant that soon spreads and is well adapted for the semi-wild garden. Double-flowered varieties should be avoided.

Family:	**Papaveraceae**
Flowering:	**April**
Cultivation:	**perennial herb**
Honey:	**no**
Honeybees:	|||||
ST Bumblebees:	|||||
LT Bumblebees:	|||||
Solitary Bees:	|||||

Bluebell — *Hyacinthoides non-scripta*

Bluebell flowers secrete large amounts of nectar, but the flower-tube is too long (9 mm) for most bees to be able to reach it from the front of the flower. The main visitors are queens of the garden bumblebee (*Bombus hortorum*), the common carder bee (*Bombus pascuorum*) and the red-tailed bumblebee (*Bombus lapidarius*). Queen bumblebees have longer tongues than workers and so are able to reach the nectar at the base of the long flower-tubes. Although bumblebees are rarely seen visiting the many flowers in bluebell woods, the flowers may be very important to the few queen bumblebees that are flying in early spring and so they may influence the survival of bumblebees, particularly long-tongued species, in many areas. The flowers provide a rich supply of nectar to queen bumblebees at

Family:	**Asparagaceae**
Flowering:	**April to June**
Cultivation:	**perennial herb, grown from bulbs**
Honey:	**no**
Honeybees:	|||||
ST Bumblebees:	||||| |||||
LT Bumblebees:	||||| ||||| |||||
Solitary Bees:	|||||

a critical time – when they are starting colonies. Honeybees and short-tongued bumblebees, such as the buff-tailed bumblebee (*Bombus terrestris*), are able to reach the nectar from the outside of the flower near the base. They poke their tongue through the space between the petals and obtain the nectar without pollinating. This behaviour is known as base working. The pollen is also collected occasionally by honeybees, bumblebees and solitary bees, such as mining bees (*Andrena* species) and mason bees (*Osmia* species). The large bee fly (*Bombylius major*) also visits the flowers and is easily mistaken for a brown bumblebee or flower bee. It is actually a fly, but it mimics bees and lays its eggs in or near the nests of solitary bees so that its immature stages can feed in their nests. The fly can be distinguished by its hovering flight and the dark band along the front edge of the wings.

Spanish bluebells (*Hyacinthoides hispanica*) are often grown in gardens and are also beneficial to bees, but they are invasive and hybridise with the native bluebell. Their stems are more erect than those of bluebells and the flowers are borne on more than one side of the stem. The species has naturalised in many areas and hybridisation poses a threat to the native bluebell. Spanish bluebells should not be grown in gardens that are within pollinating distance of populations of wild bluebells.

Scillas are closely related plants that are often grown in gardens. They have smaller flowers than the wild bluebell, are well worked by bees for nectar and pollen in the early spring, and where many have been planted are of value to the beekeeper. The Siberian squill (*Scilla siberica*) and its varieties are among the most popular and earliest to flower. Nectar collects at the bases of the stamens. The pollen is bluish-grey in colour and conspicuous in honeybees' pollen baskets as it is brought in at the hive entrance in urban areas where scillas abound. The Siberian squill is useful for edging and for naturalising on lawns, provided the grass is not cut until the plants have matured. In some seasons it is in flower as early as February and supplies much-needed pollen for honeybees when few other sources are available.

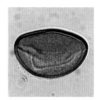

Top:
Pollen grain of bluebell (Hyacinthoides non-scripta) *(50 μm)*
Middle:
Early bumblebee (Bombus pratorum) *on bluebell* (Hyacinthoides non-scripta)
(photo: J. P. Early)
Bottom:
Mining bee (Andrena haemorrhoa) *on bluebell* (Hyacinthoides non-scripta)
(photo: T. C. Ings)

Borage — *Borago officinalis*

Borage is popular with beekeepers and has been grown by them in order to watch the bees at work on the attractive sky-blue flowers. Although it is an introduced species, it has been grown in the British Isles for many centuries, the flowers and leaves being a favourite ingredient in several summer beverages, especially Claret Cup or Pimm's. Two or three leaves impart a refreshing flavour resembling cucumber, which is often used in place of borage. Flowers are also used for garnishing salads. The plant is sometimes to be found in waste places and cultivated ground and when once established in a garden will come up year after year from self-sown seed. Over the last few decades, borage has been grown occasionally in the British Isles as a field crop for the seed oil, which is high in an essential fatty acid called gamma-linolenic acid (GLA), and is produced for its medicinal properties. This is usually sold as starflower oil. Borage crops have given beekeepers the opportunity to move beehives to

Family:	**Boraginaceae**
Flowering:	**April to October**
Cultivation:	**annual herb**
Honey:	**yes**
Honeybees:	‖‖‖ ‖‖‖ ‖‖‖
ST Bumblebees:	‖‖‖ ‖‖‖ ‖‖‖
LT Bumblebees:	‖‖‖ ‖‖‖ ‖‖‖
Solitary Bees:	‖‖‖ ‖‖

B

Bloodroot — Borage

Top:
Borage flower (Borago officinalis)
Above:
Honeybee on borage (Borago officinalis)
(photos: W. D. J. Kirk)

the fields and collect large crops of borage honey, which is very pale and runny with a mild flavour and is slow to granulate.

The plant is easy to grow and succeeds in most soils. It is best thinned to about 30 cm apart to allow the plants enough space. Flowering commences as early as April, depending on when it is sown, and continues until cold weather or until the plants are cut down by frost. It is often grown purely as an ornamental plant and violet-red and white-flowered varieties exist. For early flowering, seed may be sown in the autumn in many parts of the British Isles.

The nodding flowers of borage yield nectar freely over a long flowering season and are sometimes humming with honeybees, bumblebees and solitary bees. Owing to the inverted position of the flower, the nectar is not easily washed out by rain. They are similar in this respect to the flowers of the raspberry. Each flower has a black cone of anthers in its centre. The nectar is secreted at the base of the ovary and collects between, and is concealed by, the bases of the stamens. To obtain the nectar, the bee simply hangs under the flower and inserts its tongue between the stamens. In doing this, pollen is sprinkled on its body. The pollen of borage is a light bluish grey or almost white.

Honeybees will work borage freely, mainly for nectar, all day long but will sometimes forsake it for other plants such as lime and white clover when these are in flower and yielding well. Many bumblebee species visit the flowers for nectar and pollen, including the common carder bee (*Bombus pascuorum*) and the early bumblebee (*Bombus pratorum*). Some bumblebees, particularly the buff-tailed bumblebee (*Bombus terrestris*) and the white-tailed bumblebee (*Bombus lucorum*) buzz the anthers to produce a cloud of pollen, which allows them to groom the pollen and collect it very efficiently. The buzz only lasts about a second and is not the same as the hum that is produced as bumblebees fly. They only produce this special buzz on flowers that can be buzz-pollinated, such as kiwifruit, tomato and some types of rose (see tomato and rose). The flowers are also visited by solitary bees, such as flower bees (*Anthophora* species).

Box — *Buxus sempervirens*

Family:	**Buxaceae**
Flowering:	**March to May**
Cultivation:	**evergreen large shrub or small tree**
Honey:	**no**
Honeybees:	||||| |||||
ST Bumblebees:	—
LT Bumblebees:	—
Solitary Bees:	—

This well-known evergreen is much more abundant in other parts of Europe and Asia than in the British Isles, where it favours the chalk districts of the south, a good example being Box Hill in Surrey. The inconspicuous yellowish-green flowers appear early in the year and are sometimes, although not always, well worked by honeybees. The flowers yield both nectar and pollen, but it is probably the latter that is the chief attraction. It is yellowish green in colour and is produced abundantly.

The flowers are of two kinds, an apical female flower being surrounded by six or more male flowers. Both types of flower produce a small quantity of nectar. The action of the honeybee in collecting pollen was closely observed in the 19th century by the German botanist Hermann Müller: 'It frees the pollen from the still undehisced anthers with its mandibles, regurgitates some honey from its slightly protruded proboscis and then transfers the pollen by means of the front and mid-legs to the hind ones. All this, however, is done so quickly that the individual acts can scarcely be followed.'

Honey has been obtained from box in other countries and has been described as of indifferent quality. It is interesting to note that other members of a closely related plant family (Euphorbiaceae) are known to cause bitterness in honey. In parts of South Africa, honey from the wild tree euphorbias (Noors honey) causes a burning sensation in the mouth and throat that can last for hours.

A related plant, sweet box (*Sarcococca* species) flowers through the winter and can sometimes be of value to late/early honeybees.

Far left:
Pollen grain of box (Buxus sempervirens)
(29 µm)
Left:
Box flowers (Buxus sempervirens)
(photo: W. D. J. Kirk)

B

Box — Brassica

Bramble, see blackberry

Brassica — *Brassica* species

A large number of brassicas provide plentiful nectar and pollen for bees. The flowers are much visited by honeybees and bumblebees, such as the buff-tailed bumblebee (*Bombus terrestris*), the red-tailed bumblebee (*Bombus lapidarius*) and the common carder bee (*Bombus pascuorum*). Solitary bees, such as mining bees (*Andrena* and *Lasioglossum* species) are also frequent visitors.

Many brassicas are everyday vegetables such as cabbages, cauliflowers, broccoli, Brussels sprouts, kales, turnips and swedes. Others are less known, such as kohlrabi and Chinese cabbage, while still others, which are farm crops such as oilseed rape and mustard, are more important for bees on account of their being grown on a larger scale and maintained until flowering is completed. Some wild plants and weeds that are included in the genus *Brassica* or are closely related, such as wild cabbage (*Brassica oleracea*) and charlock (*Sinapis arvensis*) (see separate entry), are also good bee plants.

Most of the brassicas of the vegetable garden are harvested before the flowering stage is reached, but quite often unused plants or crops are left and flower before being removed. The flowers attract bees and in the case of large-scale planting for seed as on seed farms, honey may be obtained. This is basically the same as honey from oilseed rape with the same tendency to rapid granulation.

Family:	**Brassicaceae**
Flowering:	**April to August**
Cultivation:	**annual, biennial or perennial herb**
Honey:	**yes**
Honeybees:	‖‖‖ ‖‖‖ ‖‖‖
ST Bumblebees:	‖‖‖ ‖‖‖
LT Bumblebees:	‖‖‖ ‖‖‖
Solitary Bees:	‖‖‖

The flowers of all brassicas are very similar, being mostly yellow with four petals and sepals, whereas five is usual in most other plants. Nectar and pollen are usually produced freely, the nectar being secreted at the base of the flower, collecting there or in the cavities formed by the curved sepals.

Right:
*Mining bee (*Andrena nigroaenea*) on brassica (*Brassica *species)*
(photo: T. C. Ings)

Far right:
*Kale flower (*Brassica oleracea*)*
(photo: W. D. J. Kirk)

Broad bean, see field bean

Broom — *Cytisus scoparius*

Family:	**Fabaceae**
Flowering:	**May to June**
Cultivation:	**evergreen medium shrub**
Honey:	**no**
Honeybees:	|||||
ST Bumblebees:	|||||
LT Bumblebees:	|||||
Solitary Bees:	|||||

Broom is a common native shrub that occurs throughout the British Isles. In company with gorse and heather, it is found on moorland and sandy commons, often growing vigorously on bleak rocky hillsides and reaching 2 m in height. In some countries, outside its native range, the broom has become invasive, for example in New Zealand.

Its rich golden flowers appear in May and June and are frequently visited by honeybees. There is a difference of opinion as to whether bees obtain nectar from the flowers, although they certainly collect pollen, which is deep orange when packed in the bees' pollen baskets. The buff-tailed bumblebee (*Bombus terrestris*) and the white-tailed bumblebee (*Bombus lucorum*) are frequent visitors. A small, black mining bee with bands of pale hairs across the abdomen (*Lasioglossum laevigatum*) sometimes visits the flowers and occurs mainly in southern England and Wales. A very rare mason bee with a reddish brown thorax and black abdomen (*Osmia uncinata*) visits broom flowers, but is only known in a few sites in the Scottish Highlands.

Some of the cultivated or ornamental brooms, particularly the smaller-flowered sorts, are well worked by honeybees for both nectar and pollen. Notable among these is the early-flowering white Spanish broom (*Cytisus multiflorus*), which bears white flowers, and which is in bloom before most of the other species.

Above:
*Broom flower (*Cytisus scoparius*)*
(photo: D. R. Skingsley)

Right:
*Worker white-tailed bumblebee (*Bombus lucorum*) on broom (*Cytisus scoparius*)*
(photo: N. W. Owens)

Far right:
*Pollen grain of broom (*Cytisus scoparius*) (26 µm)*

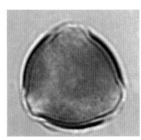

Bryony, see white bryony

Buckthorn — *Rhamnus cathartica*

This spreading shrub of woods and hedgerows is sometimes prevalent on chalk hills in the south of England. Its small greenish yellow flowers appear in dense clusters in May and are eagerly visited by bees for nectar. As the flowers are of a simple open type the nectar is exposed and available therefore to many short-tongued insects, including flies, which compete for it.

An allied shrub, the alder buckthorn (*Frangula alnus*), less dense of habit, grows mainly on damp acid soils. Like the buckthorn it was once cultivated to supply charcoal for gunpowder. Its greenish white flowers are visited for nectar and pollen in the early summer.

Many other introduced species of *Rhamnus* have been observed to be well worked for nectar at Kew Gardens. One of these is cascara buckthorn (*Rhamnus purshiana*) from western North America, the bark of which used to be harvested as the source of the drug cascara. It yields surplus honey in its native land.

Family:	Rhamnaceae
Flowering:	May
Cultivation:	deciduous large shrub
Honey:	no
Honeybees:	|||||
ST Bumblebees:	|||||
LT Bumblebees:	—
Solitary Bees:	|||||

Above:
*Flowers of buckthorn (*Rhamnus cathartica*)*
(photo: W. D. J. Kirk)

Left:
*Flowers of buckwheat (*Fagopyrum esculentum*)*
(photo: W. D. J. Kirk)

Buckwheat — *Fagopyrum esculentum*

Despite the name, buckwheat is not related to wheat and is not a cereal, but the grain can be ground to produce flour, so it is sometimes referred to as a pseudocereal. Buckwheat is extensively grown in many parts of the world, particularly Russia and China, but in the British Isles it has never been widely cultivated and is now only rarely grown as a crop. It is essentially a crop for light soils and does not thrive on heavy clay soils. The poorest of sandy or heathland soils will often grow a fair crop when all other grains are out of the question. This is the great value of buckwheat, along with its rapid growth and remarkable freedom from pests and diseases. However, there has been a major decline in the crop over the last hundred years because of the availability of nitrogenous fertilisers, which have boosted the yield of cereal crops and made buckwheat less profitable.

Buckwheat used to be cultivated in the British Isles, particularly in Norfolk and Suffolk and the fen areas, where it was called brank. It was used as a catch crop when it had not been possible to get the ground ready in time

Family:	Polygonaceae
Flowering:	June to August
Cultivation:	annual herb
Honey:	no
Honeybees:	||||| ||||| |||||
ST Bumblebees:	|||||
LT Bumblebees:	|||||
Solitary Bees:	|||||

B

Broad bean — Buckwheat

for the intended crop or when a cereal sowing had failed. Its early maturity was then of special value because of the reduced time available to grow it. Buckwheat can also be used for game coverts to attract pheasants and other game birds, in plantations to protect the roots of young trees from drought, for green manuring and for animal food.

Buckwheat is one of the few plants that offers the possibility of being sown as artificial bee pasturage on an economic basis, the value of the resulting grain crop offsetting cultivation costs. It is in those areas where sandy, acid soils of the heathland type prevail that it is likely to show most promise in this respect. In such areas clovers and lime trees are usually absent and there may be little important bee forage until late in the year when the heather is out. As bee fodder, three or four successional sowings at fortnightly intervals, commencing in early May or as soon as the danger of frost is past, is the best procedure. This ensures a long flowering period of 2–3 months. The young plants are very susceptible to frost and may be killed outright by even one light late frost.

Buckwheat has long been known to produce a good honey crop, with large quantities being obtained in the past in some countries, such as the north-eastern USA, Russia and parts of continental Europe. The honey is always dark and of characteristic strong flavour, not usually appreciated by those unaccustomed to it or those used to light, mild-flavoured honeys. It is also generally thick and difficult to extract. Buckwheat honey, however, is always in demand in the confectionery trade and used for special purposes, such as gingerbread, which it helps to keep moist. It crystallises with a coarse grain.

The buckwheat plant is of interest in that two distinct types of flower may be present, although always on different plants. One type has long stamens (the pollen-releasing part) and short styles (the pollen-receiving part) and the other has short stamens and long styles. Dimorphic flowers of this kind are known in other plants, such as the primrose. They assist in promoting cross-pollination. The white flowers are strongly fragrant and white sepals take the place of petals. Nectar is secreted by eight, sometimes nine, yellow nectaries bound together by a cushion-like swelling at the base of the ovary. The pollen grains in buckwheat are of two sizes, according to the type of flower.

Buckwheat does not always secrete nectar freely and the flow seems to be closely governed by the weather. Cool, moist conditions at flowering time are best for good nectar production. It is then that bees work the flowers all day. If the weather is inclined to be hot, bees are only attracted in the morning, and if it is very hot and dry, nectar production may cease altogether and bees pay little attention to the plants. In the USA, it has been found that cool nights and a mean temperature during the blooming period that does not exceed 21°C provide the best conditions for nectar secretion. It has been estimated that a hectare of buckwheat supplies about 100 kg (220 lb) of honey in a season. It is not sufficiently grown in the British Isles to yield a honey crop.

Buckwheat has received a lot of attention in relation to honeybees because of its value for honey production, but the shallow flowers with easily accessible nectar and pollen allow access to a wide range of insects, including bumblebees and solitary bees. Other beneficial insects, such as hoverflies are frequent visitors.

Buddleia, see butterfly bush

Bugle — *Ajuga reptans*

This common, native plant is also widely grown in gardens. There are many named varieties, including one with copper-coloured leaves. It produces dense ground cover from which emerge spikes of blue flowers. Rhizomes allow it to spread fast, so it can be somewhat invasive.

The flowers are particularly popular with bumblebees, such as the buff-tailed bumblebee (*Bombus terrestris*). A particular mason bee (*Osmia pillicornis*) is closely associated with bugle and collects pollen from the flowers. This bee has declined rapidly, but still occurs in parts of central and southern England.

Family:	**Lamiaceae**
Flowering:	**May to July**
Cultivation:	**evergreen perennial herb**
Honey:	**no**
Honeybees:	|||||
ST Bumblebees:	||||| |||||
LT Bumblebees:	||||| |||||
Solitary Bees:	||||| |||||

Left:
Bugle flowers (Ajuga reptans *'Catlin's Giant'*)
(photo: M. A. Kirk)

Burdock, see greater burdock

Burning bush — *Dictamnus albus*

This plant, which is native to central, southern and eastern Europe, has long been grown in flower gardens. Selected named varieties are available. It is also called candle plant or gas plant, because the oil secreted by the plant on hot calm days is inflammable. The pale purple, pink or white flowers with prominent stamens are visited by bees for nectar and pollen.

Family:	**Rutaceae**
Flowering:	**May to July**
Cultivation:	**perennial herb**
Honey:	**no**
Honeybees:	|||||
ST Bumblebees:	|||||
LT Bumblebees:	|||||
Solitary Bees:	—

Left:
Burning bush flowers (Dictamnus albus)
(photo: M. Kucharczyk)

Butterbur — *Petasites hybridus*

Family:	**Asteraceae**
Flowering:	**March to May**
Cultivation:	**perennial herb**
Honey:	**no**
Honeybees:	||||| |||||
ST Bumblebees:	||||| |||||
LT Bumblebees:	||||| |||||
Solitary Bees:	||||| |||||

Above:
*Butterbur flowers (*Petasites hybridus*)*
(photo: D. R. Skingsley)

This plant with downy leaves like coltsfoot, but larger, is often to be seen along river banks and in damp places. The flower stalks appear early, before the leaves from March onwards. Separate male and female flowers generally grow on different plants. They are attractive to bees, although not very conspicuous in themselves, and yield both nectar and pollen.

This plant is said to have been planted by Swedish beekeepers near their hives on account of its early flowering. For those who may wish to do likewise it is well to remember that the plant has long creeping roots with which it multiplies quickly, and that it may oust other plants or become a nuisance if not controlled. The flowers are useful to the first spring bumblebees and are also visited by solitary bees, such as mining bees (*Andrena* species).

A closely allied plant is the so-called winter heliotrope (*Petasites fragrans*) which is very like coltsfoot in leaf, and a rampant weed. It bears spikes of dingy lilac flowers from December to February. Honeybees visit the flowers when the weather is suitable. Like the butterbur it will take command of a garden if allowed to do so.

Right:
*Female mining bee (*Andrena haemorrhoa*) on buttercup*
(photo: L. A. Hislop)
Far right:
*Male sleepy mason bee (*Chelostoma florisomne*) on buttercup (*Ranunculus species*)*
(photo: N. P. Jones)

Buttercup — *Ranunculus* species

Family:	**Ranunculaceae**
Flowering:	**May to August**
Cultivation:	**annual or perennial herb**
Honey:	**no**
Honeybees:	—
ST Bumblebees:	—
LT Bumblebees:	—
Solitary Bees:	||||| |||||

The sleepy mason bee (*Chelostoma florisomne*) collects pollen almost exclusively from buttercups and so is dependent on them. It is distinctively long, thin and dark with narrow bands of short white hairs across the body. It occurs across England and Wales and is remarkable for being about the only bee that frequently visits buttercups, although some other solitary bees are occasional visitors.

The numerous buttercups so prevalent in pastures are otherwise of little consequence as bee plants. The flowers of many species seem never to be visited by honeybees at all, but those of others, for example the bulbous buttercup (*Ranunculus bulbosus*) and the closely related lesser celandine (*Ficaria verna*), both common species, may be worked for pollen on occasions.

Buttercups are, in general, unpalatable plants, owing to the presence of a poisonous compound called protoanemonin, and have caused poisoning in livestock. It is of interest, therefore, to note that the pollen of buttercups has occasionally been found to be harmful to honeybees in Switzerland and elsewhere in Europe and responsible for a form of 'May sickness'. Bad outbreaks of this malady have occurred in seasons when cold weather has retarded the flowering of the usual early pollen plants, like cherries and dandelions, but not the more hardy buttercups, causing the bees to collect larger amounts of buttercup pollen. In the British Isles, there is usually an abundance of other wholesome pollen plants in flower at the times when buttercups are in bloom, so presumably this form of bee malady is far less likely to occur. The harmful nature of buttercup pollen, or at any rate that of some species of *Ranunculus*, may be the reason why the flowers are so often completely neglected by honeybees and bumblebees.

Left:
Mining bee (Lasioglossum calceatum) *on buttercup (*Ranunculus *species)*
(photo: J. P. Early)

B

Butterbur — Buttercup

Butterfly bush — *Buddleja* species

Family:	**Scrophulariaceae**
Flowering:	**May to October**
Cultivation:	**deciduous to semi-evergreen medium shrub**
Honey:	**no**
Honeybees:	||||| |||||
ST Bumblebees:	||||| |||||
LT Bumblebees:	||||| |||||
Solitary Bees:	|||||

The common purple or white butterfly bushes or buddleias (*Buddleja davidii*) seen in gardens and on wasteland, which are so popular with butterflies, are of little use to honeybees for nectar as the flower-tubes are far too long, although they sometimes collect pollen. However, the orange-ball tree (*Buddleja globosa*) from Chile and Peru, which is very distinctive with its sweet-scented flowers in attractive orange balls, is well worked for nectar and is a good honeybee plant. Flowering usually takes place in early June, which is a dearth period in some areas, and the arrangement of the flowers in small spheres is such that a bee alighting on one of the heads is able to thrust its tongue into the separate flower-tubes one after another in an incredibly short space of time. The shrub is evergreen in mild districts and reaches 5 m. Weyer's butterfly bush (*Buddleja* x *weyeriana*) is a hybrid of the above two species and is also popular with bees. All three species of *Buddleja* are visited by a wide range of bumblebee species. They can also be visited by flower bees, such as the forked-tailed flower bee (*Anthophora furcata*), which looks like a rather hairy honeybee and occurs across England, Wales and southern Scotland.

Above:
*Pollen grain of butterfly bush (*Buddleja davidii*) (14 μm)*
Right:
*Honeybee on orange-ball tree (*Buddleja globosa*)*
(photo: T. C. Ings)
Far right:
*Honeybee on butterfly bush (*Buddleja davidii*)*
(photo: W. D. J. Kirk)

Buttonbush — *Cephalanthus occidentalis*

Family:	**Rubiaceae**
Flowering:	**August**
Cultivation:	**deciduous medium shrub**
Honey:	**no**
Honeybees:	||||| |||||
ST Bumblebees:	||||| |||||
LT Bumblebees:	||||| |||||
Solitary Bees:	|||||

This shrub is common in the eastern USA and Canada, where it is an important nectar source. The name buttonbush refers to the small white flowers, which are in globular heads. It grows well in the British Isles, but is not often seen, thriving best in moist situations and preferably peaty soils. The fact that it flowers fairly late, when few nectar sources are available in some districts, makes it potentially useful to bees and beekeepers.

Californian poppy — *Eschscholzia californica*

The Californian poppy or eschscholzia is always popular for mixed borders and thrives equally well on light and heavy soils. It has naturalised in a few places in the British Isles. Besides the original yellow and orange shades they are available in other colours, some of the pale rose and flesh coloured shades being particularly delicate. These plants are favoured by bees for pollen, which must be of a kind particularly to their liking. It is bright orange in colour. The flowers may sometimes be worked for nectar also, possibly secreted only spasmodically or in small amounts.

Family:	**Papaveraceae**
Flowering:	**July to September**
Cultivation:	**annual to perennial herb**
Honey:	**no**
Honeybees:	‖‖‖
ST Bumblebees:	‖‖‖
LT Bumblebees:	‖‖‖
Solitary Bees:	‖‖‖

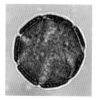 

Far left:
Pollen grain of Californian poppy (Eschscholzia californica) *(32 μm)*
Left:
Buff-tailed bumblebee (Bombus terrestris) *on Californian poppy* (Eschscholzia californica)
(photo: T. C. Ings)

Callicarpa — *Callicarpa bodinieri*

This attractive shrub is sometimes to be seen in parks and gardens, but is not widely planted. It originates from central and western China. The small pink flowers, which appear in July, are decidedly attractive to bees for nectar. Handsome foliage and violet berries are additional merits of the plant.

Family:	**Verbenaceae**
Flowering:	**July**
Cultivation:	**deciduous small shrub**
Honey:	**no**
Honeybees:	‖‖‖
ST Bumblebees:	‖‖‖
LT Bumblebees:	—
Solitary Bees:	‖‖‖

Left:
Callicarpa flowers (Callicarpa bodinieri)
(photo: W. D. J. Kirk)

C

Butterfly bush — Callicarpa

Camassia — *Camassia* species

Family:	**Asparagaceae**
Flowering:	**April to June**
Cultivation:	**perennial herb, grown from bulbs**
Honey:	**no**
Honeybees:	‖‖
ST Bumblebees:	‖‖
LT Bumblebees:	—
Solitary Bees:	‖‖

These hardy bulbous North American plants are often grown in gardens, especially for cutting. Their handsome, usually blue, flowers are attractive to bees for nectar and pollen, particularly those of Cusick's camassia (*Camassia cusickii*), large camassia (*Camassia leichtlinii*) and quamash (*Camassia quamash*). The bulbs of quamash were used as food by American Indians.

Right:
*Flowers of large camassia (*Camassia leichtlinii*)*
(photo: M. A. Kirk)

Candytuft — *Iberis* species

Family:	**Brassicaceae**
Flowering:	**July to August**
Cultivation:	**annual to perennial herb**
Honey:	**no**
Honeybees:	‖‖
ST Bumblebees:	‖‖
LT Bumblebees:	‖‖
Solitary Bees:	‖‖

Both annual and perennial forms of candytuft are much cultivated. The annual kinds, such as garden candytuft (*Iberis umbellata*), which flourish in almost any soil are probably the more favoured by bees. They are available in numerous colours besides white, including purple, lilac, crimson, rose and carmine. For early flowering, seed may safely be sown in the autumn in most districts.

Right:
*Flowers of perennial candytuft (*Iberis sempervirens*)*
(photo: W. D. J. Kirk)

Cardoon — *Cynara cardunculus* variety *cardunculus*

The large, purple, thistle-like flower-heads of this vegetable, which are
so like those of the globe artichoke (see separate entry), are much visited
by bumblebees and honeybees. Although cardoons are often cultivated
in continental Europe, the plant is seldom seen in the British Isles. The
leaves are blanched and used like celery. It can be grown as an imposing
garden ornamental, sometimes reaching a height of over 2 m.

Family:	Asteraceae
Flowering:	June to September
Cultivation:	perennial herb
Honey:	no
Honeybees:	||||| |||||
ST Bumblebees:	||||| |||||
LT Bumblebees:	||||| |||||
Solitary Bees:	|||||

Carrot — *Daucus carota*

Carrots (*Daucus carota* subspecies *sativus*) grown as vegetables are
harvested well before they can flower, but they do flower when grown for
seed and are then visited by bees, along with numerous other insects.
The nectar is exposed and consequently other short-tongued insects such
as flies have easy access to it and probably compete. This may explain
why the flowers are not as attractive to honeybees and bumblebees as
flowers with nectar that is reserved more exclusively for them. Honey
has been obtained from carrots when grown for seed in the past in
California and it was a light amber colour.

Family:	Apiaceae
Flowering:	June to August
Cultivation:	biennial herb
Honey:	no
Honeybees:	|||||
ST Bumblebees:	|||||
LT Bumblebees:	|||||
Solitary Bees:	||||| ||||| |||||

The wild carrot (*Daucus carota* subspecies *carota*), progenitor of the
cultivated sorts, and with similar flowers, is a very common plant in dry
places and the borders of fields, mainly near the coast. Honeybees and
bumblebees have been observed on it, but are not frequent visitors. The
easy access to the flowers is probably what makes the flowers popular
with such a wide range of solitary bees, including some rather unusual
ones: mining bees (*Andrena*, *Colletes* and *Lasioglossum* species);
leafcutter bees (*Megachile* species); cuckoo bees (*Epeolus*, *Nomada* and
Sphecodes species), which often look rather wasp-like; and some small,
black stem-nesting bees (*Hylaeus* species). One of the mining bees
(*Andrena nitidiuscula*) is dependent for pollen on wild carrot and closely
related plants. It is a small black bee with bands of white hairs across its
body and is restricted to southern England.

Left:
Carrot flowers (Daucus carota)
(photo: W. D. J. Kirk)

Castor oil plant— *Ricinus communis*

Family:	**Euphorbiaceae**
Flowering:	**July to September**
Cultivation:	**semi-evergreen small shrub, usually grown as an annual**
Honey:	**no**
Honeybees:	|||||
ST Bumblebees:	|||||
LT Bumblebees:	|||||
Solitary Bees:	|||||

Above:
*Flowers of castor oil plant (*Ricinus communis*)*
(photo: W. D. J. Kirk

Although this plant is an important oilseed crop in warmer countries it is grown only as an ornamental foliage plant in the British Isles. Several named varieties are available with attractively coloured foliage and fruit. Bees visit the flowers for pollen, which is produced freely. The flower spikes have the female flowers with red stigmas at the top and the male flowers with masses of creamy stamens at the base. Extrafloral nectaries exist at the base of the leaf.

There has been recent interest in growing the castor oil plant for biodiesel in tropical areas. Given that the castor oil plant contains some highly toxic substances, such as ricin, there has been concern about the possible effects of growing the plant extensively. Laboratory studies in Brazil, published in 2011, have shown that the pollen is toxic to adult honeybees and shortens their life when it forms about 10% of their diet. Although the effects have not been tested under natural conditions with ornamental varieties, there is a possibility that the pollen from garden varieties could be harmful to bees.

Catalpa, see Indian bean tree

Catmint — *Nepeta* species

Family:	**Lamiaceae**
Flowering:	**May to September**
Cultivation:	**perennial herb**
Honey:	**no**
Honeybees:	||||| |||||
ST Bumblebees:	||||| |||||
LT Bumblebees:	||||| ||||| |||||
Solitary Bees:	||||| |||||

Above:
*Garden bumblebee (*Bombus hortorum*) on catmint (*Nepeta *species)*
(photo: T. C. Ings)

The name catmint is now applied to several different plants. It used to be used more specifically for the erect-growing wild British plant bearing white flowers dotted with pink also known as catnip (*Nepeta cataria*) (see separate entry). The name has also been used for calamint (*Calamintha* species), but is more generally applied nowadays to the common garden catmints (*Nepeta* x *faassenii* and *Nepeta racemosa*) that originated from south-eastern Europe and Iran.

This is a widely cultivated perennial and is always an attractive plant with its dense prostrate habit, its grey-green foliage and blue flowers that appear in such profusion in May or June. It remains in flower for a long period and attracts bees continually. Nectar is secreted freely and the flower-tubes are just short enough for honeybees and short-tongued bumblebees, but sufficiently long to exclude flies and other insects with very short tongues. Long-tongued bumblebees, such as the garden bumblebee (*Bombus hortorum*), are very frequent visitors. Some of the larger solitary bees, such as species of flower bee (*Anthophora* species) and mason bee (*Osmia* species), also use the flowers. A scarce green-eyed flower bee (*Anthophora quadrimaculata*), which is found in southern England, but could perhaps be discovered further north, visits flowering catmint or lavender in gardens. It is a brown bee with bright green eyes. The plant is undoubtedly one of the best bee plants as any beekeeper that has observed it closely can testify, but unfortunately it is never cultivated on a sufficiently large scale for surplus honey to be obtained by honeybees – having no other use than as a garden plant. It grows well in almost any soil, even thriving on gravel. The flowers of several other allied species and named varieties of *Nepeta* that closely resemble the common catmint are also favourites with honeybees and bumblebees.

Catnip — *Nepeta cataria*

This wild plant is also known as catmint (see separate entry), but that name is now used more widely for the other species and varieties grown in gardens. It has white flowers spotted with purple or pink, which are very attractive to bees, and are held aloft on stems that can reach a metre in height. The species is much less common than it used to be and now grows in grassland and hedgerows in sites across England and Wales, mainly on chalk soils. The plant is strongly scented and the odour is attractive to cats – hence the name.

Family:	**Lamiaceae**
Flowering:	**June to September**
Cultivation:	**perennial herb**
Honey:	**no**
Honeybees:	||||| |||||
ST Bumblebees:	||||| |||||
LT Bumblebees:	||||| ||||| |||||
Solitary Bees:	||||| |||||

Early settlers from Europe introduced the herb into North America, where it has become widely naturalised and is regarded as a good bee plant. In the 19th century, Moses Quinby, who was one of the first commercial beekeepers in the USA, is said to have stated that if he were to grow any plant intensively for the honey it produces that plant would be catnip.

Catsear — *Hypochaeris radicata*

The yellow flower-heads of this weed, which somewhat resemble those of a dandelion, are visited by honeybees and bumblebees – probably mainly for pollen. A wide range of solitary bees also visit the flowers, including species of flower bee (*Anthophora* species) and mining bee (*Andrena*, *Colletes* and *Lasioglossum*) species.

Family:	**Asteraceae**
Flowering:	**June to September**
Cultivation:	**perennial herb**
Honey:	**no**
Honeybees:	|||||
ST Bumblebees:	|||||
LT Bumblebees:	|||||
Solitary Bees:	||||| |||||

Left:
Mining bee (Andrena fulvago) *on catsear* (Hypochaeris radicata)
(photo: T. C. Ings)

C

Castor oil plant — Catsear

Ceanothus — *Ceanothus* species

Family:	**Rhamnaceae**
Flowering:	**April to October**
Cultivation:	**deciduous or evergreen medium shrub**
Honey:	**no**
Honeybees:	‖‖‖
ST Bumblebees:	‖‖‖ ‖‖
LT Bumblebees:	‖‖‖
Solitary Bees:	‖‖‖

Most of these blue-flowered shrubs in cultivation are of hybrid origin. The flowers are visited by bees, but not in large numbers, and mainly for pollen. The species and varieties have a wide range of flowering seasons from spring through to autumn. Those that flower early in the year (April) seem to offer most attraction. The early bumblebee (*Bombus pratorum*) is a frequent visitor. The shrubs are generally inclined to be tender and are best with the protection of a wall. In their native home, North America, they occur in great abundance in some regions, yielding nectar and pollen. They are the plants known as 'wild lilac' in the Californian chaparral.

Right:
*Worker early bumblebee (*Bombus pratorum*) on ceanothus (Ceanothus species)*
(photo: J. P. Early)
Far right:
*Worker tree bumblebee (*Bombus hypnorum*) on ceanothus (Ceanothus species)*
(photo: T. C. Ings)

Celery — *Apium graveolens*

Family:	**Apiaceae**
Flowering:	**June to September**
Cultivation:	**biennial herb**
Honey:	**no**
Honeybees:	‖‖‖
ST Bumblebees:	‖‖‖
LT Bumblebees:	‖‖‖
Solitary Bees:	‖‖‖ ‖‖

The flowers of celery attract bees to some extent, as well as many other insects and in California, where this plant has been grown in bulk for seed, surplus honey has been obtained. Wild celery, the ancestral form of the cultivated plant, grows about ditches and rivers and in moist places generally. The clusters of small white flowers appear from June to September. White flowers of this type, arranged in a flat head with easily accessible nectar, are visited by a range of solitary bees (see carrot).

Centaurea — *Centaurea* species

Family:	**Asteraceae**
Flowering:	**June to September**
Cultivation:	**annual to perennial herb**
Honey:	**yes**
Honeybees:	‖‖‖ ‖‖
ST Bumblebees:	‖‖‖ ‖‖ ‖‖
LT Bumblebees:	‖‖‖ ‖‖ ‖‖
Solitary Bees:	‖‖‖ ‖‖ ‖‖

The centaureas are valuable to bees because they are rich in nectar. Various species occur wild as weeds or are cultivated as garden plants. One of the most frequent is common knapweed or hardheads (*Centaurea nigra*), a thistle-like plant that is a source of surplus honey in parts of Ireland. The honey is said to be golden, thin and with a sharp flavour and the pollen is greenish-yellow. The plant flowers freely and is common in fields, meadows and roadsides.

The greater knapweed (*Centaurea scabiosa*) is also a good bee plant. Clumps of it are sometimes conspicuous with their bright purple flowers on sea cliffs. The brilliant blue cornflower (*Centaurea cyanus*), which used to be a feature of ripening corn before herbicides were widely used, is also much sought after by bees, as are the garden forms of the plant often grown as annuals. Bees appear to work the blue, white, or many-coloured forms with equal fervour and do not discriminate between them.

Other centaureas that are particularly attractive to bees are the perennial cornflower (*Centaurea montana*), which is a more robust plant and is useful for cutting, Persian cornflower (*Centaurea dealbata*) and sweet sultan (*Centaurea moschata*). The yellow star-thistle (*Centaurea solstitialis*) is a Mediterranean plant that used to be widespread in the British Isles as a weed of arable crops, but changes in cultural practice have considerably reduced its abundance. It is a good plant for honeybees and surplus honey has been obtained from it in the past when it was common enough. It is unlikely to be abundant enough to be a honey source today.

Knapweeds are much visited by a range of species of bumblebee, particularly the red-tailed bumblebee (*Bombus lapidarius*). The flowers are also visited by solitary bees. The mining bee *Andrena marginata* particularly visits common knapweed (*Centaurea nigra*), field scabious (*Knautia arvensis*) and devil's bit scabious (*Succisa pratensis*) (see *scabious*). It is uncommon, with most records coming from southern England and Wales, although there are a few scattered records from Scotland and Ireland. It sometimes occurs together with the scabious bee (*Andrena hattorfiana*), which collects pollen from common knapweed, although it mainly visits field scabious (*Knautia arvensis*). This bee is scarce in southern Britain and declining rapidly. The cuckoo bee *Nomada armata* lays its eggs only in the nest of the scabious bee and so follows its decline.

Top:
*Pollen grain of cornflower (*Centaurea cyanus*) (37 μm)*

Above:
*Queen red-tailed bumblebee (*Bombus lapidarius*) on greater knapweed (*Centaurea scabiosa*)*
(photo: T. C. Ings)

Far left:
*Tree bumblebee (*Bombus hypnorum*) on centaurea (*Centaurea species*)*
(photo: J. Craig)
Left:
*Leafcutter bee (*Megachile ligniseca*) on centaurea (*Centaurea species*)*
(photo: J. P. Early)

Charlock — *Sinapis arvensis*

Early last century, charlock or wild mustard was one of the most troublesome and persistent annual weeds of farmland. Its bright yellow flowers were often conspicuous in cornfields throughout the summer months. It reduced crop yields and was a reservoir of diseases for turnips and other brassica crops. However, this problem for farmers was a major benefit to bees and beekeepers because charlock is a good source of nectar and pollen that is accessible to short-tongued as well as long-

Family:	**Brassicaceae**
Flowering:	**April to July**
Cultivation:	**annual herb**
Honey:	**yes**
Honeybees:	||||| ||||| |||||
ST Bumblebees:	||||| ||||| |||||
LT Bumblebees:	||||| ||||| |||||
Solitary Bees:	||||| |||||

C

Ceanothus — Charlock

tongued bees. Large areas of flowering charlock could appear after deep ploughing because the seeds can lie dormant for over 30 years and this allowed beekeepers to collect honey crops.

The weed is now much better controlled with herbicides and repeated ploughing, so large areas in flower are much less common. Oilseed rape (see separate entry) is closely related to charlock and similar in what it offers to bees, so the rise of oilseed rape has provided a substitute as charlock has declined.

The yellow flowers are produced in great profusion and are the same in shape and structure as those of other brassicas, such as mustard and oilseed rape. Six stamens are present, four long and two short. Nectar is secreted by nectaries at the base of the flower. Sometimes in charlock only those nectaries opposite the short stamens are functional. However, this does not seem to affect the total yield of nectar available to bees.

The flowers are very attractive to honeybees, which collect nectar and often pollen as well. The flowers are also much visited by bumblebees. The easy accessibility of pollen and nectar in the flowers of charlock and other brassicas allows many species of solitary bee to forage at the flowers, such as mining bees (*Andrena* and *Lasioglossum* species) and some small, black stem-nesting bees (*Hylaeus* species).

The honey from charlock is of excellent quality, being light coloured and of mild flavour. Colour may vary from water white to pale amber. When fresh it may have a faint hotness suggesting mustard, leaving a mild burning sensation after tasting, but this disappears as the honey ripens. Like honey from oilseed rape, the most notable feature of charlock honey is the rapidity with which it granulates. No other honeys in the British Isles can compare with them in this respect. Charlock honey can granulate within a matter of days and often granulates while still in the hive. For this reason, it should always be extracted with little delay. Its quick setting character is useful when set honey is required at short notice. It is also useful for mixing with other liquid honeys when granulated honey is required. A small quantity added to white clover honey gives a high-grade product, pure white and nearly solid.

Cherry — *Prunus avium*

The honeybee plays an important part in the pollination of the cherry, particularly in large commercial orchards where wild bees are rarely sufficiently numerous so early in the year to carry out the task adequately. Orchard owners often make special arrangements with beekeepers to have hives placed among the trees at blossom time. Skeps of bees were at one time imported from Holland just for this purpose. In return for its services, the honeybee gets both pollen and nectar in plenty from the blossoms when the weather is favourable. As a nectar producer, the cherry is considered to be second only to the apple among fruit trees. To obtain surplus honey from the cherry, stocks must usually be artificially fed to obtain the necessary size and there must be good weather conditions during the relatively short flowering period.

Top:
Pollen grain of charlock (Sinapis arvensis)
(31 µm)
Above:
Charlock flower (Sinapis arvensis)
(photo: W. D. J. Kirk)

C

Cherry

Family:	**Rosaceae**
Flowering:	**April to May**
Cultivation:	**deciduous medium tree**
Honey:	**yes**
Honeybees:	||||| ||||| |||||
ST Bumblebees:	||||| |||||
LT Bumblebees:	||||| |||||
Solitary Bees:	||||| ||||| |||||

In most parts of the British Isles, cherry trees are only sufficiently abundant to constitute a useful minor nectar source for honeybees and to be valuable in building up colony strength for the main nectar flow later in the year. In combination with other fruit trees, however, they help to supply the yields of tree fruit honey that are obtained in many areas in favourable seasons.

The flowers are visited by many solitary bees, such as the red mason bee (*Osmia rufa*), the tawny mining bee (*Andrena fulva*) and the ashy mining bee (*Andrena cineraria*). The red mason bee is a useful pollinator and is being developed as a managed pollinator of cherry and other fruit trees. Cocoons can even be purchased through the post. Although cherries flower too early for some species of bumblebee, they are visited by those that are active at the time, particularly the buff-tailed bumblebee (*Bombus terrestris*).

The wild form of the cherry, also known as the gean, and the bird cherry (*Prunus padus*), which are so conspicuous in spring in many areas are of similar value to bees. The bird cherry is common in the north, while the wild cherry is often abundant in the woods on limestone soils in the south.

The flowering or Japanese cherries are extensively planted in gardens and along streets. They are of similar value as bee plants and are well worked for nectar and pollen. One of the earliest is the Yoshino cherry (*Prunus* x *yedoensis*), which never fails to attract with its dense masses of fragrant, snow-white blossom. Double-flowered varieties are usually of no value to bees.

Morello cherries or sour cherries (*Prunus cerasus*) differ from sweet cherries in their flower characters as well as in the flavour of the fruit, but are also good sources of nectar and pollen. They flower later and are self-fertile, whereas varieties of sweet cherry are largely self-sterile and require cross-pollination with another variety in order to set fruit.

Top:
Pollen grain of cherry (Prunus avium)
(38 μm)
Above:
Flower of Morello cherry (Prunus cerasus)
(photo: M. A. Kirk)
Left:
Tawny mining bee (Andrena fulva) *on flowering cherry* (Prunus *species*)
(photo: L. A. Hislop)

C | Cherry

Cherry laurel — *Prunus laurocerasus*

Family:	**Rosaceae**
Flowering:	**evergreen large shrub**
Cultivation:	**April to June**
Honey:	**no**
Honeybees:	||||| |||||
ST Bumblebees:	||||| |||||
LT Bumblebees:	|||||
Solitary Bees:	||||| |||||

The cherry laurel, one of our most useful and quick-growing evergreens, is visited by honeybees and bumblebees. In addition to visiting the flowers, honeybees may be seen visiting the plant more or less at any time, particularly when ordinary nectar is scarce. They visit for the nectar secreted from the extrafloral nectaries on the under surfaces of the leaves, particularly on the young growth. Bushes may sometimes be found humming with honeybees working in this way.

The Portugal laurel (*Prunus lusitanica*), which starts flowering in June, and the bay laurel (*Laurus nobilis*) are also visited by honeybees and bumblebees. The bay is well known for its sweet-scented leaves, often used for flavouring soups and stews. Its small greenish-yellow flowers that appear in May or June are rich in nectar.

Right:
Cherry laurel flowers (Prunus laurocerasus)
(photo: W. D. J. Kirk)
Far right:
*Worker buff-tailed bumblebee (*Bombus terrestris) on cherry laurel (*Prunus laurocerasus)*
(photo: T. C. Ings)

Cherry plum — *Prunus cerasifera*

Family:	**Rosaceae**
Flowering:	**February to April**
Cultivation:	**deciduous large shrub or small tree**
Honey:	**no**
Honeybees:	||||| |||||
ST Bumblebees:	|||||
LT Bumblebees:	—
Solitary Bees:	|||||

The cherry plum or myrobalan is a well-known small tree in gardens and is sometimes used as a hedge plant or as a stock for grafting plums. It is among the first deciduous trees to flower and is prized on this account, trees being covered with the pure white blossoms in March. In hedges, it is easily confused with blackthorn, but it flowers earlier and the stems are generally spineless. The purple-leaved plum (cultivar 'Pissardii' or 'Atropurpurea'), which originated in Iran, is similar but has purple leaves and pale rose-coloured flowers. It is commonly cultivated on account of its foliage, often as a street tree. The flowers of both these cherry plums are a useful early source of nectar and pollen and are worked, mainly by honeybees, when the weather is suitable. They may be in flower even before the almond – in February in early seasons.

Right:
Cherry plum flower (Prunus cerasifera)
(photo: W. D. J. Kirk)
Far right:
Pollen grain of cherry plum (Prunus cerasifera) *(39 μm)*

Chicory — *Cichorium intybus*

This beautiful plant is one with many uses. It may be grown as a forage plant for stock, as a vegetable for the young leaves, as ground cover for game birds or as a crop for the roots (as a coffee substitute). It also occurs as a weed in wasteland and on the borders of fields, especially in light gravelly soils. The sky-blue star-like flowers, as large as a dandelion, appear from June onwards and are great favourites with honeybees and bumblebees. They supply nectar and pollen, but may be found to close up early in the afternoon. Chicory has been grown in the past in the British Isles for the roots and for seed and, when this was done on a field scale, honey was obtained. This was described as of a peculiar yellow colour, slightly greenish, even when granulated, and with a flavour reminiscent of chicory when fresh.

Family:	Asteraceae
Flowering:	June to October
Cultivation:	perennial herb
Honey:	yes
Honeybees:	||||| |||||
ST Bumblebees:	||||| |||||
LT Bumblebees:	||||| |||||
Solitary Bees:	|||||

Above:
Pollen grain of chicory (Cichorium intybus) *(43 μm)*
Left:
Chicory flower (Cichorium intybus)
(photo: W. D. J. Kirk)

Chinese teaplant — *Lycium chinense*

The Chinese teaplant, together with the Duke of Argyll's teaplant (*Lycium barbarum*), are the source of the wolfberry or goji berry, which is sold as a health food. The purple flowers of the Chinese teaplant are visited by honeybees and bumblebees for nectar and pollen. The plant has distinctive, long, arching, somewhat spiny branches and red berries. It has been grown, mainly near the coast, for hedging and has naturalised in some coastal areas, mainly in England.

Family:	Solanaceae
Flowering:	August to October
Cultivation:	deciduous medium shrub
Honey:	no
Honeybees:	|||||
ST Bumblebees:	|||||
LT Bumblebees:	|||||
Solitary Bees:	—

Left:
Pollen grain of Chinese teaplant (Lycium chinense) *(25 μm)*

C

Cherry laurel — Chinese teaplant

Chive, see allium

Cistus — *Cistus* species

Family:	**Cistaceae**
Flowering:	**May to July**
Cultivation:	**evergreen small to medium shrub**
Honey:	**no**
Honeybees:	||||| |||||
ST Bumblebees:	||||| |||||
LT Bumblebees:	|||||
Solitary Bees:	||||| |||||

These shrubs have mainly originated from the Mediterranean basin and are often referred to as rock roses – along with species of *Helianthemum* (see rock rose). Many of the garden forms are of hybrid origin, although there are also many species. Their brightly coloured flowers, which are usually present in great profusion, attract bees – mainly for pollen. The flowers seldom last more than a day, in some cases only for a morning. The fact that many cannot withstand severe winters accounts for their not being more generally cultivated.

Above:
Cistus flower (Cistus *x* dansereaui)
(photo: M. A. Kirk)
Right:
Mining bee (Andrena bicolor) *on cistus*
(Cistus *species*)
(photo: T. C. Ings)

Clarkia — *Clarkia unguiculata*

Family:	**Onagraceae**
Flowering:	**June to October**
Cultivation:	**annual herb**
Honey:	**no**
Honeybees:	|||||
ST Bumblebees:	|||||
LT Bumblebees:	|||||
Solitary Bees:	|||||

Right:
Pollen grain of pinkfairies (Clarkia pulchella*) (103 µm)*

The single-flowered forms of this hardy annual receive the attention of bees while the double-flowered forms, which include many of the choice newer varieties, have little or nothing to offer bees and fail to attract them. Related species, such as pinkfairies (*Clarkia pulchella*) and godetia (*Clarkia amoena*), are also visited by bees.

Claytonia — *Claytonia* species

The claytonias are native to northern Asia and North America, but two species, spring beauty (*Claytonia perfoliata*) and pink purslane (*Claytonia sibirica*), have long been naturalised in the British Isles. The first mentioned, originally introduced from northwest America as a pot-herb, is now a weed throughout much of the British Isles, but rarer in the west. It favours moist places, growing 30 cm high and bearing white flowers. Among those grown in gardens are some with pretty rose-pink flowers such as eastern spring beauty (*Claytonia virginica*). Those that bloom early in the year are attractive to bees, especially for pollen.

Family:	**Montiaceae**
Flowering:	**April to July**
Cultivation:	**annual herb**
Honey:	**no**
Honeybees:	|||||
ST Bumblebees:	|||||
LT Bumblebees:	|||||
Solitary Bees:	|||||

Left:
Flowers of pink purslane (Claytonia sibirica)
(photo: D. R. Skingsley)

C

Chive — Clematis

Clematis — *Clematis* species

These popular climbing plants produce an abundance of pollen from the many stamens of their flowers and this is often collected by bees. Some, but not all, yield nectar as well. Many of the showy garden forms are among those without nectar, including the widely grown 'Jackmanii' hybrids. The garden varieties have a wide range of flowering times from spring to late summer. The wild clematis or traveller's joy (*Clematis vitalba*) of the hedgerows yields nectar in addition to pollen, and is sometimes buzzing with bees. Short-tongued bumblebees, such as the buff-tailed bumblebee (*Bombus terrestris*) and the white-tailed bumblebee (*Bombus lucorum*), are frequent visitors. It flowers in midsummer, which is when other more important nectar plants are

Family:	**Ranunculaceae**
Flowering:	**April to August**
Cultivation:	**deciduous woody climber**
Honey:	**no**
Honeybees:	||||| |||||
ST Bumblebees:	||||| |||||
LT Bumblebees:	|||||
Solitary Bees:	|||||

Above:
Pollen grain of Himalayan clematis
(Clematis montana) *(23 μm)*
Right:
Honeybee landing on Himalayan clematis
(Clematis montana)
(photo: C. Stevens)

generally available. The flower is of interest in that the nectar is produced in droplets on the filaments (stamen stalks) and not from nectaries at the base of the flower.

Coltsfoot — *Tussilago farfara*

Family:	**Asteraceae**
Flowering:	**March to April**
Cultivation:	**perennial herb**
Honey:	**no**
Honeybees:	‖‖‖ ‖‖
ST Bumblebees:	‖‖‖ ‖‖
LT Bumblebees:	‖‖‖ ‖‖
Solitary Bees:	‖‖‖ ‖‖

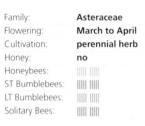

Above:
Mining bee (Andrena subopaca) *on coltsfoot* (Tussilago farfara)
(photo: N. P. Jones)

As one of the first wild flowers to appear in early spring and a source of pollen and nectar, this humble little plant is a good friend of bees and beekeepers. It is common in fields and pastures, especially on clay soils, and is one of the first plants to appear anywhere where ground has been disturbed. Railway tracks and the cuttings and embankments of main roads are sometimes covered with the plant. The felted leaves were much used medicinally at one time and collected in quantity for the manufacture of substitute tobaccos or herbal smoking mixtures.

The flowers generally spring up early in March, before the leaves, and are not unlike dandelions, but smaller. They close up at night and on dull days. Pollen is produced by the central male flowers of the flower-head and nectar by the outer female ones, a yellow circular nectary being at the base of each style (see glossary on p.290). The pollen is golden in colour and the individual grains densely spiny like other members of the same family.

As a bee plant the value of coltsfoot is primarily for pollen because weather conditions are seldom favourable enough for free nectar secretion at the early season when it flowers. It is doubtful whether the flowers are ever as freely worked as those of the dandelion are on occasions. The flowers are visited by many solitary bees, such as mining bees (*Andrena* and *Halictus* species).

Columbine — *Aquilegia vulgaris*

Family:	**Ranunculaceae**
Flowering:	**May to June**
Cultivation:	**perennial herb**
Honey:	**no**
Honeybees:	‖‖‖
ST Bumblebees:	‖‖‖
LT Bumblebees:	‖‖‖ ‖‖
Solitary Bees:	—

The wild columbine or granny's bonnet occurs locally across the British Isles in woods and damp places. The spurs of the flower, which contain the nectar, are long and only long-tongued bees, such as the garden bumblebee (*Bombus hortorum*), can reach it easily from the front of the flower. Short-tongued bumblebees poke holes at the base of the flower to access the nectar and honeybees sometimes steal the nectar through these punctures. The flowers may also be visited for pollen. This applies also to the garden aquilegias, although some varieties, particularly those with modified flowers, are not suitable for bees.

Left:
*Early bumblebee (*Bombus pratorum*)
collecting pollen from columbine
(*Aquilegia vulgaris*)*
(photo: T. C. Ings)

Comfrey — *Symphytum officinale*

Comfrey provides good ground cover and flowers over a long period. It is an excellent early source of nectar and pollen for bees. The flower tube is long, so access to the nectar from the front of the flower is restricted to long-tongued bees, such as the common carder bee (*Bombus pascuorum*). Honeybees and short-tongued bumblebees are unable to reach the nectar this way, but short-tongued bumblebees, such as the early bumblebee (*Bombus pratorum*), often pierce a hole at the base of the flower and rob the nectar. Honeybees can only access the nectar when the flower has been punctured by a bumblebee. Common carder bees (*Bombus pascuorum*) can vibrate the flowers to extract pollen more efficiently. They do this with a special kind of buzz which only lasts about a second and is not the same as the hum that is produced while bumblebees fly. Since the pollen has to be dry and powdery for this to work, they do it mainly when conditions are warm and dry. The downward-facing flowers of comfrey and creeping comfrey (*Symphytum grandiflorum*) are also often visited by hairy-footed flower bees (*Anthophora plumipes*). These large, furry bees look rather like bumblebees, but they have a darting flight. The females are black and the males are brown. They are absent from Scotland and Ireland.

Family:	**Boraginaceae**
Flowering:	**March to June**
Cultivation:	**perennial herb**
Honey:	**no**
Honeybees:	‖‖‖
ST Bumblebees:	‖‖‖ ‖‖‖ ‖‖‖
LT Bumblebees:	‖‖‖ ‖‖‖ ‖‖‖
Solitary Bees:	‖‖‖ ‖‖‖ ‖‖‖

Far left:
*Queen early bumblebee (*Bombus pratorum*) robbing nectar from creeping comfrey (*Symphytum grandiflorum*)*
Left:
*Queen ruderal bumblebee (*Bombus ruderatus*) on comfrey (*Symphytum officinale*)*
(photos: L. Hebdon)

C

Coltsfoot — Comfrey

Common fleabane — *Pulicaria dysenterica*

Family:	**Asteraceae**
Flowering:	**July to September**
Cultivation:	**perennial herb**
Honey:	**no**
Honeybees:	‖‖
ST Bumblebees:	‖‖
LT Bumblebees:	‖‖
Solitary Bees:	‖‖ ‖‖

Right:
Mining bee on common fleabane
(Pulicaria dysenterica)
(photo: J. Craig)
Far right:
*Mason bee (*Osmia spinulosa*) on common
fleabane (*Pulicaria dysenterica*)
(photo: N. W. Owens)

The yellow flower-heads of this wild plant, rather like a small marigold, are visited by honeybees and bumblebees to some extent. They are available for a long period in most areas – from July to September – and are usually to be found near streams and in moist places throughout the British Isles. Common fleabane, like many other yellow-flowered members of the daisy family (Asteraceae) that have accessible pollen and nectar, is visited by a wide range of solitary bees, including mining bees (*Lasioglossum* species) and cuckoo bees (*Stelis* species). The name 'fleabane' is also applied to several other plants, including many species of *Erigeron* (see fleabane).

Coneflower — *Rudbeckia* species

Family:	**Asteraceae**
Flowering:	**July to October**
Cultivation:	**annual to perennial herb**
Honey:	**no**
Honeybees:	‖‖ ‖‖
ST Bumblebees:	‖‖ ‖‖
LT Bumblebees:	‖‖ ‖‖
Solitary Bees:	‖‖ ‖‖

Right:
*Flower of orange coneflower (*Rudbeckia
fulgida*)*
Far right:
*Honeybee on coneflower (*Echinacea
species*)*
(photos: W. D. J. Kirk)

These North American plants, very like sunflowers with their large yellow heads but with a raised central cone, are good bee plants. They flower in the late summer and autumn and when in sufficient numbers may, along with other autumn flowers, assist in supplying winter stores for honeybees. Several related species are commonly grown in gardens, including orange coneflower (*Rudbeckia fulgida*), black-eyed Susan (*Rudbeckia hirta*) and cutleaf coneflower (*Rudbeckia laciniata*), which has deeply-divided leaves and is one of the tallest, growing to 3 m in height. Both are sometimes freely worked by honeybees and bumblebees for nectar. The name 'coneflower' is also used for the many *Echinacea* species, which are closely related and look very similar. They flower at the same time and provide the same value to bees.

Cotoneaster — *Cotoneaster* species

Bumblebees are strongly attracted to cotoneasters and the loud hum that they produce can often be heard from several metres away. Wall cotoneaster (*Cotoneaster horizontalis*) and creeping cotoneaster (*Cotoneaster adpressus*) are two of the most attractive, despite having flowers that are small and not very obvious. Short-tongued bumblebees, such as the early bumblebee (*Bombus pratorum*), the red-tailed bumblebee (*Bombus lapidarius*), the buff-tailed bumblebee (*Bombus terrestris*) and the white-tailed bumblebee (*Bombus lucorum*) are frequent visitors. Honeybees can sometimes also be abundant and solitary bees, such as mining bees (*Andrena* species), are also commonly seen.

This large group of deciduous and evergreen shrubs contains some excellent nectar plants. About two dozen different species have been recorded as well-worked by honeybees at Kew Gardens. Few flowers are so persistently visited as those of some of the commonly cultivated cotoneasters. Even in the middle of nectar flow from lime trees, certain cotoneasters have been observed covered with honeybees which suggests that the nectar may be of high sugar content or at any rate especially attractive to the honeybee. Nectar is obviously secreted very copiously in many instances. This may be seen by placing sprigs of blossom in water overnight in a warm, close atmosphere, when the bases of the flowers will be found to be covered in nectar by morning. Secretion takes place from the fleshy inner wall of the base of the flower as in the almond and other members of the rose family (Rosaceae).

The species most commonly cultivated in the British Isles as decorative shrubs, largely for their attractive berries and in some instances as hedges, are probably the Himalayan cotoneaster (*Cotoneaster simonsii*), small-leaved cotoneaster (*Cotoneaster microphyllus*), Tibetan cotoneaster (*Cotoneaster conspicuus*), tree cotoneaster (*Cotoneaster frigidus*) and wall cotoneaster (*Cotoneaster horizontalis*). These are all popular with bees and are mostly from the Himalayas. The two first mentioned have become quite extensively naturalised across the British Isles, their seed being carried by birds. The tree cotoneaster (*Cotoneaster frigidus*), as the name indicates, develops into a small tree, while the wall cotoneaster (*Cotoneaster horizontalis*), is low-growing and well-suited for training on walls or wooden fences. Cotoneasters are among the easiest subjects to grow in the garden or shrubbery and thrive in any soil. Careful choice of varieties can increase the benefit to bees by extending the flowering season over several months.

It should be noted that the wall cotoneaster (*Cotoneaster horizontalis*), entire-leaved cotoneaster (*Cotoneaster integrifolius*), Himalayan cotoneaster (*Cotoneaster simonsii*), hollyberry cotoneaster (*Cotoneaster bullatus*) and small-leaved cotoneaster (*Cotoneaster microphyllus*) are invasive non-native species in the UK. The Wildlife and Countryside Act 1981 (Variation of Schedule 9) (England and Wales) Order 2010 prohibits planting or causing them to grow in the wild.

Family:	**Rosaceae**
Flowering:	**May to July**
Cultivation:	**evergreen and deciduous small shrub to small tree**
Honey:	**no**
Honeybees:	||||| ||||| |||||
ST Bumblebees:	||||| ||||| |||||
LT Bumblebees:	||||| |||||
Solitary Bees:	||||| |||||

Top:
Pollen grain of wall cotoneaster (Cotoneaster horizontalis) *(34 μm)*
Middle:
Buff-tailed bumblebee (Bombus terrestris) *on wall cotoneaster* (Cotoneaster horizontalis)
Bottom:
Red-tailed bumblebee (Bombus lapidarius) *on wall cotoneaster* (Cotoneaster horizontalis)
(photos: W. D. J. Kirk)

C

Common fleabane — Cotoneaster

Courgette, see vegetable marrow

Cow-wheat — *Melampyrum pratense*

Family:	**Orobanchaceae**
Flowering:	**May to October**
Cultivation:	**annual herb**
Honey:	**no**
Honeybees:	|||||
ST Bumblebees:	|||||
LT Bumblebees:	||||| |||||
Solitary Bees:	|||||

This native plant has rather understated yellow flowers and, perhaps as a result, is not well known. The flower-tube is about 14–15 mm long and so only long-tongued bumblebees can obtain nectar from the front of the flower. Although this restriction might appear to make the plant less favourable to bees, such plants are reserving more nectar for long-tongued bumblebees, which are the bumblebees that are declining fastest and so need most help. Nectar is produced freely at the base of the flower and may rise 2–3 mm in the flower-tube. Short-tongued bumblebees sometimes rob the nectar by poking a hole at the base of the flower and honeybees then reach the nectar through these holes. A curious feature of the plant is that it bears nectar-secreting trichomes or hairs that attract ants.

Cranesbill — *Geranium* species

Family:	**Geraniaceae**
Flowering:	**May to September**
Cultivation:	**perennial herb**
Honey:	**no**
Honeybees:	||||| |||||
ST Bumblebees:	||||| |||||
LT Bumblebees:	||||| |||||
Solitary Bees:	||||| |||||

The common purple-flowered meadow cranesbill or wild geranium (*Geranium pratense*) that is common around thickets and in damp places is a good bee plant. So also are several other wild and garden geraniums, including the bloody cranesbill (*Geranium sanguineum*), long-stalked cranesbill (*Geranium columbinum*), marsh cranesbill (*Geranium palustre*) and dusky cranesbill (*Geranium phaeum*). The last mentioned, although rare as a wild plant, is grown in gardens. Its purplish-black flowers appear in May and are sometimes covered with bees seeking nectar from morning till night.

The open flower makes the nectar accessible to a wide range of bees, including short-tongued and long-tongued bumblebees. The flowers are regularly visited by solitary bees, such as mason bees (*Osmia* species).

In geraniums, nectar is usually secreted at the bases of the stamens. The pollen grain is large and distinctive, being rough with a fine network pattern.

The true geraniums, or cranesbills, should not be confused with the pelargoniums – to which the scarlet bedding geraniums belong – and these are not nearly such good bee plants.

Right:
Red mason bee (Osmia rufa) *on geranium*
(Geranium *species*)
(*photo: L. Hebdon*)
Far right:
Pollen grain of marsh cranesbill
(Geranium palustre) *(76 μm)*

Crimson clover — *Trifolium incarnatum*

This clover, also called Italian or carnation clover, is an annual and not a perennial like most clovers. It is a native of southern Europe and was at one time grown in flower gardens on account of its showy, deep crimson, flower-heads, which are elongate rather than globular in shape.

Early last century, it was often grown for fodder for cows and sheep, particularly in southern parts of the British Isles. Fields in flower presented a magnificent sight and were conspicuous from far away. The plants were usually grazed before they were in full flower, because the flower-heads become somewhat prickly with age and can cause digestive troubles, which meant that bees were unable to benefit from all the flowers. Despite this, the fields were still an excellent food source for bees. Honey from this crop is light in colour and similar to that of other clovers. Long-tongued bumblebees particularly visit the flowers. Unfortunately, changing agricultural practices mean that crimson clover is now rarely grown for fodder, so large expanses are very rare.

Family:	**Fabaceae**
Flowering:	**May to September**
Cultivation:	**annual herb**
Honey:	**no**
Honeybees:	||||| ||||| |||||
ST Bumblebees:	||||| ||||| |||||
LT Bumblebees:	||||| ||||| |||||
Solitary Bees:	|||||

Above:
*Flower-head of crimson clover (*Trifolium incarnatum*)*
(photo: W. D. J. Kirk)

Crocus — *Crocus* species

Crocuses produce an abundance of pollen at a time when there are few sources of fresh pollen available. They are among the plants that are most worthwhile cultivating for honeybees because they provide pollen early in the season when honeybees need it in order to build up the colony ready for the main flowering season. The first flowers are usually open in March, but this depends upon the earliness of the season and the species and variety. In exceptionally early springs, crocuses in the south of England can be out from the latter part of January. The flowering period is fortunately long and extends well over a month as a general rule. The number of different kinds of crocus in cultivation is very large, as a study of any bulb catalogue will show. Some of the commoner sorts are also to be found in a wild or semi-wild state. There is probably little or no difference in their attractiveness to bees for pollen. Nectar may also be obtained by bees in some instances, but the flowers are usually worked only for pollen. The nectar is secreted at the base of the flower and as the long narrow flower-tube is almost completely filled by the style and hairs it requires a tongue of a fair length, longer than that of a honeybee, to reach it. However, if nectar accumulates and rises

Family:	**Iridaceae**
Flowering:	**February to March**
Cultivation:	**perennial herb, grown from corms**
Honey:	**no**
Honeybees:	||||| ||||| |||||
ST Bumblebees:	|||||
LT Bumblebees:	—
Solitary Bees:	|||||

Far left:
*Queen buff-tailed bumblebee (*Bombus terrestris*) inside a crocus flower (*Crocus species*)*
(photo: T. C. Ings)

Left:
*The centre of a crocus flower (*Crocus vernus 'Pickwick'*)*
(photo: W. D. J. Kirk)

C

Courgette — Crocus

Above:
*Pollen grain of spring crocus (*Crocus
vernus*) (102 μm)*

sufficiently in the tube, short-tongued bees may be able to reach it by making great efforts.

The flowers open wide in bright sunlight and are often visited by hoverflies that bask in the protected warmth of the flower. These visitors are easily mistaken for bees. The main bees that visit are honeybees because the flowering season is too early for most other bees.

The pollen of the crocus is generally bright orange or golden in colour. The individual grain is large, smooth and spherical and is usually easily distinguished from other pollen grains by its size, shape and colour. Some of the newer garden forms of crocus (tetraploids) have an exceptionally large pollen grain. The so-called autumn 'crocus' or meadow saffron (*Colchicum autumnale*) (see separate entry), which flowers in the autumn and not in the spring, as the name indicates, also yields pollen and perhaps nectar. It exists in the wild and is also frequently cultivated.

Crown imperial — *Fritillaria imperialis*

This showy and stately garden plant, which grows 1–1.5 m high and bears a cluster of large bell-like flowers at the top, is of interest on account of the large amount of nectar each individual flower is capable of yielding. The nectar is secreted in the form of six large drops at the base of the flower. Although the nectar is generally weak with low sugar content, it is acceptable to honeybees and bumblebees on occasions. It has been shown that blue tits pollinate the flowers in British Isles gardens. Flowers vary in shade from yellow to copper or red. This large bulbous plant does best undisturbed in a rich soil. It is well suited for the edges of shrubberies.

Family:	**Liliaceae**
Flowering:	**March to May**
Cultivation:	**perennial herb, grown from a bulb**
Honey:	**no**
Honeybees:	|||||
ST Bumblebees:	|||||
LT Bumblebees:	|||||
Solitary Bees:	|||||

Cuckoo flower — *Cardamine pratensis*

The soft pink or pale lilac flowers of this native plant are common in meadows early in the year just at the time when the cuckoo's song is first heard. It is also known as lady's smock. Honeybees and bumblebees make good use of them for nectar and pollen. The nectar is secreted by two pairs of nectaries, one large and one small, at the base of the flower, and collects in the pouches formed by the bases of the sepals.

Family:	**Brassicaceae**
Flowering:	**April to July**
Cultivation:	**perennial herb**
Honey:	**no**
Honeybees:	|||||
ST Bumblebees:	|||||
LT Bumblebees:	|||||
Solitary Bees:	|||||

Right:
*Flowers of cuckoo flower (*Cardamine
pratensis*)*
(photo: M. A. Kirk)

Cucumber — *Cucumis sativus*

The cucumber, like other members of the gourd family (Cucurbitaceae), is normally dependent upon bees for pollination, the male and female organs being borne on separate flowers on the same plant. Both male and female flowers produce nectar, but only the male flowers produce pollen. However, most modern commercial varieties develop the fruit without the need for pollination, and bees are sometimes excluded from the crop to prevent pollination and the development of unwanted seeds. When grown in gardens under glass, as is usual in the British Isles, some varieties need pollination and this can be done by hand. In the past, hives of honeybees were placed in large glasshouses at flowering time and did the work efficiently, but large numbers of bees died because they beat themselves against the glass continuously until exhausted. Pickled gherkins are produced from a variety of cucumber that still needs to be pollinated and since the 1980s bumblebee colonies have been used instead of honeybees in commercial crops (see tomato).

When cucumbers are grown on a field scale out of doors, as is the case in some other countries, crops of honey may be obtained. Such honey has been described as pale yellow or amber in colour with a rather strong cucumber-like flavour at first, which largely disappears in time.

Family:	**Cucurbitaceae**
Flowering:	**June to August**
Cultivation:	**annual herb**
Honey:	**no**
Honeybees:	|||||
ST Bumblebees:	|||||
LT Bumblebees:	|||||
Solitary Bees:	|||||

C

Crown imperial — Cucumber

Left:
Cucumber flower (Cucumis sativus)
(photo: W. D. J. Kirk)

Currant — *Ribes* species

Family:	**Grossulariaceae**
Flowering:	**April to May**
Cultivation:	**deciduous medium shrub**
Honey:	**yes**
Honeybees:	||||| ||||| |||||
ST Bumblebees:	||||| ||||| ||||
LT Bumblebees:	||||| ||||
Solitary Bees:	||||| |||||

Above:
*Flowers of flowering currant (*Ribes
sanguineum*)*
(photo: W. D. J. Kirk)

The black, red, and white currants of the fruit garden are all good bee plants and yield nectar and pollen early in the season. The blackcurrant (*Ribes nigrum*) is the most extensively cultivated, and in fruit-growing districts quite large areas may be available as bee forage to beekeepers that happen to be in the vicinity. However, owing to the presence of many other nectar sources at the time flowering takes place, it is doubtful whether blackcurrant honey in anything like a pure form has ever been obtained, although it will contribute to honey yields. Awareness of the enhanced value of blackcurrants as a source of vitamins has led to increased cultivation. The inconspicuous flowers of the blackcurrant have a somewhat characteristic odour. The petals are white and the tips of the sepals tinged with red. As the bell-shaped flower is only some 5 mm deep, the honeybee has easy access to the nectar. Not only does it extract the nectar from the open flower, but may even open the older flower buds with its jaws. The flowers are frequently visited by queen bumblebees, which can visit many flowers quickly, even in cool weather. Bumblebees collect pollen from the flowers by vibrating the anthers for about a second at a time to produce a cloud of pollen over them, which allows them to groom the pollen from their body and collect it very efficiently. They dangle upside down from the flower while holding on with their legs, grasping the rim of the flower with their jaws and producing short buzzing sounds. This process is known as 'buzz pollination'. Marks around the rim of the flower indicate that pollen-collecting bumblebees have previously visited the flowers.

The flowering currants (*Ribes sanguineum*) that are popular in gardens are also good bee plants and flower early in the season. They are generally in flower in April and seldom fail to blossom freely. The flowers are very popular with both short-tongued and long-tongued bumblebees. Honeybees are often present in large numbers, working especially for pollen. There are many varieties of flowering currant. In some other species the flower-tube is too long for honeybees and short-tongued bumblebees to obtain nectar.

Right:
*Redcurrant flowers (*Ribes rubrum*)*
Far right:
*Blackcurrant flowers (*Ribes nigrum*)*
(photos: W. D. J. Kirk)

Daffodil — *Narcissus* species

Daffodils, narcissi and jonquils are of some value for pollen, especially as they appear so early, but are of little consequence as far as nectar is concerned. The cultivated kinds vary a great deal in shape, size, colour and time of flowering and those that have double flowers or flowers that are highly modified compared with the wild type of flower are unsuitable for bees. The wild daffodil (*Narcissus pseudo-narcissus*) with its pale yellow flowers, appearing usually in March, is found in moist woods and thickets in some parts of the British Isles, especially southern counties of England and Wales. Nectar collects at the base of the flower-tube and is shielded or protected by the bases of the stamens and a fairly long tongue is required to reach it. The flowers are sometimes visited by early flying bumblebees on warm days, but are rarely visited by honeybees.

Family:	**Alliaceae**
Flowering:	**February to April**
Cultivation:	**perennial herb, grown from bulbs**
Honey:	**no**
Honeybees:	—
ST Bumblebees:	|||||
LT Bumblebees:	|||||
Solitary Bees:	|||||

Far left:
*Garden bumblebee (*Bombus hortorum*) on a white daffodil (*Narcissus *species)*
(photo: J. Craig)
Left:
*Female mining bee (*Andrena flavipes*) basking on a daffodil (*Narcissus *species)*
(photo: J. V. Adams)

Dahlia — *Dahlia* species

Mexico is the original home of the parent plants of the many kinds of dahlia now in cultivation. Those that are single, whether tall or dwarf, large or small, are good bee plants and supply nectar and pollen at a time of the year when they are becoming short in most areas. Some of the dwarf bedding varieties are particularly useful in this respect, with their long blooming period and free-flowering habit right up to the time the first frosts arrive. The flowers are much visited by both short-tongued and long-tongued bumblebees, such as the common carder bee (*Bombus pascuorum*).

Family:	**Asteraceae**
Flowering:	**July to September**
Cultivation:	**perennial herb, grown from tubers**
Honey:	**no**
Honeybees:	||||| |||||
ST Bumblebees:	||||| |||||
LT Bumblebees:	||||| |||||
Solitary Bees:	|||||

Far left:
*Male buff-tailed bumblebee (*Bombus terrestris*) on dahlia (*Dahlia *species)*
Left:
*Honeybee on dahlia (*Dahlia *species)*
(photos: W. D. J. Kirk)

D

Currant — Dahlia

Daisy bush — *Olearia* x *haastei*

Family:	**Asteraceae**
Flowering:	**July to August**
Cultivation:	**evergreen medium shrub**
Honey:	**no**
Honeybees:	|||||
ST Bumblebees:	|||||
LT Bumblebees:	|||||
Solitary Bees:	|||||

This bushy evergreen shrub is often seen in gardens and is one of the few New Zealand shrubs that are hardy in the British Isles. It flowers in July and August. The flower-heads are visited by bees for nectar and pollen, but only to a limited extent. The shrub is to be seen at its best in coastal districts.

Dandelion — *Taraxacum officinale*

Right:
*Flower-head of dandelion (*Taraxacum officinale*)*
(photo: M. A. Kirk)

Family:	**Asteraceae**
Flowering:	**March to October**
Cultivation:	**perennial herb**
Honey:	**yes**
Honeybees:	||||| ||||| |||||
ST Bumblebees:	||||| ||||| |||||
LT Bumblebees:	||||| ||||| |||||
Solitary Bees:	||||| ||||| |||||

Although the dandelion is commonly thought of as a weed, it is one of the most useful of wild plants for bees and is a major honey plant for beekeepers. It occurs everywhere and is regularly visited for nectar and pollen. It is to be found in flower almost throughout the year, but flowers most freely early in the season, before the appearance of fruit blossom, when it is of most value to the beekeeper, especially for brood rearing. It occurs freely in pastures, particularly in chalk districts, where fields may be sheets of yellow at flowering time. This is not an uncommon sight and dandelion honey has been secured by beekeepers in such areas. Dandelion honey varies in density and may be deep or pale yellow in colour. It soon crystallises, doing so with a coarse grain. The flavour is strong, particularly when fresh, and the odour reminiscent of the dandelion flower, but this is lessened on ripening. However, those accustomed to mild honeys often do not care for its strong flavour.

The pollen of the dandelion is golden yellow but may appear as deep orange in bees' pollen baskets. It is produced very freely and bees are able to gather it easily. It is somewhat oily, and the honeybee wax comb built when dandelion is being freely worked is a distinctive light yellow colour. The individual pollen grain is large and spiny, and is very prevalent in English honey.

There are between 100 and 200 individual flowers or florets in a single dandelion head. The flower tubes vary from 3–7 mm in length and do not exclude honeybees and short-tongued bumblebees. At night and in dull or wet weather the heads close up. This protects the pollen and nectar and prevents it from being spoiled by dew or rain. The time of opening of the flowers in the morning varies with the time of year and is much earlier in mid-summer than in spring or autumn.

When dandelions occur in quantity in or near large orchards they can be a nuisance to the fruit grower in that bees will often forsake apple or pear blossom in favour of the dandelion flowers, to the detriment of the fruit pollination and subsequent yield of fruit. Whether it is a richer nectar in the dandelion or whether it is the pollen that is preferred is not known.

The dandelion is an important bee plant or honey yielder in many other countries. In Europe it has been listed as an important bee plant for various countries from Spain to Norway. In parts of southern Germany it is a common source of honey. The plant has become widely naturalised in North America and New Zealand where honey is obtained from it and where it is predominantly a valuable spring stimulator.

The so-called Russian dandelions (*Taraxacum kok-saghyz* and *Taraxacum megallorhizon*) that have been considered for rubber production and grown experimentally in Britain both attract the honeybee freely for nectar and pollen.

The flowers are visited by a wide range of solitary bees, such as mining bees (*Andrena, Colletes* and *Lasioglossum* species), mason bees (*Osmia* species), some small, black stem-nesting bees (*Hylaeus* species) and cuckoo bees (*Nomada* species).

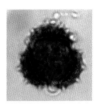

Above:
Pollen grain of dandelion (Taraxacum officinale) (36 μm)

Left:
Honeybee on dandelion (Taraxacum officinale)
(photo: C. Stevens)

Images over page
Left (p.116):
Gypsy cuckoo bee (Bombus bohemicus) on dandelion (Taraxacum officinale)
(photo: N. W. Owens)
Top right (p.117):
Female mining bee (Andrena nitida) on dandelion (Taraxacum officinale)
(photo: T. C. Ings)
Bottom right (p.117):
Female mining bee (Andrena haemorrhoa) on dandelion (Taraxacum officinale)
(photo: L. A. Hislop)

D

Daisy bush — Dandelion

D | Dandelion

Daphne — *Daphne mezereum*

Family:	**Thymelaeaceae**
Flowering:	**February to March**
Cultivation:	**deciduous small shrub**
Honey:	**no**
Honeybees:	‖‖
ST Bumblebees:	—
LT Bumblebees:	—
Solitary Bees:	—

The common daphne or mezereon is a shrub often seen in gardens, especially cottage gardens, and is favoured for its sweet-scented, bright-pink flowers that appear so early in the year and before the leaves. It is usually in flower early in February and so keeps company with the crocus and snowdrop. A white-flowered variety is also grown. The daphne exists apparently wild in woods in the south of England, but is actually a native of continental Europe and Siberia. Honeybees frequent the flowers, when the weather is warm enough, for nectar and pollen. The flowers of another daphne, the spurge laurel (*Daphne laureola*), an evergreen shrub usually to be seen in copses and woods on chalk or limestone, also attract honeybees.

Right:
*Daphne flowers (*Daphne mezereum*)*
(photo: W. D. J. Kirk)

Deadly nightshade — *Atropa belladonna*

Family:	**Solanaceae**
Flowering:	**May to August**
Cultivation:	**perennial herb**
Honey:	**no**
Honeybees:	‖‖
ST Bumblebees:	‖‖
LT Bumblebees:	‖‖
Solitary Bees:	‖‖

This toxic drug-containing plant, which is sometimes, although not frequently, to be found in the wild, is not generally regarded as a bee plant. However, plots at Kew Gardens during the Second World War were much visited by honeybees when in flower in May, obviously for nectar. It is interesting to note how some plants that appear to be ignored when solitary can be much visited when part of a larger group.

Right:
*Deadly nightshade flowers (*Atropa belladonna*)*
(photo: J. P. Early)

The bee climbs right into the large bell-shaped purple flower, out of sight, and is easily able to reach the nectar, which is secreted by a conspicuous annular yellow nectary at the base of the ovary. It has to thrust its proboscis between the hairy lower part of the stamens to get at the nectar. In crawling in and out of the flower it becomes dusted with the pale, cream-coloured pollen. There is evidence from overseas that any honey that is produced is psychoactive (affects brain function).

Dead-nettle — *Lamium* species

The white dead-nettle (*Lamium album*) and the red dead-nettle (*Lamium purpureum*) do not sting, despite their names. They both have long flower-tubes, which makes them especially valuable to long-tongued bumblebees. They can also flower over a very long period. Despite their similarity, the white dead-nettle is a perennial and the red dead-nettle is an annual.

Family:	**Lamiaceae**
Flowering:	**February to November**
Cultivation:	**annual or perennial herb**
Honey:	**no**
Honeybees:	|||||
ST Bumblebees:	||||| |||||
LT Bumblebees:	||||| ||||| |||||
Solitary Bees:	||||| |||||

The flowers of white dead-nettle are a useful source of nectar early in the season for queen common carder bees (*Bombus pascuorum*). Honeybees are sometimes to be seen around the flowers of dead-nettles, but the nectar is too deep-seated for them, only long-tongued bumblebees being able to reach it. Short-tongued bumblebees sometimes make punctures at the base of the flower to reach the nectar, in which case honeybees may also be able to obtain a certain amount.

The flowers are also visited for pollen, especially those of the red dead-nettle, which occurs along roadsides and sometimes in masses on hedge banks. This plant begins to flower as early as February when few pollen plants are available and remains in flower throughout the summer. Red dead-nettle pollen is a beautiful dark orange in colour.

White and red dead-nettles are often visited by flower bees (*Anthophora* species), including the hairy-footed flower bee (*Anthophora plumipes*). This species is a large, furry bee looking rather like a bumblebee. It has a distinctive darting flight. The females are black and the males are brown. They are absent from Scotland and Ireland.

Spotted dead-nettle (*Lamium maculatum*) and a closely related species, yellow archangel (*Lamiastrum galeobdolon*), also attracts bees. Named varieties of these perennial plants selected for their decorative leaves are available for gardens.

Above:
Female hairy-footed flower bee (Anthophora plumipes) *visiting white dead-nettle* (Lamium album)
(photo: L. Hebdon)

Far left:
*Queen red-tailed bumblebee (*Bombus lapidarius*) on white dead-nettle (*Lamium album*)
(photo: L. Hebdon)
Left:
*Male hairy-footed flower bee (*Anthophora plumipes*) visiting red dead-nettle (*Lamium purpureum*)
(photo: J. V. Adams)

D

Daphne — Dead-nettle

Delphinium, see larkspur

Devil's bit scabious, see scabious

Discaria — *Discaria* x *serratifolia*

Family:	Rhamnaceae
Flowering:	June to July
Cultivation:	deciduous medium shrub
Honey:	no
Honeybees:	||||| |||||
ST Bumblebees:	|||||
LT Bumblebees:	|||||
Solitary Bees:	|||||

This deciduous shrub from Chile with long, excessively spiny, pendulous branches is not often seen in cultivation, although quite hardy. It bears clusters of small greenish-white flowers in June or July, which are sweet scented and attract honeybees in large numbers.

Dogwood — *Cornus* species

Family:	Cornaceae
Flowering:	June to August
Cultivation:	deciduous shrub or small tree
Honey:	no
Honeybees:	|||||
ST Bumblebees:	|||||
LT Bumblebees:	—
Solitary Bees:	—

Some of the many dogwoods in cultivation attract bees, especially the Siberian dogwood (*Cornus alba* 'Sibirica') sometimes grown in gardens. The cornelian cherry (*Cornus mas*), which is covered with yellow blossoms in February and March, does not appear to be very popular with bees in spite of its unusually early flowering.

Right:
Tree bumblebee (Bombus hypnorum) *on dogwood* (Cornus *species*)
(photo: T. C. Ings)
Far right:
Pollen grain of Siberian dogwood (Cornus alba 'Sibirica') (44 μm)

Dragonhead — *Dracocephalum moldavicum*

Family:	Lamiaceae
Flowering:	June to August
Cultivation:	annual herb
Honey:	no
Honeybees:	|||||
ST Bumblebees:	|||||
LT Bumblebees:	|||||
Solitary Bees:	|||||

This is a small annual with blue and white flowers, resembling a salvia and belonging to the same family. It is a native of eastern Siberia, but grows well in the British Isles. The crushed leaves are aromatic and have been used in the past in the same way as those of lemon balm (*Melissa officinalis*) for rubbing inside skeps and hives to attract swarms of honeybees.

Dyer's greenweed — *Genista tinctoria*

The yellow gorse-like flowers of this native plant attract the honeybee for pollen at times, but do not appear to yield nectar. It is often common on clay soils. The young tops of the plant were at one time used for dying wool, hence the name 'dyer's greenweed'. There are many other species and varieties of *Genista* available for gardens, such as Spanish gorse (*Genista lydia*) that are also visited for pollen, but note that double-flowered forms are unsuitable for bees. An allied native plant, petty whin (*Genista anglica*), which occurs on moors and heaths, is also worked for pollen.

Family:	**Fabaceae**
Flowering:	**July to September**
Cultivation:	**deciduous small shrub**
Honey:	**no**
Honeybees:	‖‖
ST Bumblebees:	‖‖
LT Bumblebees:	‖‖
Solitary Bees:	‖‖

Left:
*Flowers of dyer's greenweed (*Genista tinctoria*)*
(photo: J. P. Early)

D

Delphinium — Dyer's greenweed

Elm — *Ulmus* species

Family:	**Ulmaceae**
Flowering:	**February to March**
Cultivation:	**deciduous large tree**
Honey:	**no**
Honeybees:	|||||
ST Bumblebees:	—
LT Bumblebees:	—
Solitary Bees:	—

Elms were decimated by Dutch elm disease in the 1970s and are now far less common. They can be useful early sources of pollen for honeybees, particularly when they happen to be growing in close proximity to an apiary. The purple clusters of small flowers appear in February or March and may pass unnoticed as they are so often on tall trees. Pollen is produced in abundance and is wind-borne. In favourable weather at this early season bees will make good use of it. In California, the introduced European elms have been a valued source of pollen to beekeepers, the trees being alive with bees in spring, when better bee-flying weather is likely to prevail than in the British Isles. There is some evidence that in warmer climates elm flowers may also be a source of nectar. Later in the year, the elm sometimes becomes a source of honeydew, which honeybees can collect instead of nectar.

Elsholtzia — *Elsholtzia* species

Family:	**Lamiaceae**
Flowering:	**August to October**
Cultivation:	**annual herb to deciduous small shrub**
Honey:	**no**
Honeybees:	||||| |||||
ST Bumblebees:	|||||
LT Bumblebees:	|||||
Solitary Bees:	|||||

Some good bee plants are to be found in this genus, which belongs to the mint family, and should not be confused with *Eschscholzia* (Californian poppies), which belong to an entirely different family. The most interesting is perhaps a Chinese species called mint shrub (*Elsholtzia stauntonii*), which was introduced to cultivation in the British Isles in 1909, and acquired its name because of its aromatic (mint-like) leaves. The shrub reaches 1.5 m in height, needs full sunshine and grows in almost any soil except heavy clay. It is hardy in the south of England, the shoots often dying back in the winter, but fresh ones arising in the spring. It flowers freely in about September, producing clusters of fragrant purple flowers, 8–20 cm long, at the ends of the branches. In the individual flowers the funnel-shaped flower tube is only about 6 mm in length and well suited to honeybees and short-tongued bumblebees which work it freely for nectar. Much depends, of course, on the nature of the weather so late in the year. It is undoubtedly a useful and ornamental late-flowering shrub for bees and well worth a place in the bee garden.

Crested late-summer mint (*Elsholtzia ciliata*), which is an annual, is perhaps a better-known species and is another good nectar plant. It grows 30–60 cm high and produces numerous lavender-coloured flowers on one-sided spikes in the late summer, which bees visit eagerly. The plant has aromatic leaves and is easily grown, requiring full sun.

Endive — *Cichorium endivia*

When this salad plant is grown for seed or left neglected in the vegetable garden, the blue flowers, which appear at intervals along the stem, are visited by bees for nectar. The flowers are not unlike those of chicory (see separate entry), a close relative of the plant.

Family:	Asteraceae
Flowering:	June to October
Cultivation:	perennial herb
Honey:	no
Honeybees:	||||| |||||
ST Bumblebees:	||||| |||||
LT Bumblebees:	||||| |||||
Solitary Bees:	|||||

Erect canary clover — *Dorycnium rectum*

The white to pink flowers of this small shrubby plant from southern Europe have been observed being freely worked for nectar by honeybees at Kew Gardens in July. It does not exceed 50 cm in height, grows easily from seed and, like so many Mediterranean plants, succeeds on a light dry soil.

Family:	Fabaceae
Flowering:	June to July
Cultivation:	deciduous small shrub
Honey:	no
Honeybees:	|||||
ST Bumblebees:	|||||
LT Bumblebees:	|||||
Solitary Bees:	|||||

Erodium — *Erodium* species

Known also as stork's bill, these plants are good nectar yielders, as are the hardy geraniums, their near relatives. Several species occur wild in the British Isles and may of these have been transported as seeds on wool that have then established and naturalised. They are generally most common near the sea, and selected varieties are cultivated in gardens. One of the wild species, the common stork's bill (*Erodium cicutarium*) is very prevalent in parts of the rest of Europe and has become widely naturalised in North America, where it is known as redstem filaree or pin clover and was said, in the early 20th century, to produce an abundance of pollen and considerable honey of good quality. Another British Isles species freely naturalised in other countries which has proved a good pollen and nectar plant is the musk stork's bill (*Erodium moschatum*).

Family:	Geraniaceae
Flowering:	May to September
Cultivation:	annual or perennial herb
Honey:	no
Honeybees:	|||||
ST Bumblebees:	|||||
LT Bumblebees:	|||||
Solitary Bees:	|||||

E

Elm — Erodium

Left:
Flower of erodium (Erodium *x* variabile)
(photo: W. D. J. Kirk)

Escallonia — *Escallonia* species

Family:	**Escalloniaceae**
Flowering:	**June to September**
Cultivation:	**evergreen large shrub**
Honey:	**no**
Honeybees:	||||| |||||
ST Bumblebees:	||||| |||||
LT Bumblebees:	|||||
Solitary Bees:	—

The escallonias are a group of handsome shrubs, natives of South America. They are mostly evergreen and several are from Chile and Peru. Unfortunately, the majority are too tender for most parts of the British Isles, except in the mildest parts or with the protection of a wall. A number are good bee plants, visited mainly by honeybees, which collect nectar and pollen, and by short-tongued bumblebees, such as the buff-tailed bumblebee (*Bombus terrestris*). They are more commonly cultivated in the southwest of Britain and Ireland, especially *Escallonia macrantha*, which is often used for hedges near the sea.

Escallonia x *langleyensis* (a hybrid) is fairly hardy and has pretty rosy-red flowers that are much visited by honeybees. The flowers appear in profusion in June and July, while a few may still be found as late as September. It is bushy, reaching 3 m or more in height with slender arching branches – altogether a handsome shrub. Nectar is secreted freely at the base of the flower-tube.

Right:
Flowers of escallonia (Escallonia rubra)
(photo: M. A. Kirk)
Far right:
Pollen grain of escallonia (Escallonia macrantha) *(23 μm)*

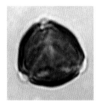

Eucryphia — *Eucryphia glutinosa*

Family:	**Cunoniaceae**
Flowering:	**July to August**
Cultivation:	**evergreen or semi-evergreen large shrub**
Honey:	**no**
Honeybees:	||||| |||||
ST Bumblebees:	||||| |||||
LT Bumblebees:	|||||
Solitary Bees:	|||||

This evergreen or partly evergreen shrub from Chile is the hardiest of the available species and bears large solitary flowers in July and August. These are striking, with their pure white petals and masses of stamens. Bees visit them for pollen and for nectar. The shrub can hardly be described as common in cultivation, probably because it is not among the easiest of plants to propagate and transplants badly. Several other species, hybrids and forms are available for gardens. One of the best known is the hybrid *Eucryphia* x *nymansensis* 'Nymansay', which is an evergreen medium-sized tree and flowers from August to September.

Leatherwood (*Eucryphia lucida*) is a small tree that flowers from June to July and is common in Tasmania. It is responsible for leatherwood honey there, which has a very distinctive flavour, and is an important export for Tasmania. In Chile, ulmo honey is obtained from the ulmo tree (*Eucryphia cordifolia*).

Left:
*Flower of eucryphia (*Eucryphia x
nymansensis *'Nymansay')*
(photo: W. D. J. Kirk)

Eupatorium — *Eupatorium* species

A number of rather coarse garden perennials belong to this genus, some better suited to the wild garden than the flower border. For the most part they flower in the autumn. Many garden plants still widely known as *Eupatorium* have now been moved by botanists to other groups of species and so may appear under names such as *Ageratina*, *Bartlettina* and *Conoclinium*. Bees work the flowers of a number of species freely for nectar and pollen. Some of those that originated in North America are regarded as good bee plants there.

Bees also visit the small flesh-coloured flowers of the wild species called hemp agrimony (*Eupatorium cannabinum*), a very common plant along streams and in moist places generally. The flowers appear in dense terminal heads in July and August and are also popular with butterflies, especially painted ladies and red admirals.

Family:	**Asteraceae**
Flowering:	**July to September**
Cultivation:	**perennial herb**
Honey:	**no**
Honeybees:	‖‖‖ ‖‖‖
ST Bumblebees:	‖‖‖ ‖‖‖
LT Bumblebees:	‖‖‖ ‖‖‖
Solitary Bees:	‖‖‖

E

Escallonia — Eupatorium

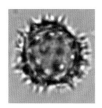

Far left:
Pollen grain of hemp agrimony
(Eupatorium cannabinum) *(24 µm)*
Left:
*Flowers of hemp agrimony (*Eupatorium
cannabinum*)*
(photo: W. D. J. Kirk)

Evening primrose — *Oenothera biennis*

Family:	**Onagraceae**
Flowering:	**June to September**
Cultivation:	**biennial herb**
Honey:	**no**
Honeybees:	|||||
ST Bumblebees:	|||||
LT Bumblebees:	|||||
Solitary Bees:	|||||

Above:
Flower of large-flowered evening primrose
(Oenothera glazioviana)
(photo: W. D. J. Kirk)

This stately plant in one or other of its many forms is to be seen both in the flower garden and as a weed in waste places. It is a naturalised rather than indigenous plant that is common in central and southern Britain. The large, attractive yellow flowers open in the evening. They are normally pollinated by night-flying moths but bees often visit them, especially in the early morning in the summer for pollen. The flowers are visited occasionally by bumblebees and mining bees (*Andrena* species).

The common evening primrose (*Oenothera biennis*) is no longer the commonest evening primrose in the wild in the British Isles. The large-flowered evening primrose (*Oenothera glazioviana*), which is also a naturalised species, has spread over recent decades and is now far more widespread. It can be recognised by the large petals (3–5 cm) and reddish sepals at the base of the flower.

The pollen grains of the evening primrose are very large and easily visible to the naked eye. They are bound together by yellow threads (strands of viscin), which may sometimes be seen trailing on the legs of honeybees working the flowers. There are many varieties of evening primrose in cultivation.

Eyebright — *Euphrasia officinalis*

Family:	**Orobanchaceae**
Flowering:	**June to September**
Cultivation:	**annual herb**
Honey:	**no**
Honeybees:	|||||
ST Bumblebees:	—
LT Bumblebees:	—
Solitary Bees:	|||||

Right:
Eyebright flowers (Euphrasia officinalis)
(photo: J. P. Early)

The brightly-coloured flowers of this variable little plant may receive the attention of the honeybee. It is common in all kinds of situations, including dry meadows and exposed hillsides or cliffs near the sea. Nectar is secreted by the lower part of the ovary and collects in the flower-tube.

False acacia — *Robinia pseudoacacia*

The false acacia or common acacia, also called robinia in France and black locust in its native region (eastern USA), is a well-known ornamental and timber tree. It is of interest in having been one of the first North American trees to be introduced to Britain. This took place as long ago as 1640. It has now become established in many other countries, particularly southern Europe, and is a valuable honey plant there when sufficiently abundant.

In the British Isles, the false acacia is not such a reliable nectar producer as it is in warmer climates or where a hot Continental type of summer is the rule. When warm sunny weather prevails during the flowering period, which usually commences in early or mid-June, it is generally well worked and seems to yield nectar freely, but in the absence of hot weather offers little attraction to bees. The bunches of white flowers are delightfully fragrant and each individual flower lasts about a week. Unfortunately, the total flowering period is short, often not more than a fortnight. The tree grows well in poor, sandy soils where many other trees would fail. Growth is very rapid in the early stages and this, combined with its habit of suckering, makes it useful for planting on sandy banks to hold the soil. It is common on railway cuttings and embankments in many parts of France. The tree yields a good honey, but there are probably few areas in the British Isles where it would be sufficiently abundant to yield surplus honey. In many other parts of Europe, however, surplus is regularly obtained, and it is sold as 'acacia honey'. It is of a superior type and considered by some to be equal to that of white clover, being light in colour and with good density and flavour, and is slow to granulate.

There are many varieties of the false acacia in cultivation, some with variegated or abnormal leaves. The most interesting for value to bees is the everblooming acacia (*Robinia pseudoacacia* 'Semperflorens'), which continues to flower more or less throughout the summer and so lacks the main drawback of the common acacia – a short flowering period. This has in the past been recommended for planting in waste sandy places on the Continent to improve the honey flow. It has the additional advantage of being thornless.

The nectar in the flower is secreted at the bottom of the stamen tube and the wide calyx allows it to be reached easily by the honeybee. A single flower has shown to yield 38 mg of nectar during its life with an average sugar concentration of 35%. The pollen grains are pale yellow.

The flowers of other species of *Robinia*, such as the clammy locust (*Robinia viscosa*) and the bristly locust or rose acacia (*Robinia hispida*) have been observed to be visited by honeybees at Kew Gardens.

It should be noted that the false acacia (*Robinia pseudoacacia*) has the potential to be an invasive species in the UK and should not be planted in the wild.

Family:	**Fabaceae**
Flowering:	**June**
Cultivation:	**deciduous large tree**
Honey:	**no**
Honeybees:	||||| |||||
ST Bumblebees:	|||||
LT Bumblebees:	|||||
Solitary Bees:	—

Above:
Flowers of false acacia (Robinia pseudoacacia)
(photo: W. D. J. Kirk)

F

Evening primrose — False acacia

Fennel — *Foeniculum vulgare*

Right:
Mining bee (Andrena wilkella) *on fennel*
(Foeniculum vulgare)
(photo: L. Hebdon)

Family:	**Apiaceae**
Flowering:	**June to August**
Cultivation:	**perennial herb**
Honey:	**no**
Honeybees:	|||||
ST Bumblebees:	|||||
LT Bumblebees:	|||||
Solitary Bees:	||||| |||||

The flowers of this herb attract bees and there are records of honey being obtained from it in other countries. It is often cultivated in gardens and smallholdings, the leaves being mainly used for flavouring fish sauces, especially for boiled salmon and mackerel. Like most plants of this family, the heads of small yellow flowers swarm with flies and other short-tongued insects, which are able to get at the relatively exposed nectar, and perhaps as a result honeybees and bumblebees are not such frequent visitors as they are with many other plants. A wide range of solitary bees, such as mining bees (*Andrena* and *Colletes* species) and small, black stem-nesting bees (*Hylaeus* species), have easy access to the pollen and nectar and are frequent visitors. The flowers of the wild fennel are similar to those of the cultivated plant. It is common in many localities, especially near the sea, where its bluish-green stems and finely divided hair-like leaves make it a conspicuous plant.

Field bean — *Vicia faba*

Family:	**Fabaceae**
Flowering:	**March to July**
Cultivation:	**annual herb**
Honey:	**yes**
Honeybees:	||||| ||||| |||||
ST Bumblebees:	||||| ||||| |||||
LT Bumblebees:	||||| ||||| |||||
Solitary Bees:	||||| ||||| |||||

Above:
Pollen grain of field bean (Vicia faba) *(44 μm)*

There are four main types of bean that are grown in the British Isles: (1) the field bean – a farm crop; (2) the closely related broad bean of the vegetable garden; (3) the French bean or kidney bean (*Phaseolus vulgaris*); and (4) the scarlet-flowered runner bean (*Phaseolus coccineus*). Of these, the field bean is far and away the most important for bees, being so extensively grown. The crop is either spring or autumn sown and the time of flowering depends on sowing and on the variety grown. The size and colour of the whitish flowers also depends upon variety, some having the side petals heavily marked with velvety black. In others, the flowers are tinged with red. The flowers are pleasantly scented and a field of beans in full bloom will scent the air on a still day. The broad beans of the vegetable garden are little more than selected forms of the field bean and are of much the same value tobees, except that they are usually grown on a small scale and often have larger flowers.

Nectar is produced by nectaries deep within the flower and only a long-tongued bee can reach from the front of the flower. When a bee lands on the front of the flower, the lower petals are forced down and pollen is pushed against the underside of the bee, simultaneously depositing pollen and picking up pollen from the visitor as it pushes into the flower. The flower is then said to have been 'tripped'. Once the lower petals have been forced apart in this way, the flower cannot be tripped again. The most frequent visitors to the front of the flower are usually long-tongued bumblebees, such as the garden bumblebee (*Bombus hortorum*), the common carder bee (*Bombus pascuorum*), and the ruderal bumblebee (*Bombus ruderatus*). Their tongues are long enough to reach the nectar at the base of the flower and their bodies are large enough to trip the flowers and bring about cross-pollination. A few species of solitary bee, such as the hairy-footed flower bee (*Anthophora plumipes*), can also reach the nectar and pollinate. Both long- and short-tongued bees can collect pollen from the front of the flower. However, honeybees, which have relatively short tongues, and short-tongued bumblebees are faced with the problem that they cannot reach the nectar from the front of the flower. Some short-tongued bees have developed the clever trick of biting through the base of the flower to reach the nectar. This remarkable behaviour is termed 'primary nectar robbing' and is done mainly by short-tongued bumblebees, such as the buff-tailed bumblebee (*Bombus terrestris*) and the white-tailed bumblebee (*Bombus lucorum*). Honeybees do not appear to bite holes in flowers under natural conditions in the field, although holes have been recorded when they have been caged with field beans. The damage from robbing does not prevent pollination by other visitors. Short-tongued bumblebees and honeybees also forage for nectar through the holes made by the primary robbers and this is termed 'secondary nectar robbing'.

Nectaries are usually within flowers, but field beans also have extrafloral nectaries on the underside of small leaf-like structures called stipules. Their presence is indicated by a pair of dark spots and they are easily accessible by bees. They secrete nectar in sunny weather and this is eagerly sought by ants. The extrafloral nectaries start to secrete nectar before flowering starts and continue to secrete nectar through to the end of flowering. They are visited by honeybees and some short-tongued bumblebees over a long period starting before the flowers open and also during flowering, particularly when no holes have been made in the flowers by primary nectar robbers.

In good weather, honeybees can store honey in quantity from this crop, and those beekeepers that have access to it are indeed fortunate. The honey varies from light to dark amber in colour and has a pleasant, mild flavour. It is inclined to granulate fairly quickly with a coarse grain.

Bee activity, particularly that of long-tongued bumblebees, usually increases the yield of field bean crops. Honeybees are used commercially for pollination of the crop and, in the UK, a rate of 2.5–5 honeybee colonies per hectare (1–2 colonies per acre) has been recommended to provide sufficient pollination for large fields. It has been suggested that colonies should not be moved to bean fields before flowering in case the bees become conditioned to visiting the extrafloral nectaries and do not visit the flowers. However, it is also claimed that extrafloral nectaries are useful in keeping honeybees in the crop rather than looking elsewhere for nectar.

F

Fennel — Field bean

Top:
Holes produced by bumblebees at the base of field bean flowers (Vicia faba)
Middle:
Common carder bee (Bombus pascuorum) on field bean (Vicia faba)
Bottom:
Buff-tailed bumblebee (Bombus terrestris) taking nectar from an extrafloral nectary of field bean (Vicia faba)
(photos: W. D. J. Kirk)

Field bindweed — *Convolvulus arvensis*

Family:	**Convolvulaceae**
Flowering:	**June to September**
Cultivation:	**perennial herb**
Honey:	**no**
Honeybees:	|||||
ST Bumblebees:	|||||
LT Bumblebees:	|||||
Solitary Bees:	|||||

Above:
Field bindweed flower (Convolvulus
arvensis)
(photo: W. D. J. Kirk)

As one of the most troublesome of farm weeds, the common convolvulus or field bindweed is well-known to all who live in country districts. It may also be a nuisance in town gardens or on the allotment because the smallest fragment of the underground stem or root left in the soil may give rise to a new plant. The funnel-shaped, scented, pink or white flowers, which are sometimes striped, vary a good deal in size. Nectar is secreted at the base of the ovary and the flower has long tubular nectar passages leading to it. The smaller-flowered kinds are visited freely by honeybees, while bumblebees work both the small and the large-flowered sorts equally well. Greater use of herbicides in agriculture have more or less eliminated bindweed infestations of cornfields, but in the past these could be worked by honeybees and produced appreciable quantities of nectar.

The flowers of sea bindweed (*Calystegia soldanella*) are sometimes visited by the coast leafcutter bee (*Megachile maritima*). This bee has been recorded mainly from coastal areas in England and Wales and very locally in southeast Ireland. Bindweeds in other countries (species of *Convolvulus* and *Ipomoea*) are known to be honey yielders. One of the best known is perhaps the campanilla of Cuba (*Ipomoea triloba*), which is of importance as a honey plant to the beekeepers there. The honey obtained from it is said to be equal to that of lucerne or sage in flavour and colour, and the comb built from it a pearly white, yielding a wax as white as tallow.

Field pennycress — *Thlaspi arvense*

Family:	**Brassicaceae**
Flowering:	**May to July**
Cultivation:	**annual herb**
Honey:	**no**
Honeybees:	|||||
ST Bumblebees:	—
LT Bumblebees:	—
Solitary Bees:	|||||

The small white flowers of this annual weed are visited by honeybees for nectar. It is often common in cultivated ground and is to be found across the British Isles, particularly in England.

Right:
Flowering stems of field pennycress
(Thlaspi arvense)
(photo: M. Kucharczyk)

Field scabious, see scabious

Figwort — *Scrophularia* species

Some of the wild figworts are excellent bee plants, their flowers secreting nectar very freely. One of the best is the common figwort (*Scrophularia nodosa*). It is a coarse perennial plant, a metre high, found in woods and moist places, and bearing much-forked bunches of small globular flowers. These are not visually attractive, being dull purple in colour and tinged with greenish yellow. The nectar is secreted in large drops at the base of the flower by a circular swelling and is protected from rain. Sometimes it collects to such an extent as to half fill the flower. Wasps are frequent visitors to the flowers. The water figwort (*Scrophularia auriculata*), which is very similar and grows by ditches and streams, is also a good nectar and pollen plant for bees. The yellow figwort (*Scrophularia vernalis*) is a smaller plant with more ornamental flowers. It blooms earlier than the other species, from April to June, but is rare in most areas. A North American species, the late figwort (*Scrophularia marilandica*), closely allied to the common figwort, also has a good reputation as a bee plant and as a profuse nectar yielder. It is sometimes known in the USA as Simpson's honey plant and has been claimed to be one of the best plants for artificial pasturage for honeybees.

Family:	Scrophulariaceae
Flowering:	June to September
Cultivation:	biennial or perennial herb
Honey:	no
Honeybees:	||||| |||||
ST Bumblebees:	||||| |||||
LT Bumblebees:	||||| |||||
Solitary Bees:	|||||

Above:
Male early bumblebee (Bombus pratorum) *on common figwort* (Scrophularia nodosa)
(photo: L. Hebdon)

Firethorn — *Pyracantha coccinea*

The masses of white blossoms of this popular evergreen shrub are attractive to a wide range of bees. Nectar is usually secreted very freely by the flowers, and pollen is also collected. In prolonged drought the nectar flow may cease, for bees are inclined to pay little attention to the blossoms during such periods. Many solitary bees, particularly mining bees (*Andrena* species) visit the flowers and have easy access to the pollen and nectar.

The firethorn or pyracantha was introduced to cultivation in the British Isles from southern Europe and it has been grown here for almost 400 years. There are several varieties and it is widely grown, particularly against walls, for which it is well adapted. Grown this way it produces its attractive fruits more freely than in the open. It provides dense cover for birds, which eat the berries. The Asian firethorn (*Pyracantha rogersiana*) is less often grown in gardens than the common firethorn, but it has the advantage of flowering earlier in spring, which means it provides nectar and pollen when foraging time for bees is more likely to be restricted because of bad weather.

Family:	Rosaceae
Flowering:	May to June
Cultivation:	evergreen large shrub
Honey:	no
Honeybees:	||||| |||||
ST Bumblebees:	||||| |||||
LT Bumblebees:	||||| |||||
Solitary Bees:	||||| |||||

Far left:
Worker white-tailed bumblebee (Bombus lucorum) *visiting firethorn* (Pyracantha coccinea)
Left:
Female mining bee (Andrena haemorrhoa) *on firethorn* (Pyracantha coccinea)
(photos: W. D. J. Kirk)

F

Field bindweed — Firethorn

Flax — *Linum usitatissimum*

Family:	**Linaceae**
Flowering:	**May to September**
Cultivation:	**annual herb**
Honey:	**no**
Honeybees:	‖‖‖ ‖‖‖
ST Bumblebees:	‖‖‖
LT Bumblebees:	‖‖‖
Solitary Bees:	‖‖‖

Above:
*Flax flower (*Linum usitatissimum*)*
(photo: W. D. J. Kirk)

The flax or linseed plant is cultivated in many temperate countries, both for flax fibre, which is the raw material of the linen industry, and for seed, which yields linseed oil and linseed cake for animal feed. The names flax and linseed are used according to whether the crop is grown mainly for fibre or for seed. Flax varieties are tall to give long fibres whereas linseed varieties are shorter. Flax was much grown for linen in Ireland, particularly in the north, until the first half of the 20th century, but the industry has now almost disappeared. Linseed has been grown in Britain for many centuries and is now grown mainly for oil. The area grown in the British Isles has fluctuated considerably over the last few decades as world prices have changed. The plant is an annual with an attractive blue flower and a field of linseed in full bloom is indeed a pretty sight. The flowers only last a day and most of the petals have fallen off by the afternoon. Honeybees visit the flowers, but it is doubtful whether they are a very important sources of nectar, although the flowers can be visited very freely, particularly in the early morning. Some honeybees stand on the flower stem and poke their tongue between the petals to reach the nectar from the outside, rather than land on the front of the flower, perhaps because the petals are delicate and liable to drop off. The crop is said to yield honey in some other countries, but the yield, if any, is generally poor in the British Isles.

The wild and the cultivated flax plants of the flower garden appear to be of about the same value as bee plants. Purging flax or fairy flax (*Linum catharticum*) is a common plant in meadows and on chalk hills and cliffs. It is in bloom from June to August and has small white, not blue, flowers. In these and other species of *Linum* the stamens are fused together at the base into a fleshy ring where the nectar is secreted in five drops from the five small pits or nectaries.

Fleabane — *Erigeron* species

Family:	**Asteraceae**
Flowering:	**July to August**
Cultivation:	**annual to perennial herb**
Honey:	**no**
Honeybees:	‖‖‖ ‖‖‖
ST Bumblebees:	‖‖‖ ‖‖‖
LT Bumblebees:	‖‖‖ ‖‖‖
Solitary Bees:	‖‖‖ ‖‖‖

Right:
*Flower of seaside fleabane (*Erigeron glaucus*)*
(photo: W. D. J. Kirk)
Far right:
*Blue mason bee (*Osmia caerulescens*) on fleabane (*Erigeron *species)*
(photo: J. V. Adams)

The name 'fleabane' is used for several types of daisy-like flower, including the common fleabane (see separate entry) and a range of species of *Erigeron*. These popular border perennials generally produce their flowers in July and August when there may be rather few other sources for bees in gardens.

They are white, pink or purple and rather like a Michaelmas daisy. Among the better known of these fleabanes, the Aspen fleabane (*Erigeron speciosus*) and Himalayan fleabane (*Erigeron multiradiatus*) are freely visited by bees for nectar, as are doubtless many others. The first of these is perhaps the best of the taller kinds, reaching up to about 75 cm in height with masses of large purple flowers.

Forget-me-not — *Myosotis* species

The forget-me-nots, whether wild or cultivated, are always popular with bees. Among the wild kinds, the field forget-me-not (*Myosotis arvensis*) is the most abundant, its small sapphire flowers being common in fields and woods alike. A larger and more attractive flower is that of the water forget-me-not (*Myosotis scorpioides*), which is also wild in many other parts of Europe and known by the same name, for example 'Vergissmeinnicht' in German. Its dainty blue flowers are most prevalent on the banks of rivers and streams. Forget-me-nots start to flower early in the season and so can be a valuable source of nectar and pollen when few other sources are available.

Where forget-me-nots abound, the pollen of the plants is often very prevalent in honey. The reason is that the mouth of the flower tube is very narrow and there is barely room for the honeybee to insert its tongue. In doing so, it is forced to dislodge a good deal of pollen, which must get mixed with the nectar. The pollen grains of forget-me-not are exceedingly minute, among the smallest known from any plant, and so are probably drawn up with the nectar. They also get lodged in the hairs of the tongue. The result is that they reach the honey stomach of the honeybee in much greater quantity than the pollen of other flowers. The grains can measure as little as 3–4 µm in length and when compared under the microscope with large pollens, such as those of crocus or hollyhock, look rather like a marble next to a football. In shape they are not round, but appear as two small spheres joined together by a narrow neck.

Family:	**Boraginaceae**
Flowering:	**April to September**
Cultivation:	**annual to perennial herb**
Honey:	**no**
Honeybees:	‖‖‖ ‖‖‖
ST Bumblebees:	‖‖‖ ‖‖‖
LT Bumblebees:	‖‖‖ ‖‖‖
Solitary Bees:	‖‖‖ ‖‖‖

Above:
Pollen grains of wood forget-me-not (Myosotis sylvatica) (7 µm)

Far left:
Male mining bee (Andrena haemorrhoa) on forget-me-not (Myosotis species)
(photo: N. W. Owens)

Left:
Cuckoo bee (Nomada species) on forget-me-not (Myosotis species)
(photo: T. C. Ings)

Foxglove — *Digitalis purpurea*

Family:	**Veronicaceae**
Flowering:	**June to September**
Cultivation:	**biennial to perennial herb**
Honey:	**no**
Honeybees:	—
ST Bumblebees:	||||| ||||| |||||
LT Bumblebees:	||||| ||||| |||||
Solitary Bees:	|||||

Above:
Garden bumblebee (Bombus hortorum) *on foxglove* (Digitalis purpurea)
(photo: M. A. Kirk)

The foxglove is also sometimes called finger flower because the long tubular flowers are the right size and length to fit over the end of a small finger. The flowers are also an excellent fit to a bumblebee and these are the main visitors. The flower narrows further at the base so that bumblebees need to poke their tongue out to reach the nectar. Long-tongued bumblebees can reach further and so can suck up more nectar than the other bumblebees. As a result, the flowers are much visited by long-tongued bumblebees, including the garden bumblebee (*Bombus hortorum*), the common carder bee (*Bombus pascuorum*) and the ruderal bumblebee (*Bombus ruderatus*), which is restricted to southern and central England. The purple flowers have a lip on which bumblebees land and a pattern of spots that leads them to the nectar. As they push deep within the flower, anthers on the roof of the flower brush pollen onto the upper surface of the bee.

The wild foxglove is reliably good for bumblebees whereas garden forms of foxglove may or may not be so good. The wool-carder bee (*Anthidium manicatum*) has been recorded visiting flowers of the woolly foxglove (*Digitalis lanata*), apparently for nectar, but perhaps also to gather plant hairs to line its nest (see stachys). These bees can be recognised by the rows of distinctive yellow spots down the body.

French honeysuckle — *Hedysarum* species

Family:	**Fabaceae**
Flowering:	**June to September**
Cultivation:	**biennial to perennial herb or small shrub**
Honey:	**no**
Honeybees:	|||||
ST Bumblebees:	|||||
LT Bumblebees:	|||||
Solitary Bees:	—

The flowers of several kinds are visited by bees for nectar. Two of the best known in gardens are French honeysuckle or cock's head (*Hedysarum coronarium*), with red or white flowers, and alpine French honeysuckle (*Hedysarum hedysaroides*), a much smaller plant with racemes of showy purple flowers. The plant is not related to the common honeysuckle (see honeysuckle), but is instead related to sainfoin (see separate entry). A related species, purple hedysarum (*Hedysarum multijugum*), is not often grown in gardens but is available. It is a deciduous shrub that can reach a height of 1.5 m and flowers later over a long season from June to September.

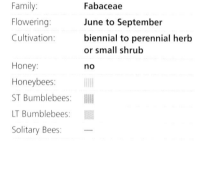

Right:
Flower of purple hedysarum (Hedysarum multijugum)
(photo: W. D. J. Kirk)

Fuchsia — *Fuchsia magellanica*

This South American plant is hardy in the milder parts of the British Isles and attains the dimensions of a small tree if unpruned. In less mild districts it may be killed to the ground in the winter but sends up fresh-flowering shoots each year. In Devon and Cornwall and western Ireland it grows vigorously and has become naturalised in some areas. It is quite commonly used there as a hedge plant, even for farm hedges, for it makes bushy compact growth and withstands the sea breezes. The red and purple flowers are rich in nectar and are pollinated by hummingbirds in their native land, but in the British Isles they are visited mainly by long-tongued bumblebees, such as the common carder bee (*Bombus pascuorum*), and by honeybees. They are an important source of nectar for bees in Ireland. The pendent nature of the flower protects the nectar well from rain. At Kew Gardens, beds of the plant have attracted bees in large numbers in August year after year. Honey has been obtained from fuchsia in the USA and is described as very light in colour, but of little flavour.

Family:	Onagraceae
Flowering:	June to September
Cultivation:	deciduous small shrub or small tree
Honey:	no
Honeybees:	||||| |||||
ST Bumblebees:	|||||
LT Bumblebees:	||||| |||||
Solitary Bees:	—

F

Foxglove — Fuchsia

Left:
*Common carder bee (*Bombus pascuorum*)*
*and honeybee on fuchsia (*Fuchsia*
'Countess of Aberdeen')
(photo: J. Craig)

Gaillardia — *Gaillardia* species

Family:	**Asteraceae**
Flowering:	**June to September**
Cultivation:	**annual to perennial herb**
Honey:	**no**
Honeybees:	||||| |||||
ST Bumblebees:	||||| |||||
LT Bumblebees:	||||| |||||
Solitary Bees:	||||| |||||

This very popular garden plant, which is sometimes known as blanket flower, is available in annual or perennial forms and has striking yellow, orange and red flowers. It is attractive to bees, which probe the flower-heads for nectar and pollen. Some varieties have the advantage of flowering more or less continuously throughout the summer. The annual gaillardia (*Gaillardia pulchella*) was considered, during the early 20th century, to be one of the main honey-producing plants of Texas.

Right:
Flower of gaillardia (Gaillardia 'Gallo Yellow')
(photo: W. D. J. Kirk)
Far right:
Buff-tailed bumblebee (Bombus terrestris) on gaillardia (Gaillardia aristata 'Kobold')
(photo: C. Stevens)

Garlic mustard — *Alliaria petiolata*

Family:	**Brassicaceae**
Flowering:	**April to June**
Cultivation:	**biennial herb**
Honey:	**no**
Honeybees:	|||||
ST Bumblebees:	|||||
LT Bumblebees:	|||||
Solitary Bees:	|||||

The white flowers of this well-known wild plant are visited by bees for nectar, which is secreted in four drops at the base of each flower. Known also as hedge garlic on account of the strong smell when bruised, this plant is very prevalent in hedges and ditches. Some closely related wild species are also visited for nectar, such as hedge mustard (*Sisymbrium officinale*) and flixweed (*Descurainia sophia*).

Right:
Garlic mustard flowers (Alliaria petiolata)
(photo: W. D. J. Kirk)
Far right:
Worker ruderal bumblebee (Bombus ruderatus) on garlic mustard (Alliaria petiolata)
(photo: L. Hebdon)

Garrya — *Garrya elliptica*

This evergreen shrub has male and female forms. The pollen-producing catkins on the male forms are sometimes visited by early honeybees for pollen. It grows best in the warmer districts, such as Devon and Cornwall, where the catkins can reach 30 cm in length.

Family:	**Garryaceae**
Flowering:	**January to March**
Cultivation:	**evergreen large shrub**
Honey:	**no**
Honeybees:	‖‖‖
ST Bumblebees:	—
LT Bumblebees:	—
Solitary Bees:	—

Gaultheria, see shallon

Geranium, see cranesbill

Geum, see avens

Gilia — *Gilia* species

These hardy annuals with their colourful flowers of various shades are in bloom for a long time and also last well in vases. They are generally sown in spring, but in milder districts they may be sown in the autumn for early blooming the following season. Several species are available for gardens and one of the best known is Queen Anne's thimble (*Gilia capitata*). In parts of North America, their original home, the wild gilias are useful sources of nectar, especially in burnt-over forest country, and, in the past, have been reported to yield surplus honey. Some yield dark blue pollen that is very distinctive on the hind legs of bees.

Family:	**Polemoniaceae**
Flowering:	**June to September**
Cultivation:	**annual herb**
Honey:	**no**
Honeybees:	‖‖‖
ST Bumblebees:	‖‖‖
LT Bumblebees:	‖‖‖
Solitary Bees:	‖‖‖

Globe artichoke — *Cynara cardunculus* variety *scolymus*

When globe artichokes are grown as vegetables, the flower-heads are cut before they open, but if they are allowed to flower, either decoratively in gardens or commercially for seed production, they are visited freely by bees. The large, purple, thistle-like flower-heads are similar to those of the cardoon (see separate entry). The Jerusalem artichoke (*Helianthus tuberosus*), a native of North America in spite of its name, is also a good bee plant in countries where it flowers. In the British Isles, it does not normally flower because the autumn frosts arrive first.

Family:	**Asteraceae**
Flowering:	**June to September**
Cultivation:	**perennial herb**
Honey:	**no**
Honeybees:	‖‖‖ ‖‖‖
ST Bumblebees:	‖‖‖ ‖‖‖
LT Bumblebees:	‖‖‖ ‖‖‖
Solitary Bees:	‖‖‖

Far left:
Flower-head of globe artichoke (Cynara cardunculus variety *scolymus)*
Left:
Honeybees on globe artichoke (Cynara cardunculus variety *scolymus)*
(photos: W. D. J. Kirk)

Globe thistle — *Echinops* species

Family:	**Asteraceae**
Flowering:	**July to August**
Cultivation:	**perennial herb**
Honey:	**no**
Honeybees:	||||| |||||
ST Bumblebees:	||||| |||||
LT Bumblebees:	||||| |||||
Solitary Bees:	||||| |||||

Top:
*Buff-tailed bumblebees (*Bombus
terrestris*), hoverflies and a honeybee on
globe thistle (*Echinops *species)*
Above:
*Honeybee on globe thistle (*Echinops
species)
(photos: W. D. J. Kirk)

The globe thistle or echinops, with its large prickly heads of blue flowers, never fails to attract bees in good weather in the summer. The name echinops is from the Greek meaning 'looking like a hedgehog', which is very appropriate. There are well over a hundred species and they occur in the wild state mainly from Spain and Portugal eastwards to India. Bumblebees and honeybees visit the flowers for nectar and sometimes pollen, in company with numerous hoverflies and wasps. The following species are much visited by bees: globe thistle (*Echinops bannaticus*), which is common in gardens; tall globe thistle (*Echinops exaltatus*), which has white to pale blue flowers; globe thistle (*Echinops niveus*); globe thistle (*Echinops ritro*); and great globe thistle (*Echinops sphaerocephalus*). These thistle-like plants are well suited to herbaceous borders and shrubberies and are all easy to grow. Globe thistles have long been grown in gardens and several selected garden varieties are available, such as 'Veitch's Blue' which is a form of globe thistle (*Echinops ritro*) and 'Arctic Glow', which is a form of the great globe thistle (*Echinops sphaerocephalus*).

After the great globe thistle (*Echinops sphaerocephalus*) was introduced to the USA in the 1880s, a beekeeper in New York state called Hiram Chapman grew about a hectare of it. Glowing reports at the time about its attractiveness to honeybees caused the plant to become known as the 'Chapman honey plant' in beekeeping circles. Although the plant attracts many bees, some have doubted whether it is really of as much value as a nectar plant as the number of bees suggests and have observed that the bees do not work as fast as they usually do when there is a high yield and that many do not feed at all. The issue has not been resolved at the time of writing.

Globe thistles could makes a good apiary hedge or boundary plant if given two wires for support, the dead stalks being left in position through the winter.

In the individual flowers of this plant the nectar is secreted at the base and may rise in the flower-tube, which is 5–6 mm deep, and overflow into the bell or expanded part of the flower. As the petals are split almost to the base, the nectar is easily available to bees with short or long tongues.

Glory of the snow — *Scilla luciliae*

Family:	**Asparagaceae**
Flowering:	**March to May**
Cultivation:	**perennial herb, grown from bulbs**
Honey:	**no**
Honeybees:	|||||
ST Bumblebees:	|||||
LT Bumblebees:	|||||
Solitary Bees:	|||||

This little plant (formerly known as *Chionodoxa luciliae*) comes from Asia Minor. It is one of the most handsome of the early spring-flowering bulbs and is quite hardy. Any ordinary garden soil will suit it and it increases rapidly. The blue and white or pure white flowers appear in March and April and are useful for early pollen and nectar. The earliness of the flowers means that they are mainly visited by honeybees, but as with the bluebell (see separate entry) may be of particular value to the few bumblebees and solitary bees that visit it because of the shortage of other flowers so early in the season. There are several other closely related species, such as the lesser glory of the snow (*Scilla sardensis*) and Siberian squill (*Scilla siberica*), which are of similar value to bees.

Far left:
Pollen grain of lesser glory of the snow
(Scilla sardensis) *(33 μm)*
Left:
Flower of glory of the snow (Scilla
luciliae)
(photo: W. D. J. Kirk)

Goat's rue — *Galega* species

The name 'goat's rue' is used for several species in the genus *Galega*, but only two of these species are likely to be seen in the British Isles. The species that is most often seen in gardens is common goat's rue (*Galega officinalis*). It is native to central and southern Europe, but has naturalised in parts of central and southern Britain. It is considered a noxious weed in some countries because of toxic alkaloids in the leaves. An alternative name is 'French lilac', although the flowers do not look much like those of lilac. The species that is grown as a fodder crop in eastern Europe and is starting to become more popular as a garden plant is oriental goat's rue or fodder galega (*Galega orientalis*). It does not contain toxic alkaloids. Both plants can grow to a height of about 1.5 m and have racemes of white to bluish mauve pea-like flowers.

Bumblebees and honeybees are frequent visitors, including the common carder bee (*Bombus pascuorum*), the buff-tailed bumblebee (*Bombus terrestris*), the white-tailed bumblebee (*Bombus lucorum*), the red-tailed bumblebee (*Bombus lapidarius*), the early bumblebee (*Bombus pratorum*) and the garden bumblebee (*Bombus hortorum*). Most visiting bees can be seen to be collecting pollen because of the presence of orange pollen loads on their hind legs.

There are reports from eastern Europe that goat's rue is an excellent nectar source and good honey yields have been obtained by honeybees. However, there are also claims that the plant does not produce nectar and attempts to measure nectar production on plants grown in England have failed to detect any nectar. A possible explanation of these contradictory reports is that the plant is fickle and only yields nectar under particular soil conditions.

Family:	**Fabaceae**
Flowering:	**May to August**
Cultivation:	**perennial herb**
Honey:	**no**
Honeybees:	||||| |||||
ST Bumblebees:	||||| |||||
LT Bumblebees:	||||| |||||
Solitary Bees:	|||||

Above:
Buff-tailed bumblebee (Bombus terrestris)
visiting common goat's rue (Galega
officinalis)
Left:
Buff-tailed bumblebee (Bombus terrestris)
on common goat's rue (Galega officinalis)
(photos: T. C. Ings)

Godetia, see clarkia

Golden honey plant — *Verbesina alternifolia*

Family:	**Asteraceae**
Flowering:	**August to September**
Cultivation:	**perennial herb**
Honey:	**no**
Honeybees:	||||| |||||
ST Bumblebees:	|||||
LT Bumblebees:	|||||
Solitary Bees:	|||||

This plant is native to eastern North America and has been favourably reported on as a honey plant there. It is also known by the name wingstem or yellow ironweed. The flowers are like small sunflowers and produce plenty of nectar and pollen. It grows best on rich lowlands, reaching a height of 2–3 m and blooming in August and September. Its yellow flowers are freely worked by honeybees. As it is somewhat coarse in appearance it does not appear to have been grown in gardens in the British Isles, but is an interesting possibility for the bee garden.

Goldenrod — *Solidago* species

Family:	**Asteraceae**
Flowering:	**July to October**
Cultivation:	**perennial herb**
Honey:	**no**
Honeybees:	||||| |||||
ST Bumblebees:	||||| |||||
LT Bumblebees:	||||| |||||
Solitary Bees:	||||| |||||

There are about a hundred different species of goldenrod, the great majority of which are natives of North America, where they are important autumn honey plants. One species, common goldenrod (*Solidago virgaurea*), is wild in the British Isles and is prevalent in some areas, particularly near heaths and on rocky banks and cliffs near the sea. The same species occurs freely in many other European countries. It grows in the poorest soils and produces its abundance of yellow flowers from July to October. These are very attractive to bees as well as to numerous other insects and must constitute a useful source of late nectar and pollen where they are sufficiently abundant. The same applies to the many garden forms of goldenrod that are popular in herbaceous borders and the shrubbery or wild garden where they are well able to hold their own with other plants. Some of these introduced kinds have also become naturalised to some extent in the British Isles. Most goldenrods are freely worked for nectar and pollen by bees late in the season, including Canadian goldenrod (*Solidago canadensis*), downy goldenrod (*Solidago puberula*), grass-leaved goldenrod (*Solidago graminifolia*), rough-stemmed goldenrod (*Solidago rugosa*) and Short's goldenrod (*Solidago shortii*). However, some species of goldenrod, particularly Canadian goldenrod (*Solidago canadensis*), can be highly invasive.

A range of bumblebee species are frequent visitors, including the common carder bee (*Bombus pascuorum*), the buff-tailed bumblebee (*Bombus terrestris*) and the garden bumblebee (*Bombus hortorum*). Solitary bees, such as mining bees (*Lasioglossum* species) and cuckoo bees (*Nomada* species) also visit the flowers.

In many parts of eastern Canada and the USA, goldenrod and aster are the two important late-season honey plants. Their main value is in providing winter stores for honeybees, but surplus honey is taken from goldenrod in some areas, often in conjunction with nectar from other plants. This is described as golden yellow in colour, thick and heavy and of fine flavour. The flavour improves markedly during ripening. It crystallises in about two months with a coarse grain. Little is known regarding the nectar value of the actual individual species, but some contend that all goldenrods will yield nectar under conditions favourable to them. However, in some parts of the USA where goldenrod is common it yields little or no honey.

Above:
*Mining bee (*Lasioglossum *species) on goldenrod (*Solidago *species)*
(photo: T. C. Ings)

Gooseberry — *Ribes uva-crispa*

The gooseberry occurs as a wild plant across most of the British Isles. In Britain, some may be native, but many are escapes that have naturalised. The native plant is the progenitor or parent plant of the numerous varieties now cultivated with rough or smooth, green, yellow, red or purplish berries. The gooseberry has been cultivated in the British Isles for many centuries, every cottage garden, however small, having its own gooseberry bushes at one time. These sometimes attain a large size and great age of 50 years or more.

The leaves of the gooseberry are among the first to show signs of growth in early spring, and the greenish-white, inconspicuous flowers are generally out in April. These are attractive to honeybees for their nectar, which is secreted at the base of the bell-shaped flower, and is protected by the hairs projecting from the style in the centre. The hairs may impede other insects but offer no obstruction to the honeybee. The flower is in fact well constructed for its visits. Early bumblebees and solitary bees, such as the tawny mining bee (*Andrena fulva*), sometimes visit the flowers.

Surplus honey from gooseberries may be obtained from hives near fruit farms where gooseberries are extensively grown, but this probably rarely occurs. However, such honey has been described as medium coloured and of excellent flavour. It has been found that where currants and gooseberries are inter-planted with cherries, as is sometimes done, honeybees may desert the currant and gooseberry flowers in favour of those of the cherries.

The gooseberry is regarded as a better nectar plant than the currant. The pollen of the gooseberry is not produced in great abundance and is pale greenish yellow in colour. It is not in separate granules like that of the common tree fruits, but is stuck together in glutinous masses. That of the currant is similar. It is collected as a sideline while bees work for nectar.

Family:	Grossulariaceae
Flowering:	March to May
Cultivation:	deciduous small shrub
Honey:	no
Honeybees:	||||| |||||
ST Bumblebees:	|||||
LT Bumblebees:	|||||
Solitary Bees:	|||||

Top:
*Pollen grain of gooseberry (*Ribes uva-crispa) (25 µm)*
Above:
*Male tawny mining bee (*Andrena fulva)
*on a gooseberry leaf (*Ribes uva-crispa)
(photo: L. Hebdon)

Gorse — *Ulex europaeus*

The prickly gorse or furze bush with its familiar yellow flowers is one of the commonest plants in the British Isles and covers large areas of moors, commons and heathland. It thrives on poor, light sandy soils, often coming up freely wherever soil is disturbed and is usually found with at least some flowers throughout the year. However, the main flowering period is around April, when the bushes are covered with their golden blossoms. At this time, early in the season, they are a useful source of pollen for beekeepers, helping build up colonies ahead of the main nectar flows. Whether they supply nectar as well is rather open to question, but they probably do at times. However, the main benefit of the plant to bees is the pollen. This is produced in abundance and is bright yellow or orange in colour, assuming a darker or duller shade when packed on the hind legs of honeybees or bumblebees. In the early spring it is especially valuable. Flowers often start to appear freely as early as February and so may take the place of willow

Family:	Fabaceae
Flowering:	February to June
Cultivation:	evergreen medium shrub
Honey:	no
Honeybees:	||||| |||||
ST Bumblebees:	||||| |||||
LT Bumblebees:	||||| |||||
Solitary Bees:	|||||

G

Godetia — Gorse

Above:
*Queen buff-tailed bumblebee (*Bombus terrestris*) on gorse (*Ulex europaeus*). The pale dots above her legs are mites, which are commonly found as passengers on queen bumblebees.*
(*photo: J. V. Adams*)
Right:
*Female hairy-footed flower bee (*Anthophora plumipes*) on gorse (*Ulex europaeus*)*
(*photo: T. C. Ings*)
Far right:
*Pollen grain of gorse (*Ulex europaeus*) (32 μm)*

and hazel in other districts. Bees commonly forsake gorse once other flowers become available. The dwarf gorse (*Ulex minor*) is also very common on heaths and commons in southern England. It differs from ordinary gorse in its more trailing habit, smaller size and smaller flowers, the latter being about half the size of ordinary gorse and probably more easily worked by smaller bees, such as honeybees and solitary bees. It flowers from June to December, but most freely in September when those of ordinary gorse are mainly over. In company with heather (*Calluna vulgaris*), it is the main source of pollen in August and September in some heathland areas, with the two pollens being often found mixed in the pollen loads on honeybees' hind legs.

Gorse is a valuable source of pollen in early spring for bumblebees such as the red-tailed bumblebee (*Bombus lapidarius*) and the buff-tailed bumblebee (*Bombus terrestris*). The flowers are also visited by the larger solitary bees, such as hairy-footed flower bees (*Anthophora plumipes*) and mining bees (*Andrena* species).

Gourd — *Cucurbita* species

Family:	**Cucurbitaceae**
Flowering:	**June to August**
Cultivation:	**annual herb**
Honey:	**no**
Honeybees:	|||||
ST Bumblebees:	|||||
LT Bumblebees:	|||||
Solitary Bees:	|||||

All the gourd plants are useful sources of nectar and pollen for bees. They include vegetable marrows, courgettes, pumpkins, cucumbers, squashes, melons and the ornamental gourds sometimes grown in gardens for their decorative value or quaint appearance. Only the first two of these can be said to be commonly cultivated out of doors in the British Isles (see vegetable marrow). Pumpkins are being increasingly grown commercially for sale for Halloween.

Right:
*Honeybees on giant pumpkin (*Cucurbita maxima*)*
(*photo: W. D. J. Kirk*)

Grape hyacinth — *Muscari* species

The pretty blue flowers of these ever-popular spring bulbs are very attractive to honeybees early in the year and yield pollen and much nectar at a time when rather few other sources are available. The flowers are also visited by bumblebees and by solitary bees. There are many different kinds of grape hyacinth in cultivation. All are hardy and easy to grow, which is rather surprising as they are for the most part of Mediterranean origin. One species (*Muscari neglectum*) occurs wild in some parts of eastern England, but is not common.

Family:	Asparagaceae
Flowering:	March to May
Cultivation:	perennial herb, grown from bulbs
Honey:	no
Honeybees:	||||| |||||
ST Bumblebees:	|||||
LT Bumblebees:	|||||
Solitary Bees:	|||||

Far left:
*Garden grape hyacinth flowers (*Muscari armeniacum*)*
(photo: M. A. Kirk)
Left:
*Male hairy-footed flower bee (*Anthophora plumipes*) on garden grape hyacinth (*Muscari armeniacum*)*
(photo: N. W. Owens)

Grass — *Alopecurus pratensis* and *Dactylis glomerata*

Grasses are wind-pollinated plants. They yield a light powdery type of pollen and do not produce nectar. Bees generally do not favour this type of pollen when others are available, but they do sometimes collect pollen from grasses. There are many well-authenticated cases of this. Probably any grass that is producing pollen may be visited, but the two grasses often concerned are cock's foot (*Dactylis glomerata*) and meadow foxtail (*Alopecurus pratensis*). The last mentioned has been observed to be worked for pollen by honeybees at Kew Gardens in May, a time when numerous other pollen sources are available in the area, which goes to show that bee behaviour is not easy to predict.

Family:	Poaceae
Flowering:	April to August
Cultivation:	perennial herb
Honey:	no
Honeybees:	|||||
ST Bumblebees:	||||| |||||
LT Bumblebees:	||||| |||||
Solitary Bees:	|||||

Grasses are of benefit to several species of bumblebee that build their nests either in long grass, such as the brown-banded carder bee (*Bombus humilis*) and the moss carder bee (*Bombus muscorum*), or in old mouse nests in long grass, such as the red-shanked carder bee (*Bombus ruderarius*). Leaving an area of uncut grass may provide nesting areas for bumblebees, although the success rate of providing nest sites for bumblebees is usually low.

The tawny mining bee (*Andrena fulva*) often nests in bare patches in lawns. It is common in England and Wales, rare in Scotland and absent from Ireland. The female digs a burrow and the ejected soil piles up around the entrance like a mini volcano. Her appearance is distinctive, with bright reddish brown hair above and black hair underneath.

Above:
*Female tawny mining bee (*Andrena fulva*) at her nest entrance in a patch of bare soil*
(photo: L. A. Hislop)

G

Gourd — Grass

Greater burdock — *Arctium lappa*

Family:	**Asteraceae**
Flowering:	**July to September**
Cultivation:	**biennial herb**
Honey:	**no**
Honeybees:	||||| |||||
ST Bumblebees:	||||| |||||
LT Bumblebees:	||||| |||||
Solitary Bees:	|||||

This common weed is well-known for its burr-like seed heads that cling tenaciously to man and beast. The purple flowers that appear from July onwards closely resemble those of thistles. They are much frequented by honeybees and bumblebees, particularly the common carder bee (*Bombus pascuorum*). They may be observed collecting the white pollen and probing the flowers for nectar. As the flower-tube of the individual flowers generally exceeds 8 mm in length it may be that the honeybee is only able to get nectar when it is secreted freely and rises in the base of the tube to within reach of the bee's tongue. Bumblebees with longer tongues would be able to draw the nectar at any time, so it is doubtful whether the greater burdock can be of much value for nectar to honeybees where bumblebees are plentiful. These remarks do not apply to the lesser burdock (*Arctium minus*) in which the whole plant, including leaves and flower-heads, is smaller.

Right:
*Honeybee on greater burdock (*Arctium lappa*)*
(photo: W. D. J. Kirk)
Far right:
*Pollen grain of lesser burdock (*Arctium minus*) (38 μm)*

Gromwell — *Lithospermum* species

Family:	**Boraginaceae**
Flowering:	**May to July**
Cultivation:	**annual to perennial herb**
Honey:	**no**
Honeybees:	|||||
ST Bumblebees:	|||||
LT Bumblebees:	|||||
Solitary Bees:	|||||

Both the wild and garden species of gromwell often flower in great profusion. Of these, the purple gromwell is common in gardens and is known by various scientific names (*Lithospermum diffusum*, *Lithodora diffusa* and *Glandora diffusa*). The garden species are generally blue-flowered rock-garden plants. They are sometimes visited by honeybees and bumblebees. Nectar collects at the base of the flower tube, which in the case of the field gromwell (*Lithospermum arvense*) is 4.5 mm long, so all the nectar is available to honeybees and short-tongued bumblebees, not just long-tongued bumblebees. They are probably not of any special importance as honey plants. The field gromwell, bearing whitish flowers in May and June, occurs as a weed in cultivated ground.

Right:
*Purple gromwell flower (*Glandora diffusa 'Heavenly Blue'*)*
(photo: W. D. J. Kirk)

Gypsywort — *Lycopus europaeus*

Although found throughout the British Isles, this plant is commonest in England and Wales. It grows mainly along the margins of rivers and pools and has distinctive, deeply lobed leaves. The small white flowers with purple dots are in clusters on the upper part of the stem and are present from June to September. They are rich in nectar, which honeybees and short-tongued bumblebees have no difficulty in extracting. The plants are a useful late, though minor, source of nectar for beekeepers in some districts. The name 'gypsywort' arose because gypsies were reputed to use the juice as a dye.

Family:	**Lamiaceae**
Flowering:	**June to September**
Cultivation:	**perennial herb**
Honey:	**no**
Honeybees:	|||||
ST Bumblebees:	|||||
LT Bumblebees:	|||||
Solitary Bees:	|||||

Left:
Gypsywort flowers (Lycopus europaeus)
(photo: W. D. J. Kirk)

G

Greater burdock — Gypsywort

Harebell, see bellflower

Hawkbit, see autumn hawkbit

Hawksbeard — *Crepis* species

Family:	Asteraceae
Flowering:	June to September
Cultivation:	annual to perennial herb
Honey:	no
Honeybees:	‖‖‖
ST Bumblebees:	‖‖‖
LT Bumblebees:	‖‖‖
Solitary Bees:	‖‖‖ ‖‖‖ ‖‖‖

These plants, with flowers like those of a small dandelion, are common weeds of cultivated ground. Smooth hawksbeard (*Crepis capillaris*) is common throughout the British Isles. Honeybees visit the flowers for nectar and pollen in July and August but they can only be regarded as very minor sources in most areas. Bumblebees, particularly the red-tailed bumblebee (*Bombus lapidarius*), are frequent visitors. Hawksbeards, along with several other yellow-flowered members of the daisy family (Asteraceae), provide easy access to pollen and nectar and are visited by an impressively wide range of solitary bees. These include mining bees (*Andrena* and *Lasioglossum* species); leafcutter bees (*Megachile* species); mason bees (*Osmia* species); and cuckoo bees (*Nomada* and *Stelis* species). A few species of solitary bee, such as the hairy-legged mining bee (*Dasypoda hirtipes*), which occurs mainly in southern England and Wales, appear to be strongly associated with yellow-flowered members of the daisy family. The female of this species has distinctive long golden hairs on the hind legs.

Right:
Smooth hawksbeard flower-head (Crepis capillaris)
(photo: W. D. J. Kirk)
Far right:
Female hairy-legged mining bee (Dasypoda hirtipes) on hawksbeard (Crepis species)
(photo: J. P. Early)

Hawkweed — *Hieracium* species and *Pilosella* species

Family:	Asteraceae
Flowering:	May to November
Cultivation:	perennial herb
Honey:	no
Honeybees:	‖‖‖
ST Bumblebees:	‖‖‖
LT Bumblebees:	‖‖‖
Solitary Bees:	‖‖‖ ‖‖‖

Hawkweed (*Hieracium* species) and mouse-ear hawkweed (*Pilosella* species) are very closely related and include many species that are difficult to separate. They have yellow or orange flowers like those of a small dandelion, but on the ends of long stems about 20–30 cm tall. Honeybees collect nectar and pollen from some of the many different kinds of hawkweed, especially leafy hawkweed (*Hieracium umbellatum*) and mouse-ear hawkweed (*Pilosella officinarum*), which are widely distributed throughout the British Isles. The flowers are particularly valuable to the red-tailed bumblebee (*Bombus lapidarius*). Hawkweed, like several other yellow-flowered members of the daisy family (Asteraceae), has easily accessible pollen and nectar and is visited by a wide range of solitary bees, similar to those that visit hawksbeard (see separate entry).

Left:
Male wool-carder bee (Anthidium manicatum) *on orange hawkweed* (Pilosella aurantiaca)
(*photo: J. V. Adams*)

Hawthorn — *Crataegus* species

The hawthorn, may or whitethorn is one of our most common native shrubs or small trees. Its strongly-scented white blossoms that appear around the middle of May are familiar to everyone. It is not a fastidious plant and will grow in sun or shade and in all soils except acid peat, which it avoids. Often it is the only shrub to be seen in pastures, where it sometimes becomes far too prevalent for the farmer's liking. Its virtues as a hedge plant are well recognised and as a farm hedge or fence plant it stands supreme.

The shallow flowers have easily accessible nectar, which can be reached even by bees with very short tongues. It attracts large numbers of honeybees collecting nectar and pollen as well as short- and long-tongued bumblebees. The flowers are also visited by a range of solitary bees, such as mining bees (*Andrena*, *Halictus* and *Lasioglossum* species).

As a nectar plant, the hawthorn is notoriously fickle, being a good source of nectar in some seasons or in some districts. Attempts to correlate this with soil or with moisture and temperature conditions have not so far met with success and the reasons for this fickleness remain obscure at present. The seasons when hawthorn is a good honey source only come round at long intervals.

Sometimes hawthorn blossoms will be worked well and yield honey freely in one area while in apparently similar conditions just a kilometre or two away the blossoms may be deserted by bees. In a district that gives a good hawthorn flow one year, the flowers for several succeeding years may offer little attraction. When the flow from hawthorn does occur it is usually very rapid and the smell of the flowers is easily detected in the hives while the nectar is being brought in.

In the hawthorn flower the nectar is secreted by the base of the flower and is half concealed. In cold or dull weather the inner stamens remain curved inwards but open out in sunshine, exposing the nectar more fully.

There are two native species of hawthorn, although the differences between them are slight and they seem to be of similar value as bee plants. The hawthorn (*Crataegus monogyna*) is the more abundant and widespread species throughout the British Isles, while the midland hawthorn (*Crataegus laevigata*) is confined more to the southeast of Britain although it is introduced and naturalised elsewhere. The numerous ornamental forms

Family:	Rosaceae
Flowering:	May to June
Cultivation:	deciduous large shrub or small tree
Honey:	yes
Honeybees:	||||| ||||| |||||
ST Bumblebees:	|||||
LT Bumblebees:	|||||
Solitary Bees:	||||| ||||| |||||

H

Harebell — Hawthorn

Top:
Hawthorn flowers (Crataegus *species*)
(*photo: M. A. Kirk*)
Above:
Mining bee (Andrena nitida) *on hawthorn* (Crataegus *species*)
(*photo: T. C. Ings*)

of hawthorn with pink or red flowers attract bees when the flowers are single, but not the double forms. So also do the flowers of several introduced species of *Crataegus*, mainly from North America, which are sometimes grown in gardens or as street trees.

Honey from hawthorn is of very high quality. It is usually a dark amber in colour, very thick and of an appetising rich flavour. Owing to its dark colour and density it has been mistaken for heather honey. It is not usually bright or sparkling and sometimes has a greenish tinge that can detract from its appearance. The flavour has been described in various ways, although always favourable, such as exquisite, nutty or suggestive of almond.

Usually hawthorn blossoms do not appear until those of apple are over but in some seasons flowering overlaps. The resulting honey, when procurable, which is a blend of apple and hawthorn, is considered by some to be one of the finest flavoured that could be desired.

The pale, whitish pollen of hawthorn is freely collected by bees and is often found in honey. The individual grain is similar to that of apple and rose.

Hazel — *Corylus avellana*

Family:	**Betulaceae**
Flowering:	**January to March**
Cultivation:	**deciduous small tree or large shrub**
Honey:	**no**
Honeybees:	|||| |||||
ST Bumblebees:	—
LT Bumblebees:	—
Solitary Bees:	—

Above:
Hazel catkins (Corylus avellana)
(photo: W. D. J. Kirk)

Like the hawthorn, the hazel is very widespread throughout the British Isles (although avoids acid, peaty soils) and even extends to the extreme north of Scotland. In oak and ash woods it is common, having often been grown in the past for coppicing, and flourishing best on calcareous soils where pure thickets or copses of it may occur. It provides an early source of pollen that is often collected by honeybees on warm spring days. Other bees are not around early enough in the season to make use of the pollen. The tassels of male flowers are conspicuous from late January until early March according to season and district. They yield an abundance of a light yellow powdery pollen, that honeybees will collect eagerly in suitable weather when hazel bushes are near their hives. It is unusual for them to visit bushes a long way from home at this early season. The flowers are wind-pollinated and not dependent on insect visits for fertilisation. The plants produce no nectar. The catkins are available for quite a long period, usually about a month, but this is governed by weather conditions at flowering time. In Kent, hazelnut and cobnut orchards used to be common. The varieties grown for their nuts are fundamentally the same with regard to flowering as the wild hazel bushes, except that the tassels are sometimes much longer.

Heath — *Erica* species

Family:	**Ericaceae**
Flowering:	**March to September**
Cultivation:	**evergreen dwarf shrub**
Honey:	**yes**
Honeybees:	||||| ||||| |||||
ST Bumblebees:	||||| ||||| |||||
LT Bumblebees:	||||| ||||| |||||
Solitary Bees:	||||| ||||| |||||

The term heath is here used to denote all the true heaths or species of *Erica*, as distinct from heather or ling (*Calluna vulgaris*) (see heather). Several heaths occur wild in the British Isles but only two are widely distributed or common: the bell heath or bell heather (*Erica cinerea*) and the cross-leaved heath (*Erica tetralix*).

The bell heath is an excellent bee plant and is to be found on moors and heathlands in company with heather. Its degree of prevalence varies.

It can occur more or less on its own or it may form patches among the heather. It blooms much earlier than heather and its flowers are a deeper purple, larger and more handsome. They are crowded together in clusters, mainly at the ends of the branches. Their rich hue can be seen from far away and it is to them that heathlands owe much of their beauty. They are a good source of nectar and the bell-shaped corolla is the right length (5 mm) for the honeybee and other short-tongued bees to negotiate. Despite this, short-tongued bumblebees pierce the corolla at the base to steal the nectar, presumably because this gives them easier access than probing from the front of the flower. The following historical observations of bees on bell heath recorded by J.T. Powell in 1884 (*Journal of Botany*) can be repeated easily today: 'I watched for some time the visits of bees. ... *Apis mellifica* [the honeybee] was present in great numbers, and was doing its work in beneficial fashion. I noticed, however, that it also took advantage of holes already pierced in the corollas [flower-tubes] of very many of the flowers. Both myself and a botanical friend who was with me watched narrowly to see if the honey-bees made these holes, but in no case did we observe them do so. We also saw numerous humble-bees [bumblebees] busy with the same flowers, which they visited in both the above ways. Presently we saw a *Bombus* [bumblebee] pierce a sound corolla, and afterwards several other insects of the same kind repeated the operation. The action was rather boring than biting, and was comparable to pushing an awl without twisting through a thin deal-board. In some cases a distinct sound was heard, as when paper is pricked with a pin. ... The advantage to both bees of the perforation seemed to be that they could sip their sweets in greater comfort in the nearly erect position they assumed during their illegitimate visits than when turned half-over and hanging sideways to insert their tongues into the mouth of the flower; and this comfort seems to be a sufficient motive for the exercise of intelligence in the humble-bee.'

Honey is frequently obtained from bell heath, either pure or mixed with that of heather. When pure, it is of a reddish port wine colour with distinctive or pronounced flavour which somewhat resembles heather honey. Some prefer it to heather but others do not rate it very highly. The honey is thick, but not enough to prevent the beekeeper from removing it from the comb with an ordinary honey extractor, as is the case with heather honey for which a special heather honey press is needed. As the plant flowers so much earlier than heather – it may be in flower in June in the south – it is often possible to obtain it in a pure or relatively pure state. Later on in the year of course it is always blended with that of heather. Bell heath honey is not the best of winter foods for bees, being inclined to granulate in the comb, but does not cause bee dysentery as heather may do.

Cross-leaved heath (*Erica tetralix*) with its leaves characteristically arranged in fours in the form of a cross, and its drooping clusters of pale pink, wax-like flowers, is also common on heathlands. However, it is of doubtful value as a honeybee plant, the flower-tubes being on the long side (7–8 mm). Flowers have been seen with punctures at the base, so they are clearly visited by short-tongued bumblebees.

In parts of Cornwall, the Cornish heath (*Erica vagans*) is common and beekeepers have obtained surplus from it. The honey resembles that of bell

Top:
Male heath bumblebee (Bombus jonellus) *on bell heath* (Erica cinerea)
(*photo: N. W. Owens*)

Above:
White-tailed bumblebee (Bombus lucorum) *on heath* (Erica *species*) *with holes at the base of the flower*
(*photo: T. C. Ings*)

H

Hazel — Heath

Above:
Tetrad of four pollen grains of Cornish heath (Erica vagans) *(27 μm)*

heath rather than heather in that it is not thick or jelly-like, i.e. it is not thixotropic. Irish heath (*Erica erigena*) occurs wild only in the west of Ireland although common in southern Europe and cultivated in gardens. It is also popular with honeybees.

The numerous garden forms of heath that are so much admired are for the most part good bee plants, having been mainly derived from the wild species already mentioned. It is possible to make a selection so that some will be in flower at all times of the year including the early spring. The majority are much relished by bees. Varieties of winter heath (*Erica carnea*) and Darley Dale heath (*Erica* x *darleyensis*), which are in flower in March, are particularly noticeable in this respect. Beds of winter heath varieties, especially 'Springwood White' and 'King George', have been observed on bright sunny days in March covered with honeybees all feverishly working for nectar. Among the later (August-September) flowering heaths are many forms of bell heath (*Erica cinerea*) and Cornish heath (*Erica vagans*).

Bumblebees collect nectar and pollen from heaths. The white-tailed bumblebee (*Bombus lucorum*), the garden bumblebee (*Bombus hortorum*) and the heath bumblebee (*Bombus jonellus*) are frequent visitors. In late summer, the bilberry bumblebee (*Bombus monticola*), which is seriously declining in many areas, particularly visits flowers of heath and bilberry (see separate entry). It can be recognised fairly easily by the two yellow stripes on the thorax and the large red tail.

Mining bees are classed as solitary bees because each female has its own nest, but a species of heathland mining bee (*Colletes succinctus*) is notably gregarious and many females often dig their nests near each other. The females forage for pollen from heath (*Erica* species) and heather (*Calluna vulgaris*) and impressive numbers of these bees can be seen in some areas on sunny days. The bee is widespread across the British Isles. The flowers are also visited by other solitary bees, such as mining bees (*Andrena* species).

The pollen of the heaths, like that of heather, is characteristic, for it is in the form of a tetrad of four pollen grains together.

Heather — *Calluna vulgaris*

The production of heather or ling honey is one of the few specialised types of honey production in the British Isles. The main crop is in Scotland, but the yield is uncertain and usually obtained by migratory beekeeping, with hives moved to the heather specifically for the flowering season. A really good season only occurs about one year in seven and often no honey surplus at all is obtained, although the hives may become well stocked with stores for the winter. This is often considered by the owner to be sufficient recompense for the cost and trouble of transportation of hives to and from the moors. Heather is the dominant plant in heathlands in the south of England but these are not important for honey. In general the production of heather honey only appeals to beekeepers situated within easy distance of the moors. Heather is in flower from August, usually mid-August, to about the end of September,

Family:	**Ericaceae**
Flowering:	**August to September**
Cultivation:	**evergreen dwarf shrub**
Honey:	**yes**
Honeybees:	||||| ||||| |||||
ST Bumblebees:	||||| ||||| |||||
LT Bumblebees:	||||| ||||| |||||
Solitary Bees:	||||| ||||| |||||

H

Heather

and so has a longer flowering period than most honey plants, although the main period of nectar secretion may be much shorter then this. In the south, some flowers may be found open in July. The flowers are smaller than those of the true heaths (*Erica* species) (see heath), with the flower tubes only 2–3 mm long. Nectar is concealed at the base of the flower and is secreted by eight tiny swellings or nectaries which alternate with the bases of the stamens. As the flower ages, nectar secretion ceases and the stamens elongate. Honeybees also collect the pollen, which is slate grey in colour. It is always present in heather honey in great abundance. The grains are in groups of four, called tetrads, as in the heaths.

Conflicting views are held and have been freely expressed regarding the best conditions for the free secretion of nectar in heather. All are agreed on certain points, however, and that the following factors are important: (1) the age of the heather; (2) the nature of the soil and subsoil; (3) rainfall; and (4) possibly altitude. All these factors may of course be discounted if rain or cold wind prevents honeybees from flying while the heather is out. This often happens owing to the lateness of the season when heather blooms and the fact that it generally grows in areas that are bleak and exposed. Actually, the heather flower will secrete nectar at quite a low temperature, probably lower than that required for bees to fly. It is thought that the best yield of nectar is obtained from young shoots about 30 cm tall and that large bushes that are several years old, despite being covered in flowers, yield very little nectar. Subsoil is also important and a subsoil of granite and ironstone is said to give much higher yields than peat and bog land.

Some have claimed that the honey obtained from heather in the south of England is different from that obtained in the north, and that in some parts of the south the plant is of no use at all as a honey producer and does not secrete nectar. The fact that the honey itself may differ from Scottish heather honey is probably because the heathlands in the south are much less extensive and less uniform than those in the north and there is therefore a much greater chance of admixture with nectar from other floral sources.

Sandy, hilly districts are liable to be easily affected by drought in dry seasons, when only the heather in the low-lying areas may yield. In wet seasons the reverse may apply, the plants on the drier well-drained slopes yielding better than those in the low-lying boggy situations. It may well be, therefore, that the optimum conditions for heather honey production in the south differ radically from those in the different, more moist, climate of Scotland. Heavy rain will put a temporary check to the nectar flow in heather, as is the case with many other honey plants.

Heather honey is sometimes a bad winter food for bees because it is prone to cause bee dysentery. This is exacerbated if bees are confined to the hive and cannot void their faeces for long periods during the cold winter months. Many beekeepers in the south of England, who have made use of heather areas for furnishing winter stores, have not experienced this trouble. Possibly the reason is that in the south, where winters are milder than in Scotland, a sufficient number of mild days

Top:
A jar of heather honey
Above:
*Heather flowers (*Calluna vulgaris *'Red Pimpernel')*
(photos: W. D. J. Kirk)

Images over page
Left (p.152):
*Mining bee (*Colletes succinctus*) on heather (*Calluna vulgaris*)*
(photo: W. George)
Right (p.153):
*Female mining bee (*Andrena fuscipes*) on heather (*Calluna vulgaris*)*
(photo: T. C. Ings)

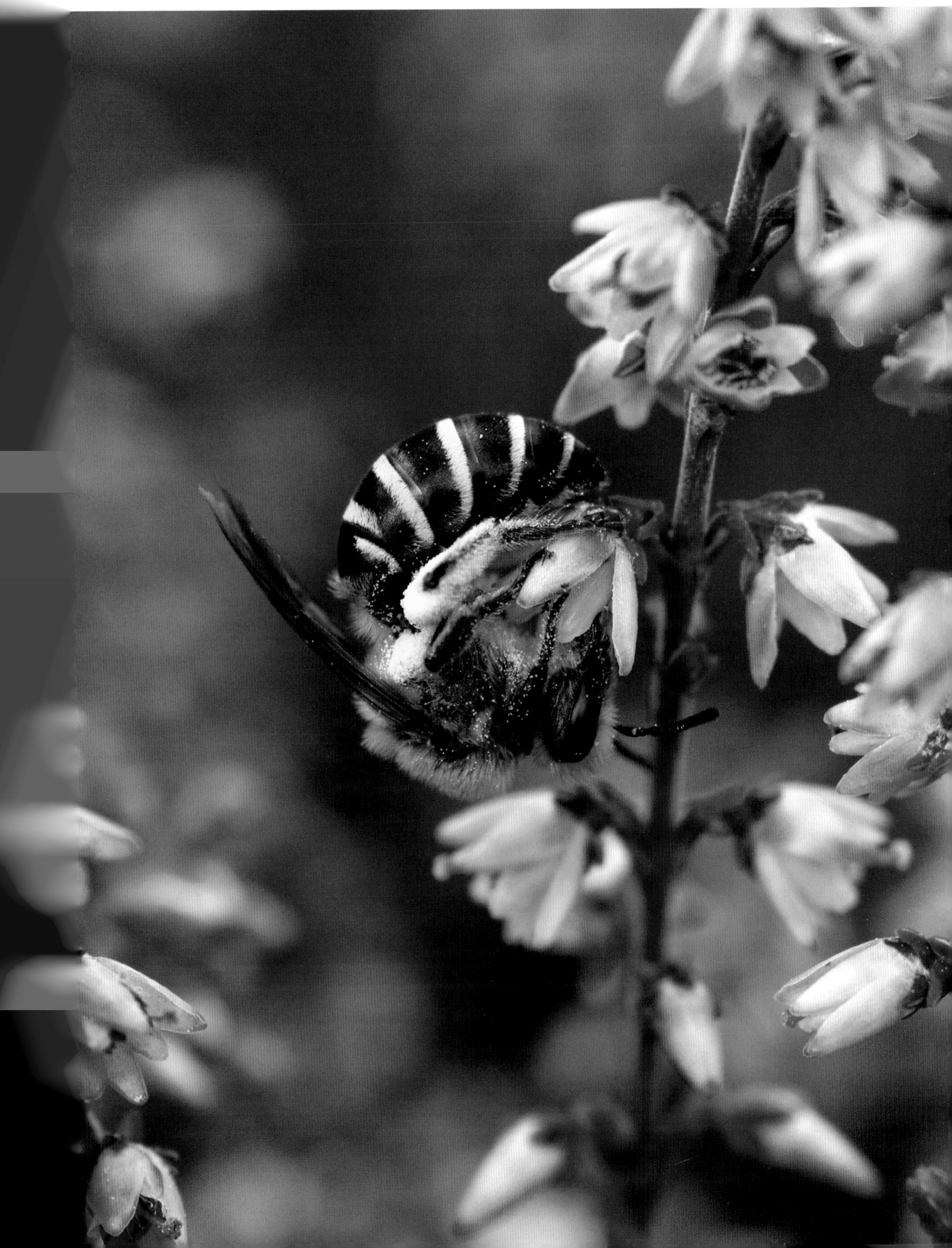

H

Heather

Above:
*Male mining bee (*Andrena fuscipes*) on heather (*Calluna vulgaris*)
(photo: N. W. Owens)*

occur during the average winter to enable honeybees to take the necessary cleansing flights.

Heather honey has many characteristics that distinguish it from other honeys and place it in a class by itself. It is considered by many to be the best of all honeys and is much sought after, commanding a higher price than other honey. Some people do not care for it or its strong, slightly bitter flavour. This is particularly the case among those unaccustomed to it or those used to the light, mild-flavoured honeys. It is appreciated most as comb honey, the wax cappings of which are usually white. The honey is thick and will not flow unless agitated (i.e. it is thixotropic). This property means it cannot be extracted by ordinary rotary extractors and special heather honey presses have to be used to obtain the honey. In colour it is a shade of light, dark or reddish brown and numerous small air bubbles that are introduced during pressing remain in it and do not rise to the surface. This imparts a distinctive appearance. True heather honey does not granulate quickly but admixture with other honey will cause it to do so, even that of bell heath (*Erica cinerea*), which is often present on heather moors. The flavour and aroma are very distinct and if a pot of good heather honey is opened in a warm room the aroma can usually soon be detected.

Bumblebees collect nectar and pollen from heather. The white-tailed bumblebee (*Bombus lucorum*) is a frequent visitor. Mining bees are classed as solitary bees because each female has its own nest, but a species of heathland mining bee (*Colletes succinctus*) nests gregariously and many females can dig their nests close to each other. The females forage for pollen from heather and heath (*Erica* species) (see separate entry) and large numbers can sometimes be seen on heaths and moors on sunny days. The bee is widespread across the British Isles. The flowers are also visited by other solitary bees, such as mining bees (*Andrena* species). One of these (*Andrena fuscipes*) appears to feed exclusively at heather flowers and is probably dependent on the plant. It occurs in scattered locations across Britain and Ireland. A cuckoo bee (*Nomada rufipes*) lays its eggs in the nests of *Andrena fuscipes* and is also likely to be found on heather flowers.

Hebe — *Hebe* species

Family:	**Plantaginaceae**
Flowering:	**May to July**
Cultivation:	**evergreen dwarf, small or medium shrub**
Honey:	**no**
Honeybees:	|||||
ST Bumblebees:	||||| |||||
LT Bumblebees:	||||| |||||
Solitary Bees:	|||||

There are about 90 species of hebe and they are nearly all natives of New Zealand. There is dispute among botanists about whether they should all join the large genus *Veronica* or remain separate in the genus *Hebe*, so the same species may appear under both names. The flower spikes contain a large number of small flowers, which are popular with bees and provide both nectar and pollen. Just as with the much larger racemes of the butterfly bush (*Buddleja* species) (see separate entry), bees can often settle on the flower spikes and walk between flowers, so that foraging is made easy for a wide range of bees. Many species or varieties are available for gardens and the flower colour can be white or pink through to lilac or blue. Although most flower from May to July, some, such as *Hebe* 'Autumn Glory', continue flowering late into the autumn, so it is possible to extend the season for bees by careful choice of varieties. Bumblebee visitors include the buff-tailed bumblebee (*Bombus terrestris*), the early bumblebee (*Bombus pratorum*) and the red-tailed bumblebee (*Bombus lapidarius*).

Left:
Male red-tailed bumblebee (Bombus lapidarius) *on hebe* (Hebe *species*)
(photo: J. Craig)

Heliotrope — *Heliotropium arborescens*

The delicate fragrance always associated with the garden heliotrope or cherry pie is well known and it is not surprising that bees should think the flowers worth a visit. Some of the varieties used for bedding are a great attraction to bees for nectar in August. Although the plant can grow into a small shrub, it is frost tender and so is usually grown as an annual in gardens. Several named varieties, such as 'Princess Marina', are available.

Family:	**Boraginaceae**
Flowering:	**June to September**
Cultivation:	**evergreen small shrub, grown as an annual**
Honey:	**no**
Honeybees:	|||||
ST Bumblebees:	|||||
LT Bumblebees:	|||||
Solitary Bees:	|||||

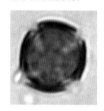

Far left:
Pollen grain of heliotrope (Heliotropium arborescens) *(18 μm)*
Left:
Flowers of heliotrope (Heliotropium arborescens)
(photo: W. D. J. Kirk)

Hellebore — *Helleborus* species

These hardy perennials, which bloom in the winter or early spring when there is little else in flower, are attractive to honeybees on those occasions when the weather is sufficiently mild for them to fly. Honeybees collect whitish pollen loads while clinging to the downward-facing flowers. A wide range of flower colours is available, including white, green, yellow, pink, red and purple. The old-fashioned white-flowered Christmas rose (*Helleborus niger*), is the first to flower and may be in bloom at Christmas.

Family:	**Ranunculaceae**
Flowering:	**December to March**
Cultivation:	**perennial herb**
Honey:	**no**
Honeybees:	|||||
ST Bumblebees:	|||||
LT Bumblebees:	—
Solitary Bees:	|||||

Above:
*Pollen grain of lenten rose (*Helleborus orientalis*) (34 µm)*

Right:
Centre of a white lenten rose flower
(Helleborus x hybridus)
Far right:
Centre of a purple lenten rose flower
(Helleborus x hybridus)
(photos: W. D. J. Kirk)

Other kinds, such as the lenten rose (*Helleborus orientalis*) and the many selected hybrids (*Helleborus* x *hybridus*), flower throughout the spring. The two wild British Isles species, the green hellebore (*Helleborus viridis*) and the stinking hellebore (*Helleborus foetidus*), although hardly garden plants, are useful for the wild garden, flowering in March. Both yield nectar freely. The flowers of all hellebores are interesting in that the petals are modified into raised funnel-shaped nectaries, which hold the nectar perfectly, like miniature vases. What appear to be the petals of the flower are actually the coloured sepals. This same ingenious type of nectary is also to be seen in the winter aconite (see separate entry), another early spring-flowering plant of the same family.

Hemp agrimony, see eupatorium

Hemp nettle — *Galeopsis tetrahit*

Family:	Lamiaceae
Flowering:	July to September
Cultivation:	annual herb
Honey:	no
Honeybees:	|||||
ST Bumblebees:	|||||
LT Bumblebees:	||||| |||||
Solitary Bees:	|||||

The common hemp nettle with its white to pinkish red flowers is common across most of the British Isles. It used to be particularly common in the stubble of cornfields, but is now found mostly in arable areas and on rough ground. Honeybees visit the flowers of the hemp nettles, but only for pollen, the nectar being too deep-seated. Long-tongued bumblebees, such as the common carder bee (*Bombus pascuorum*), can reach the nectar easily.

Right:
*Common carder bee (*Bombus pascuorum*)*
*on hemp nettle (*Galeopsis tetrahit*)*
(photo: L. Hebdon)

Henbane — *Hyoscyamus niger*

Henbane occurs wild or semi-wild in the British Isles, mainly in southern Britain, but is not common, nor is it generally regarded as a bee plant. The plant is highly toxic and contains the alkaloids hyoscyamine and scopolamine. It has been grown on a field scale for medicinal purposes and when this was done during the Second World War honey was said to have been stored from it in one instance. The field in question was cut while in flower and several workers got stung in the process. Bees kept returning to the bare patch where the plants had recently been. The honey alleged to have been obtained from it was of quite good flavour but crystallised very soon.

Family:	**Solanaceae**
Flowering:	**June to August**
Cultivation:	**annual or biennial herb**
Honey:	**no**
Honeybees:	|||||
ST Bumblebees:	|||||
LT Bumblebees:	|||||
Solitary Bees:	|||||

Left:
Henbane flowers (Hyoscyamus niger)
(photo: M. Kucharczyk)

Heuchera — *Heuchera* species

Heuchera or coral flower is a perennial usually grown for the sake of the decorative leaves rather than for the flowers. Bees have been observed visiting the flowers for nectar. The early bumblebee (*Bombus pratorum*) is a frequent visitor.

Family:	**Saxifragaceae**
Flowering:	**July to September**
Cultivation:	**perennial herb**
Honey:	**no**
Honeybees:	|||||
ST Bumblebees:	|||||
LT Bumblebees:	|||||
Solitary Bees:	|||||

Left:
Worker buff-tailed bumblebee (Bombus terrestris) *on heuchera* (Heuchera *species*)
(photo: M. A. Kirk)

H

Hemp agrimony — Heuchera

Himalayan balsam, see balsam

Hogweed — *Heracleum* species

Family:	**Apiaceae**
Flowering:	**June to September**
Cultivation:	**biennial to perennial herb**
Honey:	**no**
Honeybees:	‖‖
ST Bumblebees:	‖‖ ‖‖
LT Bumblebees:	‖‖
Solitary Bees:	‖‖ ‖‖ ‖‖

Top:
*Mining bee (*Andrena carantonica*) on hogweed (*Heracleum sphondylium*)*
(photo: N. W. Owens)
Above:
*Cuckoo bee (*Sphecodes *species) on hogweed (*Heracleum sphondylium*)*
(photo: T. C. Ings)

These coarse-growing perennials usually attract attention on account of their large size and commanding appearance but are better suited for odd corners than for the flower border. Bees visit the flowers and compete with numerous other insects, such as hoverflies. The common hogweed (*Heracleum sphondylium*) is common in hedgerows throughout the British Isles, whereas the giant hogweed (*Heracleum mantegazzianum*), a species from the Caucasus, up to about 5 m high with flower-heads a metre across, is found in scattered sites across the British Isles. Honeybees visit them occasionally for nectar and pollen, but they are not good honey plants. The nectar is easily accessible by short-tongued bees, so the buff-tailed bumblebee (*Bombus terrestris*) and the white-tailed bumblebee (*Bombus lucorum*) are frequent visitors. The presence of many flowers that form a platform to stand on while foraging also encourages visits from the red-tailed bumblebee (*Bombus lapidarius*). A wide range of solitary bees are attracted by the easily available pollen and nectar. These include mining bees (*Andrena, Colletes* and *Lasioglossum* species), cuckoo bees (*Sphecodes* species) and some small, black stem-nesting bees (*Hylaeus* species). Some species, for example a rare mining bee (*Andrena proxima*) from southern England and an even rarer mining bee (*Andrena rosae*) collect pollen only from common hogweed and a few other closely-related species, so hogweed may be critical for them.

It should be noted that giant hogweed (*Heracleum mantegazzianum*) is an invasive non-native species in the UK. The Wildlife and Countryside Act 1981 (Schedule 9) prohibits planting or causing it to grow in the wild. The sap is toxic and can cause severe skin reactions.

Holly — *Ilex aquifolium*

Family:	**Aquifoliaceae**
Flowering:	**May to June**
Cultivation:	**evergreen large shrub to medium tree**
Honey:	**no**
Honeybees:	‖‖ ‖‖
ST Bumblebees:	‖‖ ‖‖
LT Bumblebees:	‖‖
Solitary Bees:	‖‖

The holly is a common evergreen tree in the British Isles and is to be found throughout, except in the extreme north. It is abundant in woodland, where the wet climate seems to suit it. It more often occurs as a shrub than a tree, although trees with large trunks do occur. The holly is also found wild in most other countries of Europe.

Flowering takes place in May or June but the small fragrant white flowers, in clusters where the leaf stalks meet the stem, are by no means conspicuous and would pass unnoticed by some people. They secrete nectar freely and this is easily reached by the honeybee. Short-tongued bumblebees and solitary bees, such as mining bees (*Andrena* species), also visit the flowers.

Holly is probably a much more useful nectar source than many beekeepers realise, especially as it may be in flower after the fruit blossom has finished. It is unfortunate that the flowering period is rather short, generally 2–3 weeks, and that the trees or bushes do not always flower freely. The holly is strange in this respect for sometimes a tree will flower well on one side or on some branches but not on the others, or some trees will flower freely while others in the same area and a few metres away have hardly any flowers at all.

It is generally agreed that holly makes one of the best hedges. Its one drawback is its slow growth. Nevertheless, it is extensively planted for hedges but unfortunately for bees, the periodical clipping prevents flowering. The flowers of the many varieties of holly with variegated leaves or other characteristics that are seen in gardens are probably of similar value for nectar as the wild type and attract bees in the same way.

Some of the American hollies that have been cultivated in this country are good honey plants in their native land, such as the American holly (*Ilex opaca*) and the inkberry or gallberry (*Ilex glabra*). The latter has in the past been described as one of the best honey plants of the USA, especially in Georgia, the honey being light amber, very heavy and very mild and pleasant in flavour.

Far left:
Holly flowers (Ilex aquifolium)
(photo: M. A. Kirk)
Left:
Mining bee (Andrena species) on holly (Ilex aquifolium)
(photo: T. C. Ings)

Hollyhock — *Alcea rosea*

Flowers of single hollyhocks afford regular feasts for honeybees and bumblebees. It is not unusual to see two or three bees in a single flower at the same time. The pollen is the main attraction and this seems to be of a kind that is particularly to their liking. Late in the season, when pollen is in demand and the number of sources are diminishing daily, it is not unusual to find flowers stripped of every vestige of pollen as soon as it appears. When working hollyhock flowers, honeybees often arrive at the hive dusted all over with pollen or bearing a distinct white mark on the back of the thorax as though white-washed. Besides yielding pollen the flowers are also worked for nectar to some extent. The buff-tailed bumblebee (*Bombus terrestris*) is a frequent visitor.

The pollen grain of the hollyhock, often present in the honey of urban or suburban beekeepers, is interesting on account of its large size (about 130 μm compared with as little as 3–4 μm in forget-me-not).

Various other species of *Alcea* and the closely related genus *Althaea* are worked for pollen and nectar, including hemp-leaved hollyhock (*Althaea cannabina*) from southern Europe to Central Asia and the native marshmallow (*Althaea officinalis*).

Family:	**Malvaceae**
Flowering:	**July to September**
Cultivation:	**biennial to perennial herb**
Honey:	**no**
Honeybees:	‖‖‖
ST Bumblebees:	‖‖‖ ‖‖‖
LT Bumblebees:	‖‖‖
Solitary Bees:	—

Above:
Honeybee on hollyhock (Alcea rosea)
(photo: W. D. J. Kirk)

Honesty — *Lunaria annua*

Family:	**Brassicaceae**
Flowering:	**April to June**
Cultivation:	**biennial herb**
Honey:	**no**
Honeybees:	‖‖
ST Bumblebees:	‖‖
LT Bumblebees:	‖‖
Solitary Bees:	‖‖

This old-fashioned plant remains popular in gardens both for its sweet-scented purple flowers and the silvery flat seed pods, which are often dried and used for winter decoration. It starts flowering early, in April or May, and honeybees visit the flowers for pollen and nectar, but not so freely as in most other members of the cabbage family where the nectar is more easily obtained.

Right:
*Fork-tailed flower bee (*Anthophora furcata*) on honesty (*Lunaria annua*)*
(photo: T. C. Ings)

Honey locust — *Gleditsia triacanthos*

Family:	**Fabaceae**
Flowering:	**May to June**
Cultivation:	**deciduous large tree**
Honey:	**no**
Honeybees:	‖‖
ST Bumblebees:	‖‖
LT Bumblebees:	‖‖
Solitary Bees:	—

The honey locust originates from North America, where its fragrant flowers are useful to beekeepers for the nectar, although it is seldom a source of surplus honey and is not so important as the related false acacia or black locust (*Robinia pseudoacacia*) (see false acacia). The word 'honey' in the name refers to the sweetness of pulp from the pods and not to honey yield from the plant. This tree is sometimes to be seen in cultivation and always creates interest on account of the long, branched, woody spines on the trunk. These do not develop as well here as in warmer climates such as the south of Europe, where it is sometimes grown as a hedge. Named varieties, including ones without thorns, are available for gardens.

Honeysuckle — *Lonicera* species

Family:	**Caprifoliaceae**
Flowering:	**June to September**
Cultivation:	**deciduous to evergreen woody climber**
Honey:	**no**
Honeybees:	‖‖
ST Bumblebees:	‖‖
LT Bumblebees:	‖‖ ‖‖
Solitary Bees:	—

The flowers of the honeysuckle or woodbine (*Lonicera periclymenum*), so prevalent in thickets and hedgerows, and so much loved for their fragrance and beauty, have a long, narrow flower-tube, which restricts normal access to the nectar to long-tongued bumblebees. These include the garden bumblebee (*Bombus hortorum*), the common carder bee (*Bombus pascuorum*) and the ruderal bumblebee (*Bombus ruderatus*), which only occurs in southern and central England. Sometimes the flower is robbed by short-tongued bumblebees, which puncture the base of the flower and suck out the nectar. Honeybees may also obtain some nectar by using these punctures.

Most of the climbing honeysuckles seen in gardens also have long flower-tubes. Besides the climbing honeysuckles there are a number of shrubby or bush honeysuckles in cultivation. In some of these the flower-tubes are quite short. Among them is the fly honeysuckle (*Lonicera xylosteum*), which is naturalised across much of the British Isles. It has a flower-tube of only some 3 mm in length, and honeybees frequent the flowers for nectar. Other species that honeybees visit are the winter honeysuckle (*Lonicera fragrantissima*) from China, the shrubby honeysuckle (*Lonicera* x *purpusii*) and the Tartarian honeysuckle (*Lonicera tatarica*) from Central Asia. The two first mentioned are particularly valuable for early pollen, for they flower in February. In some seasons at Kew Gardens the flowers have been observed humming with honeybees, whereas in other years the blossoms may be destroyed by frost, or the weather may be against bees visiting them. Wilson's honeysuckle (*Lonicera nitida*), a popular hedge plant, is a useful source of nectar to honeybees in some countries but in most parts of the British Isles this shrub does not flower.

Far left:
*Honeysuckle flowers (*Lonicera periclymenum*)*
(photo: W. D. J. Kirk)
Left:
*Buff-tailed bumblebee (*Bombus terrestris*) on winter honeysuckle (*Lonicera fragrantissima*) in December*
(photo: T. C. Ings)

Hop tree — *Ptelea trifoliata*

This plant usually grows as a small tree and originates from North America, but has been cultivated in the British Isles since as far back as 1704. It is sometimes to be seen in gardens, the curious disc-shaped seed pods always attracting attention. These have been used as a hop substitute in home-brewed beer, hence the name. Small greenish-white flowers appear in clusters in June and July. They are scented and very attractive to honeybees for nectar, the whole tree humming with them at flowering time. The flowering period is short and may barely exceed a week in hot weather. In the eastern USA the tree is widely distributed and reputed to be a good honey plant in favourable seasons. Observations are needed to assess the value of this plant to bumblebees and solitary bees.

Family:	**Rutaceae**
Flowering:	**June to July**
Cultivation:	**deciduous large shrub to small tree**
Honey:	**no**
Honeybees:	||||| |||||
ST Bumblebees:	—
LT Bumblebees:	—
Solitary Bees:	—

Left:
*Hop tree flowers (*Ptelea trifoliata*)*
(photo: M. Kucharczyk)

Hop trefoil — *Trifolium campestre*

Family:	**Fabaceae**
Flowering:	**June to August**
Cultivation:	**annual herb**
Honey:	**no**
Honeybees:	|||||
ST Bumblebees:	||||| |||||
LT Bumblebees:	|||||
Solitary Bees:	|||||

Hop trefoil or hop clover is another of the small or insignificant clovers common in pastures and the borders of fields. It bears hop-shaped heads of yellow flowers from June to August. This clover may be used in seed mixtures to give good bottom cover. It is sometimes confused with ordinary trefoil or black medick (*Medicago lupulina*). The flowers are a minor source of nectar for honeybees. Honeybees also visit the flowers of two other less well-known clovers, strawberry clover (*Trifolium fragiferum*) and hare's foot clover (*Trifolium arvense*). They are both wild plants but not cultivated, the latter being often common on sandy soils near the sea. Like most clovers, these are all of value to bumblebees. Since the flower tube is short in these clovers, they are visited more by short-tongued bumblebees than by long-tongued bumblebees.

Hornbeam — *Carpinus betulus*

Family:	**Betulaceae**
Flowering:	**April to May**
Cultivation:	**deciduous medium tree**
Honey:	**no**
Honeybees:	|||||
ST Bumblebees:	—
LT Bumblebees:	—
Solitary Bees:	—

The tree is wind-pollinated and produces much pollen. The yellowish-green catkins are occasionally visited by honeybees for pollen only. The tree is of little account to the beekeeper, but it may be a minor source of honeydew in some seasons, which honeybees can use to make honey.

Right:
Hornbeam flowers (Carpinus betulus)
(photo: T. C. Ings)

Horse-chestnut — *Aesculus hippocastanum*

Family:	**Sapindaceae**
Flowering:	**April to June**
Cultivation:	**deciduous large tree**
Honey:	**yes**
Honeybees:	||||| ||||| |||||
ST Bumblebees:	||||| |||||
LT Bumblebees:	||||| |||||
Solitary Bees:	|||||

The horse-chestnut is perhaps the most commonly planted of the larger ornamental trees in the British Isles, although a native of southeastern Europe. It is a good bee plant with its masses of blossoms that start to flower in the latter part of April or May, for these are well worked for pollen and nectar.

Close study of the horse-chestnut in flower will show that there are three kinds of flower present: male only, female only and hermaphrodite (male and female together). Most of the flowers are male and produce pollen only, a few are female and produce conkers, and the rest are hermaphrodite flowers which produce pollen and conkers and are chiefly at the base of the flower spike. The nectar is sometimes clearly visible and is secreted at the base of the flowers between the stamens and the claws of the upper petals. It is protected by woolly hairs. In working the flowers for nectar the honeybee frequently gets at the nectar from the side of the flower or from behind. The nectar guides on the petals guide bees to the nectar and are at first yellow but later turn dark red. The flowering period generally lasts for about a month but the petals remain attached and unfaded long after the stamens have withered and the flowers have ceased to secrete nectar. It may be observed that bees do not visit such flowers.

Horse-chestnut pollen is very distinctive on account of its bright, almost brick-red colour. Honeybees returning to their hives with reddish-brown pollen loads in their pollen baskets when the horse-chestnut is in flower are a common sight, and familiar to most beekeepers in or near towns because of urban planting, as well as in rural areas. Sometimes the bees themselves look as though they have been sprinkled with brick dust as they enter the hive.

Various other horse-chestnuts are cultivated and seem to be equally popular with the honeybee, except of course the double-flowered forms. The variety 'Praecox' that comes into leaf and flower about two weeks before the ordinary form is of interest because it extends the flowering season. but appears to be no longer in cultivation in the British Isles. The red horse-chestnut (*Aesculus carnea*) flowers about a fortnight later than the common horse-chestnut and the blossoms are freely worked. So also are those of the Indian horse-chestnut (*Aesculus indica*), a magnificent tree from the Himalayas, not much grown in the British Isles but quite hardy, at least in the south. It flowers three weeks to a month later than the ordinary horse-chestnut and so is a source of nectar and pollen during the early summer when relatively few other sources are available. The California buckeye (*Aesculus californica*) flowers later still (July to August) and the blossoms are much visited by bumblebees and honeybees, but this species causes poisoning and paralysis of honeybees because of a type of toxic saponin called aesculin in the pollen and nectar. It is best not to plant it in order to help bees.

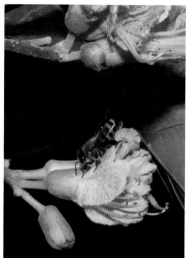

Top:
*Horse-chestnut flowers (*Aesculus hippocastanum*)*
(photo: M. A. Kirk)
Above:
*Honeybee on red horse-chestnut (*Aesculus carnea*)*
(photo: T. C. Ings)

Hottentot fig — *Carpobrotus edulis*

This plant from the Cape region of South Africa is now naturalised on cliffs along the coast in some parts of Devon and Cornwall and elsewhere and has been used at seaside towns on the south coast of England to cover and maintain banks and other exposed places. It soon carpets the ground with its creeping stems and fleshy leaves. The large showy flowers only open in the sunshine when they attract honeybees in numbers for nectar and pollen. The closely allied ice plant (*Mesembryanthemum crystallinum*), which is often cultivated, has been recorded as a good honeybee plant in warmer climates where it grows freely out of doors. Honey from it is said to granulate very quickly. The flowers are also visited by bumblebees and solitary bees.

Family:	**Aizoaceae**
Flowering:	**May to July**
Cultivation:	**perennial herb**
Honey:	**no**
Honeybees:	‖‖‖
ST Bumblebees:	‖‖‖
LT Bumblebees:	‖‖‖
Solitary Bees:	‖‖‖

H

Hop trefoil — Hottentot fig

It should be noted that the hottentot fig (*Carpobrotus edulis*) is an invasive non-native species in the UK. The Wildlife and Countryside Act 1981 (Variation of Schedule 9) (England and Wales) Order 2010 prohibits planting or causing it to grow in the wild.

Above:
*Buff-tailed bumblebee (*Bombus terrestris*)*
*on hottentot fig (*Carpobrotus edulis*)*
(photo: T. C. Ings)
Right:
*Hottentot fig flower (*Carpobrotus edulis*)*
(photo: P. A. Thomas)

Hound's tongue — *Cynoglossum* species

Family:	**Boraginaceae**
Flowering:	**June to August**
Cultivation:	**annual, biennial or perennial herb**
Honey:	**no**
Honeybees:	‖‖
ST Bumblebees:	‖‖ ‖‖
LT Bumblebees:	‖‖ ‖‖
Solitary Bees:	‖‖

The hound's tongue of the flower garden may include various plants (annuals, biennials or perennials), which thrive in any garden soil in a sunny position. Their deep blue forget-me-not-like flowers start to appear in June or July and attract bees. There are several selected varieties for gardens, such as Chinese hound's tongue 'Firmament' (*Cynoglossum amabile*). The resemblance to forget-me-not (*Myosotis* species) (see separate entry) means that the plants are sometimes also known by this name. Bees also visit the claret-coloured flowers of the wild biennial hound's tongue (*Cynoglossum officinale*), which occurs by roadsides, in waste places and around sand dunes. The nectar, protected by velvety hairs, is secreted by a fleshy nectary at the base of the flower-tube, which is only some 3 mm long and so can be reached by short-tongued bees.

The main visitors are bumblebees, particularly the early bumblebee (*Bombus pratorum*) and the common carder bee (*Bombus pascuorum*). Honeybees are less frequent. A few solitary bees visit hound's tongue, such as the cuckoo bee *Melecta luctuosa*, a distinctive black bee with white spots, which lays its eggs in the nest of the potter flower bee (*Anthophora retusa*). Unfortunately, the last British Isles record of the species was a hundred years ago in southeast England! The only English record of a flower visit was to wild hound's tongue. This bee still occurs on the Continent and could return to or even be rediscovered in the UK. Its host, the potter flower bee, which visits a wider range of flowers, has also declined but still occurs in a few scattered sites across southeast England.

Above:
*Male early bumblebee (*Bombus pratorum*)*
*on hound's tongue (*Cynoglossum officinale*)*
(photo: L. Hebdon)

Hyacinth — *Hyacinthus orientalis*

The ordinary hyacinth, so popular for forcing and for growing indoors in bowls, is attractive to honeybees when grown outside in the flower border. It is in flower early and is visited for nectar and pollen. The nectar is secreted in an unusual manner. Instead of being produced at the base of the flower it is secreted in three large drops from three nectaries appearing as dots near the tip of the ovary.

Family:	Asparagaceae
Flowering:	March to April
Cultivation:	perennial herb, grown from bulbs
Honey:	no
Honeybees:	|||||
ST Bumblebees:	—
LT Bumblebees:	—
Solitary Bees:	—

Far left:
*Hyacinth flowers (*Hyacinthus orientalis*)*
(photo: W. D. J. Kirk)
Left:
*Honeybee on hyacinth (*Hyacinthus orientalis*)*
(photo: J. Craig)

Hydrangea — *Hydrangea* species

The ordinary garden hydrangea (*Hydrangea macrophylla*) with blue or pink flowers does not usually attract bees very much, for the bulk of the flowers in the flower-head are of the sterile type. There are other hydrangeas, less ornamental perhaps, that are sometimes cultivated and which are of more use to bees. The best known is probably the climbing hydrangea (*Hydrangea petiolaris*), a deciduous climber from Japan that attaches itself to walls and trees by means of aerial roots just as ivy does. Its large, white flower-heads, up to 25 cm across, appear in June when the inner fertile florets are sometimes freely worked by honeybees. The plant is useful for covering old tree trunks, walls and mounds.

Family:	Hydrangeaceae
Flowering:	June to August
Cultivation:	deciduous small shrub or woody climber
Honey:	no
Honeybees:	||||| |||||
ST Bumblebees:	|||||
LT Bumblebees:	|||||
Solitary Bees:	|||||

Above:
Pollen grain of climbing hydrangea
*(*Hydrangea petiolaris*) (14 µm)*

Far left:
Flowers of climbing hydrangea
*(*Hydrangea petiolaris*)*
(photo: W. D. J. Kirk)
Left:
Honeybee on rough-leaved hydrangea
*(*Hydrangea aspera*)*
(photo: L. Hebdon)

Hyssop — *Hyssopus officinalis*

Family:	**Lamiaceae**
Flowering:	**June to October**
Cultivation:	**evergreen small shrub**
Honey:	**no**
Honeybees:	||||| |||||
ST Bumblebees:	||||| |||||
LT Bumblebees:	||||| |||||
Solitary Bees:	|||||

This fully hardy, fragrant herb from the Mediterranean region, the oil of which has been used in perfumery and the leaves in salads, grows well and is sometimes planted as an edging. There are several varieties of it, with blue, red or white flowers, which are out from June to October. It looks well with catmint and these may be backed by lavender and rosemary by the lover of bee plants, thereby providing a useful quartet!

Honeybees revel in the blossoms, helping themselves to nectar and pollen. The corolla tube is some 10 mm in length, but as it widens into a funnel in the upper part the honeybee and other short-tongued bees are able to reach the nectar. Bumblebees are also frequent visitors, including the buff-tailed bumblebee (*Bombus terrestris*) and the common carder bee (*Bombus pascuorum*).

Right:
*Honeybee on hyssop (*Hyssopus officinalis*)*
(photo: W. D. J. Kirk)
Below:
*Pollen grain of hyssop (*Hyssopus officinalis*) (29 μm)*

Indian bean tree — *Catalpa bignonioides*

The Indian bean or southern catalpa originates from the southeastern USA and has been grown in English gardens for almost 300 years. It is popular on account of its small size and elegant shape, its attractive flowers, and its quaint bean-like seed-pods. The white blossoms appear in July and August in large panicles or bunches and are available when few other trees are in flower. They attract honeybees and bumblebees in large numbers for nectar. Because the individual flowers are bell-shaped and about 3–4 cm long and across, bees can crawl right into them. Bees have been observed collecting nectar from the extrafloral nectaries on the under surface of the leaves. These secrete before, during and after the blossoming period.

Other catalpas not in general cultivation have been observed to be popular with bees at Kew Gardens. Notable among them is yellow catalpa (*Catalpa ovata*), a Chinese tree with smaller flowers and more deeply lobed leaves than the common sort. It flowers equally freely and at about the same time.

Family:	**Bignoniaceae**
Flowering:	**July to August**
Cultivation:	**deciduous medium tree**
Honey:	**no**
Honeybees:	||||| |||||
ST Bumblebees:	||||| |||||
LT Bumblebees:	||||| |||||
Solitary Bees:	|||||

Ivy — *Hedera helix*

The ivy and the honeysuckle are the two most common and widespread climbing plants in the British Isles. Ivy is to be seen clinging to the trunks of trees in all classes of woodland except on acid soils and is very prevalent as ground cover, on rock surfaces and old walls, with the plants sometimes attaining huge dimensions. Many garden varieties are also available.

Family:	**Araliaceae**
Flowering:	**September to November**
Cultivation:	**evergreen woody climber**
Honey:	**yes**
Honeybees:	||||| |||||
ST Bumblebees:	|||||
LT Bumblebees:	—
Solitary Bees:	||||| ||||| |||||

The small greenish-yellow flowers of ivy appear very late in the year, from the latter part of September as a rule until hard weather appears. They are an excellent source of nectar and pollen for the honeybee, and where they are prevalent and the weather is warm enough for bees to work them they may make a welcome contribution to the hive's winter stores of both honey and pollen. It is the last important nectar and honey plant of the season to be available to honeybees. In mild winters, fresh flowers may be found on the plants right up to Christmas.

Above:
Pollen grain of ivy (Hedera helix) *(30 μm)*

As if to make up for the lateness of the flowers and the difficulty honeybees might have in driving off the moisture from the nectar and converting it into honey, the nectar happens to be very concentrated. It is produced very freely sometimes and may even drip from the flowers. If insects are excluded, the base of the flower may be covered with a sugary crust after the flower has faded, so rich is the nectar in sugar and so lavishly is it produced. The nectar is actually secreted by a yellowish-green disc surrounding the female parts of the flower and is freely exposed. It provides an open feast for all manner of insects besides bees. Carrion flies are often common visitors, attracted by the strong, somewhat unpleasant odour of the flowers. Little nectar is secreted by the freshly-opened flowers but it increases as the flower ages and reaches the female stage.

Bumblebee colonies have usually deteriorated before ivy comes into flower, so they are not around to take advantage of the nectar and pollen. However, in recent years, the buff-tailed bumblebee (*Bombus terrestris*) has been observed foraging during the winter in southern England. Milder winters may allow this bumblebee and perhaps others to establish a second generation, in which case plants such as ivy may become useful.

The ivy bee (*Colletes hederae*) almost always restricts its pollen foraging to ivy, so this plant is essential for it. The bee has expanded its range across Europe and was first recorded in Britain in 2001 in Dorset. It has now spread across southern England. It is unusual in having such a late flying season.

The pollen of ivy is dull yellow in colour and the individual grain is heavily granulated. Honey from ivy is greenish in colour with a pleasantly aromatic flavour.

Top right:
*Male buff-tailed bumblebee (*Bombus terrestris*) on ivy (*Hedera helix*)*
(*photo: N. W. Owens*)

Bottom right:
*Ivy bee (*Colletes hederae*) on ivy (*Hedera helix*)*
(*photo: T. C. Ings*)

Jacob's ladder — *Polemonium caeruleum*

This bright little perennial is popular in flower borders and rock gardens. It also occurs wild as a native plant in a few places in northern England and is rare, but garden forms of the plant have naturalised quite widely. Bees industriously work the blue flowers for nectar and pollen. The latter is a bright orange when packed in a bee's pollen baskets. It is worth noting that, as in this case, pollen colours are often quite different from the flower colour. Bumblebee visitors particularly include the early bumblebee (*Bombus pratorum*) and the common carder bee (*Bombus pascuorum*). Flowers of many of the garden varieties of Jacob's ladder, offering attractive foliage or a longer flowering season, are also visited.

Family:	**Polemoniaceae**
Flowering:	**June to August**
Cultivation:	**perennial herb**
Honey:	**no**
Honeybees:	||||| |||||
ST Bumblebees:	||||| |||||
LT Bumblebees:	||||| |||||
Solitary Bees:	|||||

Far left:
Pollen grain of Jacob's ladder (Polemonium caeruleum) (42 μm)
Left:
Early bumblebee (Bombus pratorum) on Jacob's ladder (Polemonium caeruleum)
(photo: T. C. Ings)

Japanese pagoda tree — *Styphnolobium japonicum*

The Japanese pagoda tree or Japanese acacia (formerly *Sophora japonica*) is a handsome tree of Oriental origin sometimes cultivated for ornament in the British Isles and elsewhere. It bears masses of sweet-scented cream-coloured flowers in September, which fall while still fresh, literally carpeting the ground. Flowering lasts for about a month and the flowers are actively worked by honeybees and bumblebees for both nectar and pollen. They must constitute a useful late food source for the bees. In good flowering seasons at Kew Gardens, trees have been observed alive with bees, the busy hum being audible several metres away, bees even buzzing about the carpet of fallen flowers.

Family:	**Fabaceae**
Flowering:	**September**
Cultivation:	**deciduous medium to large tree**
Honey:	**no**
Honeybees:	|||||
ST Bumblebees:	|||||
LT Bumblebees:	|||||
Solitary Bees:	—

The tree is one of the last to blossom in the year. Unfortunately it is rather uncertain as a honey plant in the British Isles, for after poor or wet summers it hardly flowers at all. Another drawback is that it does not flower until 30 or 40 years of age. There are records from central Europe that the flowers poison honeybees, and in the 1920s beekeepers at Marienfeld (Teremia Mare) in Romania were in the habit of moving their hives from the vicinity of the trees at blossoming time to avoid mortality. However, no signs of poisoning were observed at Kew Gardens during several seasons.

Other closely related species are worked by honeybees, notably the shrub pagoda tree (*Sophora davidii*), which is a handsome June-flowering, prickly shrub, about 2 m in height and is a native of China.

J

Jacob's ladder — Japanese pagoda tree

J

Japanese quince — Juneberry

Japanese quince — *Chaenomeles speciosa*

Family:	**Rosaceae**
Flowering:	**February to June**
Cultivation:	**evergreen medium shrub**
Honey:	**no**
Honeybees:	‖‖‖
ST Bumblebees:	‖‖‖
LT Bumblebees:	‖‖‖
Solitary Bees:	‖‖‖

The Japanese quince or japonica is one of the popular early-flowering shrubs that are useful for bees flying early in the season. The blood-red flowers may appear as early as Christmas in some cases, but usually not until February or early March. Flowering extends over a long period, often till June. It is mainly for pollen that the flowers are visited, but honeybees have been observed at Kew Gardens obtaining nectar in warm weather later in the season. Many varieties of this hardy oriental shrub exist, with white, pink or salmon flowers. A closely related species (*Chaenomeles japonica*) and hybrids between the two species are also known as Japanese quince or japonica and are of similar value to bees.

Above:
Pollen grain of Japanese quince (Chaenomeles speciosa) *(35 μm)*
Right:
Queen buff-tailed bumblebee (Bombus terrestris) on Japanese quince (Chaenomeles *species*)
(photo: L. Hebdon)

Japonica, see Japanese quince

Judas tree — *Cercis siliquastrum*

Family:	**Fabaceae**
Flowering:	**April to June**
Cultivation:	**deciduous small tree**
Honey:	**no**
Honeybees:	‖‖‖
ST Bumblebees:	‖‖‖
LT Bumblebees:	‖‖‖
Solitary Bees:	‖‖‖

This handsome small tree from the Mediterranean region has been cultivated in the south of England for several hundred years and owes its name to the belief that it was the tree on which Judas hanged himself after the Betrayal. It grows best in the milder parts of the British Isles and flowers between April and June, which is before or during the time that the young leaves appear. It is then very picturesque, the deep pink to purple flowers being borne in profusion, often in clusters on the old wood, including the trunk. The flowers may be used in salads. Bees visit the flowers freely for nectar but the trees are never sufficiently common to be of much consequence. An allied species, eastern redbud (*Cercis canadensis*) is common in the southeastern USA and is a good early honeybee plant there, but does not provide surplus honey. Native species of redbud (*Cercis* species) in the USA are pollinated by bumblebees and the orchard mason bee (*Osmia lignaria*).

Left:
*Early bumblebee (*Bombus pratorum*) on*
*Judas tree (*Cercis siliquastrum*)*
(photo: J. Craig)

Juneberry — *Amelanchier* x *lamarckii*

The juneberry or snowy mespilus appears to be of hybrid origin and has been cultivated in the British Isles for over 250 years. It usually flowers in April and is then a mass of white, the flowers being followed by edible dark purple fruits ripening in June. While the blossoms may be visited for pollen they do not appear to be especially attractive to bees or to be much worked for nectar. In North America the plant seems to be of some nectar value for honeybees.

Family:	Rosaceae
Flowering:	March to May
Cultivation:	deciduous large shrub or medium tree
Honey:	no
Honeybees:	‖‖
ST Bumblebees:	‖‖
LT Bumblebees:	‖‖
Solitary Bees:	‖‖

Left:
*Juneberry flowers (*Amelanchier x lamarckii*)*
(photo: W. D. J. Kirk)

J

Japanese quince — Juneberry

K

Kalmia — Laurustinus

Kalmia — *Kalmia* species

Family:	**Ericaceae**
Flowering:	**June**
Cultivation:	**evergreen small to medium shrub**
Honey:	**no**
Honeybees:	‖‖
ST Bumblebees:	‖‖ ‖‖
LT Bumblebees:	‖‖ ‖‖
Solitary Bees:	‖‖

These shrubs, which are mostly evergreen and do best in peaty, moist soils, are often to be seen in gardens and have become more or less naturalised in some instances. The species most generally grown is the sheep laurel (*Kalmia angustifolia*), which may form thickets 5 m across through sucker growth and bears clusters of rosy-red flowers in June. This and the mountain laurel or calico bush (*Kalmia latifolia*), also much cultivated and one of the most beautiful of evergreen shrubs, have both been described as useful nectar plants for honeybees in their native land (eastern North America). Mountain laurel has been credited with being a source of honey that is bitter and poisonous to humans without being harmful to the honeybees themselves. However, very large expanses of the plant would have to be present for this to occur. Bumblebees visit both species and are considered to be the specialised pollinators of mountain laurel in its native land.

Right:
*Flowers of mountain laurel (*Kalmia latifolia*)*
(photo: W. D. J. Kirk)

Knapweed, see centaurea

Lamb's ears, see stachys

Larkspur — *Consolida* and *Delphinium* species

The name larkspur is used for two closely related groups of plants. In general, the annuals with a looser spike of flowers are *Consolida* species, whereas the perennials with denser spikes of flowers are *Delphinium* species. None of these species is native to the British Isles, although some can occur in the wild as introduced species or garden escapes. There are very many named varieties of *Consolida* and *Delphinium* available for gardens. Tall spikes of blue, mauve, pink, cream or white flowers are stunning additions to a flower bed in summer, and the flowering period can be extended by cutting them back hard after flowering to get a second flush of flowers later in the season.

The flowers have a long spur, hence the name larkspur, which holds the nectar and restricts access to only animals with long tongues. The species that are native to the USA are pollinated by bumblebees and hummingbirds, so it is not surprising that the main visitors in the British Isles are bumblebees, particularly the long-tongued garden bumblebee (*Bombus hortorum*). It may also be visited by some of the rare long-tongued bumblebees when these occur near gardens.

Family:	**Ranunculaceae**
Flowering:	**June to July**
Cultivation:	**annual or perennial herb**
Honey:	**no**
Honeybees:	—
ST Bumblebees:	||||| |||||
LT Bumblebees:	||||| ||||| |||||
Solitary Bees:	—

Left:
*Larkspur flower (*Delphinium *species)*
(photo: M. A. Kirk)

Laurel, see cherry laurel

Laurustinus — *Viburnum tinus*

This much-grown ornamental shrub flowers mainly in the winter months, between autumn and early spring. Its pinkish-white flowers are fragrant and in dense bunches. On fine days in early spring they may be visited for pollen by honeybees and bumblebees, but do not seem to attract much attention later in the year. In view of its prevalence in gardens in southern England this well-known evergreen is doubtless a useful early pollen source to urban beekeepers there. The pollen is of a pale slate-grey colour in the bees' pollen baskets. The early flowers are useful for queen bumblebees,

Family:	**Caprifoliaceae**
Flowering:	**October to April**
Cultivation:	**evergreen large shrub**
Honey:	**no**
Honeybees:	|||||
ST Bumblebees:	||||| |||||
LT Bumblebees:	|||||
Solitary Bees:	—

L

Kalmia — Laurustinus

particularly the buff-tailed bumblebee (*Bombus terrestris*). Several related winter-flowering species are of similar value to late/early bees, such as the Bodnant viburnum (*Viburnum* x *bodnantense*) and Farrer's viburnum (*Viburnum farreri*).

Lavatera — *Malva* species

Family:	**Malvaceae**
Flowering:	**June to September**
Cultivation:	**annual to perennial herb or semi-evergreen medium shrub**
Honey:	**no**
Honeybees:	||||| |||||
ST Bumblebees:	||||| |||||
LT Bumblebees:	||||| |||||
Solitary Bees:	|||||

There are annuals, biennials, and perennials among the lavateras or tree mallows. The names can be confusing because a group of species formerly classed as species of *Lavatera* have now been renamed as species of *Malva*. These plants are still commonly referred to as lavatera though and may still be listed as *Lavatera* species, even though their scientific name should, strictly, be *Malva*. Selected forms are available for gardens, such as *Malva* x *clementii* 'Rosea' (often listed as *Lavatera* 'Rosea') and *Malva* x *clementii* 'Barnsley' (often listed as *Lavatera* 'Barnsley'). All have the same type of flower structure and yield pollen in abundance, which honeybees readily collect. They also obtain nectar. Bumblebees are frequent visitors, particularly the common carder bee (*Bombus pascuorum*). In milder areas, the pink-flowered tree mallow (*Malva arborea*) is one of the best of the taller perennial kinds and an imposing plant. It grows to 3 m in height. However, on some Scottish islands this plant has become invasive and appears to be threatening populations of seabirds, including puffins. The wild mallows (see mallow) are also useful to bees.

Right:
*Flower of lavatera (*Malva x clementii *'Rosea')*
(photo: M. A. Kirk)

Lavender — *Lavandula angustifolia*

Family:	**Lamiaceae**
Flowering:	**June to August**
Cultivation:	**evergreen small shrub**
Honey:	**yes**
Honeybees:	||||| ||||| |||||
ST Bumblebees:	||||| ||||| |||||
LT Bumblebees:	||||| ||||| |||||
Solitary Bees:	||||| |||||

It is common knowledge that the fragrant blue flowers of lavender are always a great attraction for bees and that much buzzing always accompanies their visits. June and July are the months when the flowers are at their best in most districts. The flowers produce nectar freely, which is stored at the base of the flower and protected by a ring of hairs. The flower-tube of the usual garden lavenders is about 6 mm long – just short enough for the honeybee and short-tongued bumblebees to reach.

Lavender needs to be grown in full sun and does best on light or chalky well-drained soils. These are the conditions in many parts of southern Europe where the plant occurs wild over large tracts of country and supplies good-quality honey. This has been described as dark, of very pleasant flavour, and granulating with a grain almost as smooth as butter. Along with the orange and rosemary, it is one of the three most important honey plants in parts of Spain. Lavender is sometimes grown on a field scale in some areas of England (e.g. Norfolk) for perfumery purposes, and should afford opportunities for nearby beekeepers. Unfortunately, the flowers have to be harvested while still in their prime.

A wide range of bumblebee species frequent the flowers, particularly the red-tailed bumblebee (*Bombus lapidarius*) and the common carder bee (*Bombus pascuorum*). The flowers are visited by solitary bees, such as flower bees (*Anthophora* species) and the blue mason bee (*Osmia caerulescens*). A scarce green-eyed flower bee (*Anthophora quadrimaculata*), which is found in southern England, but could perhaps be discovered further north, visits flowering lavender or catmint in gardens. It is a brown bee with bright green eyes.

Far left:
*Common carder bee (*Bombus pascuorum*) visiting lavender (*Lavandula angustifolia*)*
(photo: C. Stevens)

Left:
*Buff-tailed bumblebee (*Bombus terrestris*) on lavender (*Lavandula angustifolia*)*
(photo: D. R. Skingsley)

Lemon balm — *Melissa officinalis*

The lemon balm or balm is sometimes also referred to as bee balm, but this can be confusing because that name is also used for species of *Monarda* (see bee balm), which also have sweet-scented leaves but are unrelated. Lemon balm is a native of the Mediterranean region, but is common in gardens in the British Isles. It naturalises freely and is almost a weed in some instances. The white flowers attract honeybees to a moderate extent, but the flowers have too long a flower-tube for the honeybee to extract all the nectar and it is unable to force its head into the widened part of the tube.

However, the real interest of lemon balm to the beekeeper is in the aromatic, lemon-scented leaves. If these are crushed and rubbed inside a skep it is said to render it attractive to bees and that if convenient branches of trees near an apiary be rubbed with the herb at swarming time, swarms will settle there. There is, however, a difference of opinion as to its value in attracting swarms. Most of those who have tried it in the British Isles consider it quite ineffective, but it has been claimed to be quite effective in the former Yugoslavia. Possibly the climate or strain of honeybee makes a

Family:	**Lamiaceae**
Flowering:	**August to September**
Cultivation:	**perennial herb**
Honey:	**no**
Honeybees:	‖‖
ST Bumblebees:	‖‖
LT Bumblebees:	‖‖ ‖‖
Solitary Bees:	‖‖

Above:
Lemon balm flowers (Melissa officinalis)
(photo: W. D. J. Kirk)

difference. Rubbing the hands with the leaves is claimed to, and probably does, help in preventing stings. The scented water in which leaves have been macerated and soaked has been used to sprinkle bees to pacify them when uniting colonies – before the general adoption of the 'newspaper method', which uses a sheet of newspaper between colonies to allow them to adjust to each other gradually without fighting. The fragrant oil from the leaves, known as melissa oil and used in perfumery, has in the past been recommended for making scented syrup for introducing new queen bees into colonies. The plant's historical relationship with bees is recorded in the scientific name *Melissa*, which is Greek for honeybee.

The flowers are visited by bumblebees, particularly the common carder bee (*Bombus pascuorum*), which has a long enough tongue to reach the nectar at the base of the flower tube.

Leopard's bane — *Doronicum* species

Bees visit the sunflower-like flowers for nectar and pollen. The most useful are undoubtedly those that flower early in the spring, from March onwards (such as *Doronicum* x *excelsum* or *Doronicum orientale*), and these are the most generally cultivated. They are unusual in being some of the few members of the daisy family that flower in spring. Avoid the double-flowered varieties as these are of little benefit to bees. The leopard's banes are of vigorous growth and thrive in any soil. Several introduced species have naturalised and can be found in the wild in some parts of the British Isles.

L

Leopard's bane — Lily-of-the-valley

Family:	Asteraceae
Flowering:	March to July
Cultivation:	perennial herb
Honey:	no
Honeybees:	|||||
ST Bumblebees:	|||||
LT Bumblebees:	|||||
Solitary Bees:	|||||

Right:
*Flower of leopard's bane (*Doronicum orientale*)
(photo: M. A. Kirk)

Lesser trefoil — *Trifolium dubium*

This tufted annual bears small yellow flower-heads of about a dozen flowers and is common in grassland. The seed used to be incorporated in seed mixtures for temporary pastures in soils well-suited to cocksfoot grass, when abundant secondary growth or aftermath was desired. It was useful on poor, light land, but the plant is rarely used now because it competes poorly in well-fertilised pasture and is not very productive. In spite of their insignificant appearance, the flowers are attractive to bees and yield nectar abundantly.

Family:	Fabaceae
Flowering:	June to July
Cultivation:	annual herb
Honey:	no
Honeybees:	||||| |||||
ST Bumblebees:	||||| |||||
LT Bumblebees:	|||||
Solitary Bees:	|||||

They appear in June and July, but no longer contribute to the honey crop to the extent they would have done in the past when sown for grazing. The plant is also known as small yellow trefoil or yellow suckling clover.

Lilac — *Syringa* species

The sweet-scented flowers of this favourite ornamental shrub secrete nectar freely but in most varieties of the common lilac (*Syringa vulgaris*) the flower-tube is too long for honeybees or short-tongued bumblebees. When nectar is produced abundantly it may rise from 2–4 mm or even more in the flower-tube, and so become within reach of short-tongued bees. Under such conditions honeybees may be seen working lilac. Honeybees have been observed working the masses of pink sweetly scented flowers of *Syringa tomentella* (from western China) at Kew Gardens on occasions. Nodding lilac (*Syringa komarowii*) from central China is also worked by honeybees.

Family:	**Oleaceae**
Flowering:	**May to June**
Cultivation:	**deciduous large shrub or small tree**
Honey:	**no**
Honeybees:	|||||
ST Bumblebees:	|||||
LT Bumblebees:	|||
Solitary Bees:	—

Left:
Lilac flowers (Syringa vulgaris)
(photo: W. D. J. Kirk)

Lily-of-the-valley — *Convallaria majalis*

The honeybee is known to visit these sweet-scented flowers, but only for pollen. Other bees also visit. The flowers appear in May and June when there are many other, possibly more appetising, sources of pollen available. Several named varieties are available for gardens, but avoid those with double flowers as they are of little value to bees. The plant is native to Britain and most other parts of Europe, but not Ireland although it has naturalised there.

Family:	**Asparagaceae**
Flowering:	**May to June**
Cultivation:	**perennial herb, grown from rhizomes**
Honey:	**no**
Honeybees:	|||||
ST Bumblebees:	|||||
LT Bumblebees:	|||||
Solitary Bees:	|||||

Left:
Lily-of-the-valley flowers (Convallaria majalis)
(photo: M. A. Kirk)

Lime — *Tilia* species

Family:	**Malvaceae**
Flowering:	**June to July**
Cultivation:	**deciduous medium to large tree**
Honey:	**yes**
Honeybees:	||||| ||||| |||||
ST Bumblebees:	||||| ||||| |||||
LT Bumblebees:	||||| |||||
Solitary Bees:	|||||

Above:
*Flowers of large-leaved lime (*Tilia platyphyllos*)*
(photo: W. D. J. Kirk)

The lime or linden tree should not be confused with the tree that bears the lime citrus fruit. The two plants are unrelated, despite having the same name. Lime flowers secrete large volumes of nectar and are much visited by honeybees and short-tongued bumblebees, such as the buff-tailed bumblebee (*Bombus terrestris*) and the red-tailed bumblebee (*Bombus lapidarius*). The tree is a major honey source for beekeepers and because limes are often planted in towns and cities it is of particular value to urban beekeepers.

There are some thirty different species of lime or *Tilia* known to science. All are natives of the north temperate zone – Europe, North America and Asia, including China and Japan. They all have many characteristics in common, such as type of leaf and an unusual flower structure, the flowers being borne on a conspicuous, long, ribbon-like bract. They all appear to be fragrant and yield much nectar, although it would seem that some secrete nectar more freely than others. Three limes are native to the British Isles. These are listed in order of prevalence.

The lime (*Tilia* x *europaea*) is the common lime of streets, parks and private gardens. It is a hybrid and occurs in the wild in a few places where the two parent species, the large-leaved lime and the small-leaved lime, occur together. Different individual trees may vary somewhat in their time of flowering, even in the same area. They may reach large dimensions – over 40 m in height – and bear smooth branches and heart-shaped leaves 5–10 cm long. Trees may reach a great age and many old trees and avenues exist. It is common throughout the British Isles.

The large-leaved lime (*Tilia platyphyllos*), also called the broad-leaved lime, is wild in localised areas of England and Wales, but is widespread as a naturalised plant throughout the British Isles. It is very like the above species, but with larger leaves, downy shoots and fewer flowers on each bract. It is often planted in place of the above and has roughly the same flowering period. Hybrid forms, or forms intermediate between the common lime and the large-leaved lime are not uncommon. Like the common lime, different trees in the same area may vary a good deal in their time of flowering, some being several days earlier or later every year than others. If trees that consistently flower early or late were propagated (vegetatively rather than by seed) it is probable that this valuable characteristic would be maintained and so could be used to extend the period over which the species is useful to bees.

The small-leaved lime (*Tilia cordata*) occurs wild or apparently wild in some parts of England and Wales. It is characterised by its smaller leaves and flowers, which are not all pendent and therefore probably more liable to have their nectar spoiled by rain. It flowers later than the above two limes but is not often planted. It is much more important for honey on the mainland of Europe than in the British Isles, for extensive woods occur there and it is commonly planted as a street tree.

A few of the other species of *Tilia* are sometimes planted as ornamental trees, such as the silver-lime (*Tilia tomentosa*), the pendent silver-lime (*Tilia* 'Petiolaris'), and occasionally the Caucasian lime (*Tilia* x *euchlora*).

The common lime and the large-leaved lime supply practically all the lime honey harvested in the British Isles and generally come into flower in mid-June in the southeast of England, but later farther north and earlier in the west. The flowering period does not generally last for more than 2–3 weeks or perhaps a month if cold or wet weather intervenes. The individual flowers open at night and last for about a week, turning to a darker shade of cream or yellow on about the third day. Nectar is secreted during the whole of the time and more copiously when the darker coloured or 'female' stage of the flower is reached. For some unknown reason, some of the flower buds never open.

The intense fragrance of the lime in flower is well known and even suggests honey. It may often be detected many metres away from the tree. The flowers are commonly collected and dried in other European countries and used for making a kind of tea or tisane. It is only rarely that the lime ripens its seed properly in the climate of the British Isles, because it requires a hot or Continental type of summer to do so. This applies also to most of the other introduced limes.

Nectar secretion in the lime flower is rather unusual in that it takes place on the inner side of the five boat-shaped sepals, and is held in position there by small hairs aided by surface tension. The sepal may become only moist with nectar but when secretion is copious as sometimes happens on sultry mornings, the nectar collects in large drops and is to be seen glistening in the flowers. Shaking a branch then may cause quite a shower of nectar. The secretion of nectar in the five sepals of a single flower is not always uniform, some often containing more than others. In working a lime flower for nectar, especially if it is only moist, a honeybee often scoops the end of the tongue round the inside of the sepal, removing all traces of nectar. This may easily be seen from above the flower owing to the transparent nature of the sepal. Sometimes a honeybee will alight on a flower that obviously has nectar and yet proceed to another flower before taking any nectar. Perhaps the sugar concentration in different flowers varies, as with age, and the bee knows how to select the ones with the highest sugar content.

Observant beekeepers in the British Isles with experience of lime districts generally consider the best conditions for a good lime flow are warm nights and warm sultry days (high atmospheric humidity), with the sky perhaps overcast; but certainly not hot, dry, bright sunny days such as might be the most favourable for many other nectar plants. It must be remembered the lime secretes its nectar mainly, if not entirely, before midday. Bees may often be seen working limes very early in the morning. With hot dry days or drying winds there is a tendency for the nectar to be dried out early in the day and little more is secreted, with the result that the bees find little or nothing to bring in during the afternoon and evening. The open nature of the lime flower is also conducive to this. Temperature is of course of great importance for there is little or no secretion in cold weather. The optimum temperature for lime nectar secretion is about 20°C.

The lime does not appear to be particular with regard to soil and will thrive and secrete nectar in a variety of soils that may differ from one another considerably in physical texture and in chemical composition. While soil moisture may be important in countries with a naturally dry

Above:
*Flower of small-leaved lime (*Tilia cordata*)*
(photo: W. D. J. Kirk)

L

Lime

climate it is doubtful whether it is of much significance in the relatively wet climate of the British Isles. Furthermore, being a tree and deep rooted, the lime is able to draw moisture from a considerable depth in the soil and is not dependent on the moisture in the surface layers like many honey plants that are of short duration.

In the early 20th century, beekeepers reported that lime produced good honey flows in most years and in most districts in Britain, where it was sufficiently abundant, and really good or bumper years came round once in every three or four seasons. More recently, beekeepers have found lime to be a less reliable source, with fewer good years and often years with no honey at all. When it fails, it is probably due to unfavourable weather at blossoming time, such as prolonged rain or low temperatures. Cold winds are definitely inimical to the nectar flow but fortunately are not usual at the time of year when the lime flowers. All winds, however, are not necessarily harmful for the production of nectar. After rain, mild drying winds may have a beneficial effect in raising the sugar concentration of the nectar. In spite of the pendent nature of the flowers and the nectar being secreted on the under-surface of the sepals, where it would appear to be well protected, heavy rain does cause serious dilution of the nectar. The age of flowers also affects nectar concentration, older flowers having a more copious and richer nectar than those newly opened.

To obtain surplus honey from limes it is of course essential to have a sufficient number of trees for the number of hives in the neighbourhood, a few isolated trees having little effect. Where there are many trees and the flow is heavy, honeybees may get all the nectar they can deal with from trees close at hand and not bother to visit those further afield. Probably no other plant or tree secretes such quantities of nectar as the lime when at its best. Lime honey is well liked by most people, in spite of its distinctive flavour, usually described as 'minty' or 'like peppermint'. It is usually light amber with a greenish tinge, which may be due to traces of honeydew, for there is always a certain amount produced by aphids on the leaves of the lime. Its density, however, is not good for it is always thin. It crystallises after a few months with a fine smooth grain.

The common lime is the worst offender among British Isles trees for honeydew, although the large-leaved lime can also be a problem. Honeydew is a sugary liquid secreted by aphids and it is collected most by bees when hot dry weather coincides with blossoming time, for then nectar ceases to be available early in the day and the bees turn to honeydew. While plenty of nectar is available they do not seem to bother with it. As the honeydew itself is always darkened by fungus (sooty moulds) it causes the honey to be dark. This may vary from olive green to almost black and the flavour is considered inferior to those accustomed to milder honeys.

Unfortunately, large numbers of dead and dying bees can sometimes be found on the ground beneath some species of late-flowering lime. The limes concerned are: (1) the silver-lime (*Tilia tomentosa*) and its named varieties; (2) the pendent silver-lime (*Tilia* 'Petiolaris'), which is probably just a distinct form of the silver-lime; and (3) a hybrid lime *Tilia* 'Orbicularis', which has the silver-lime as one parent. In addition, there are occasional reports of bees looking groggy on the ground below trees of common lime

Above:
*Flowers of Caucasian lime (*Tilia x euchlora*)*
(photo: W. D. J. Kirk)

Left:
Dead bumblebees beneath a lime tree
(photo: T. C. Ings)

L

Lime

(*Tilia* x *europaea*) and Caucasian lime (*Tilia* x *euchlora*), particularly in dry years. Bumblebees are far more affected than honeybees. They lie on their backs making jerky movements and are unable to fly, appearing to be paralysed or 'drunk'. In this prone state they are often attacked and fed on by great tits. Honeybees are much less affected and in many seasons, no dead honeybees are to be seen under the trees, only bumblebees. It is probable that the actual amount of honeybee death connected with limes is small having regard to the total population and that their merits to the colony as honey producers far outweigh their demerits.

In the 1970s, research on these bee deaths suggested that the nectar was unusually high in a sugar called mannose. Although humans can digest this sugar easily, which means it is perfectly safe for us, bumblebees and honeybees are unable to digest it adequately because they have low levels of an enzyme that is important for the process. Compounds that build up as a result of incomplete digestion would interfere with other essential processes and eventually kill the bee. It was therefore concluded that the cause of the problem was nectar toxic to bees. However, research in Germany in the 1990s and 2000s has contradicted this. No evidence was found for mannose in the nectar from trees with dead bees beneath them. It was noted that bees were most affected at the end of flowering or in dry years when there was very little nectar in the flowers, which would not be expected if nectar was the problem. When bees below a tree were fed with nectar from the same tree they were able to recover, so there was no evidence for toxic nectar. Instead, the evidence indicated that bees were starving or running out of the nectar they needed as fuel to be able to fly back to their nest. Bumblebees were particularly affected because, unlike honeybees, they continued to forage on the trees at the end of flowering when there was insufficient nectar left.

The lime has been much planted as an avenue tree in the past and many fine avenues still exist, especially as approaches to country mansions. It has also been much used in street planting but there has been a falling off in lime planting over recent years. This is unfortunate for honeybees and bumblebees and also for the beekeeper, or rather for future generations of beekeepers. Present-day beekeepers benefit from the lime planting of previous generations, the lime being a long-lived tree and requiring 10–15 years before it commences to blossom as a rule. Some of the newer limes, however, along with those from the Orient do not have the weaknesses of the common lime for general planting although quite hardy and equally good as nectar sources for bees. If these trees were used as street and avenue trees, and for parks, pleasure grounds and open spaces generally the honey-producing capacity of many parts of the British Isles might be greatly improved and future generations of beekeepers would be thankful to those responsible.

The reasons why the lime has fallen into disrepute as an avenue and street tree are: (1) its susceptibility to aphids that produce honeydew and the sticky mess this produces; (2) early leaf fall; (3) habit of suckering from the base and trunk; (4) large size for suburban streets; and (5) soft nature of the bark of young trees and susceptibility to injury.

The honeydew menace is without doubt the main popular objection to the lime. Not because it may occasionally mean spoiled honey, but because the sticky secretion falls on pavements and streets making them slippery and on anything that may be under them, such as parked cars and public seats. There have been instances of falls caused by this honeydew, resulting in broken limbs and even litigation. Lime honeydew has been so bad in some years that a local authority has had sand or gravel strewn on certain streets to render them safer.

Early leaf fall causes premature littering of the streets and an autumnal aspect that is objected to on aesthetic grounds. Some limes hold their leaves later in the year than the common lime. The suckering and production of young shoots from the trunk means constant pruning on the part of the local authority. This means labour and therefore expense. It is only the common lime (*Tilia* x *europaea*) that is a serious offender in this respect. With regard to size and suitability for small suburban streets or grounds of limited extent, there are limes that have a much smaller habit than the common lime.

The following are some of the limes that may be worthy of consideration by those interested in the planting of limes to help bees or to provide honey sources:

Caucasian lime (*Tilia* x *euchlora*).
This is a hybrid from eastern Europe that was introduced to Britain in about 1860. It is a medium tree of upright growth with dark green glossy leaves and pendulous branches that is remarkably free from aphid honeydew. It flowers and casts its leaves later than the common lime. The flowers are apparently not so freely worked by honeybees as those of some limes. It is much planted as a street tree in some European countries but not in Britain. It is probably the most beautiful of limes and an ideal avenue tree.

Mongolian lime (*Tilia mongolica*).
This tree was introduced to Britain in 1904. It is a small tree of slow growth with small maple-like leaves and reddish leaf-stalks. It flowers a month later than the common lime and is very free flowering with

blossoms that are small, fragrant and freely worked by bees. The tree is very hardy, of handsome erect appearance, and should be suitable as a small avenue or street tree.

Large-leaved lime variety 'Asplenifolia'.
This tree is also known as the cut-leaved lime. It is another small lime for where large free-growing trees are not desired and is of dense, compact growth with small deeply dissected leaves. It is exceptionally free flowering and is much worked by honeybees. The leaves and flower bracts are shed early. This variety may be hard to locate, but other named varieties, such as 'Laciniata', are available.

Small-leaved lime variety 'Greenspire'.
This is a fast-growing, upright well-branched tree and plants of this variety have consistent growth. Other named varieties, such as 'Rancho', which is smaller, are available.

Japanese lime (*Tilia maximowicziana*).
This tree was introduced to Kew Gardens in 1904. It is a large forest tree in Japan and bears large clusters of flowers which hum with bees year after year. It is more intensively worked by honeybees than any other species.

Left:
Flowers of basswood (Tilia americana)
(photo: W. D. J. Kirk)

L

Lime

Other Oriental limes attractive to bees, but not so easily available are: Manchurian lime (*Tilia mandshurica*) from northeast Asia, Henry's lime (*Tilia henryana*) from central China, and three limes with no common names – *Tilia insularis* from Korea, *Tilia oliveri* from central China and *Tilia miqueliana* from Japan. The North American limes, known as basswood (*Tilia americana*) and white basswood (*Tilia heterophylla*) in their native land and the source of much honey, are also good bee plants in the British Isles, but are rarely seen. They flower 2–3 weeks later than the common lime.

It would help bees if the lime flowering season could be extended by planting both early- and late-flowering species. The large-leaved lime (*Tilia platyphyllos*) flowers early, but unfortunately the late-flowering limes are the pendent silver-lime (*Tilia* 'Petiolaris') and the hybrid lime *Tilia* 'Orbicularis', which are associated with bumblebee deaths.

Ling, see heather

Linseed, see flax

Loganberry — *Rubus loganobaccus*

Family:	**Rosaceae**
Flowering:	**June to August**
Cultivation:	**perennial root with biennial stems**
Honey:	**no**
Honeybees:	||||| ||||| |||||
ST Bumblebees:	||||| ||||| |||||
LT Bumblebees:	||||| |||||
Solitary Bees:	|||||

The loganberry was introduced to Britain in 1900 from the USA where it had been raised by James Logan of California in 1881 by crossing a raspberry with a blackberry. Seedling plants have not always kept true to type and other berries like the tayberry and boysenberry have been derived from it. With proper management the loganberry will succeed on all manner of soils but gives the highest yields on deep, rich loams. Bees are the main pollinators of the crop and are important to raise the quality of the harvested fruit.

The flowers are rich in nectar and resemble those of raspberries with which they are probably on a par as bee fodder, for they are frequented continually by bees in suitable weather during the period of several weeks when they are available in early summer. They would be a major honey source if they were more widely grown. Pollen is also collected.

The flowers are much visited by short-tongued bumblebees, such as the early bumblebee (*Bombus pratorum*) and the rapidly spreading tree bumblebee (*Bombus hypnorum*). The red mason bee (*Osmia rufa*) visits the flowers as well as the blossom of other fruit.

Love-in-a-mist — *Nigella damascena*

Family:	**Ranunculaceae**
Flowering:	**May to September**
Cultivation:	**annual herb**
Honey:	**no**
Honeybees:	|||||
ST Bumblebees:	|||||
LT Bumblebees:	|||||
Solitary Bees:	—

The many varieties of love-in-a-mist are popular garden annuals that are visited by honeybees and bumblebees for nectar and pollen, but usually only in a moderate degree. The flowers are interesting in having an unusual type of nectary with nectar secreted into a small pit. Sow seed in the autumn to flower early the next year or sow in spring to flower later the same year.

Above:
*Pollen grain of love-in-a-mist (*Nigella damascena*) (39 µm)*
Right:
*Buff-tailed bumblebee (*Bombus terrestris*) on love-in-a-mist (*Nigella damascena*)*
Far right:
*Buff-tailed bumblebee (*Bombus terrestris*) on love-in-a-mist (*Nigella damascena*)*
(photos: T. C. Ings)

Lucerne — *Medicago sativa*

Lucerne, or alfalfa as it is sometimes called, is not the important crop in the British Isles that it is in other countries, such as France and the USA. It is grown for cattle fodder and is usually cut for hay or silage. This clover-like plant is perennial and once established yields several cuts in a season, the plants lasting for many years. In the moist conditions of the British Isles the plant appears to make more leafage than it does in other countries and is cut before flowering, whether for hay or fodder, otherwise the plants become too fibrous. Sometimes three or even four cuts may be made throughout the summer, all before any flowers have a chance to appear. So the crop may be quite useless for bees. In some cases, however, there are flowers available to bees later in the season and these may prove a useful source of nectar, particularly towards the end of hot dry summers. Seed is easily available because it is sold for garden use as a green manure or to produce sprouting seeds for salads.

Lucerne is sometimes found by the sides of paths and fields as a relic of cultivation. The small, purple flowers do not appear to attract honeybees much until later in the year when other sources of nectar become scarce. In other countries, lucerne or alfalfa honey is known to vary much according to locality but is of good quality and generally resembles clover honey, but with a more spicy flavour and a tendency to granulate early.

When lucerne is grown for seed production, it needs to be pollinated by bees. The flowers have a 'tripping' mechanism (see field bean) and need to be 'tripped' in order to be pollinated. The process hits the bee on the head and honeybees learn to avoid this by poking their tongue between the petals at the base of the flower to obtain the nectar. Solitary bees particularly need pollen for their nests, so they continue to trip the flowers and, as a result, are much better pollinators. In the USA, the alfalfa leafcutter bee (*Megachile rotundata*) is reared commercially and the ground-nesting alkali bee (*Nomia melanderi*) is encouraged for lucerne pollination. Neither of these species occurs in the British Isles.

The main bumblebee visitor is the common carder bee (*Bombus pascuorum*). The flowers are visited by several solitary bees, such as the blue mason bee (*Osmia caerulescens*), which occurs in Britain but not Ireland. The long-horned bee (*Eucera longicornis*) collects pollen from lucerne and a few other related plants with similar flowers, such as meadow vetchling (*Lathyrus pratensis*) (see vetchling). This large, dark brown bee has remarkably long antennae in the male. It is found in southern Britain and can be locally common, but is declining rapidly.

Other plants allied to lucerne that the honeybee visits for nectar are sand lucerne (*Medicago sativa* subspecies *varia*), sickle medick (*Medicago sativa* subspecies *falcata*), toothed medick (*Medicago polymorpha*) and black medick (*Medicago lupulina*). The last mentioned is widely distributed in the British Isles, being most prevalent on limestone soils. Seed can be used in seed mixtures for grassland, especially for light or chalky land. Flowering is generally earlier than is the case with white or red clover, the small yellow flower-heads being followed by distinctive black seed-pods. The flowers are often very freely worked for nectar by honeybees and short-tongued bumblebees.

Family:	**Fabaceae**
Flowering:	**June to July**
Cultivation:	**perennial herb**
Honey:	**no**
Honeybees:	|||||
ST Bumblebees:	|||||
LT Bumblebees:	||||| |||||
Solitary Bees:	||||| |||||

Top:
*Lucerne flowers (*Medicago sativa*)*
(photo: W. D. J. Kirk)
Above:
*Female mining bee (*Melitta leporina*) on lucerne (*Medicago sativa*)*
(photo: J. P. Early)

L

Ling — Lucerne

Lungwort — *Pulmonaria* species

Family:	**Boraginaceae**
Flowering:	**March to May**
Cultivation:	**perennial herb**
Honey:	**no**
Honeybees:	—
ST Bumblebees:	‖‖‖
LT Bumblebees:	‖‖‖ ‖‖‖ ‖‖‖
Solitary Bees:	‖‖‖ ‖‖

Lungwort is widely grown in gardens for the early flowers and attractive white-spotted leaves. It also provides good ground cover and a large patch can be covered in flowers in early spring. Many named varieties with blue, pink or white flowers and various leaf patterns are available, such as *Pulmonaria angustifolia* 'Munstead Blue', which flowers early, or *Pulmonaria* 'Blue Ensign'. The traditional cottage-garden lungwort is *Pulmonaria officinalis*.

The flower-tube is quite deep and so honeybees and short-tongued bumblebees cannot reach the nectar, although they can still reach the pollen. For those bees that can reach, it is a useful early source of nectar. The main bumblebee visitor is the common carder bee (*Bombus pascuorum*). The hairy-footed flower bee (*Anthophora plumipes*) is also a frequent visitor. These large, furry bees look rather like bumblebees, but they have a darting flight. The females are black and the males are brown. They are absent from Scotland and Ireland. The large bee fly (*Bombylius major*) visits the flowers and is easily mistaken for a brown bumblebee or flower bee because it is a fly that mimics a bee. It can be distinguished by its hovering flight, extraordinarily long tongue and dark band along the front edge of the wings.

Narrow-leaved lungwort (*Pulmonaria longifolia*) is a native species that is rare in southern England, although it may occur as a garden escape elsewhere.

Right:
*Queen common carder bee (*Bombus pascuorum*) on lungwort (*Pulmonaria 'Opal')*
(photo: W. D. J. Kirk)

Far right:
*Female hairy-footed flower bee (*Anthophora plumipes*) on lungwort (*Pulmonaria *species)*
(photo T. C. Ings)

Right:
*Queen garden bumblebee (*Bombus hortorum*) on lungwort (*Pulmonaria species)*
(photo T. C. Ings)

Far right:
*Two-coloured mason bee (*Osmia bicolor*) on lungwort (*Pulmonaria angustifolia 'Azurea')*
(photo: J. V. Adams)

Lupin — *Lupinus* species

The original garden lupin (*Lupinus polyphyllus*) has been displaced in gardens by the many new hybrids, particularly the Russell hybrids. The colourful flowers of perennial garden lupins are generally regarded as more or less nectarless, honeybees and bumblebees visiting them mainly for pollen, the latter with its greater weight being better able to manipulate the flowers. They are particularly visited by the buff-tailed bumblebee (*Bombus terrestris*) and the white-tailed bumblebee (*Bombus lucorum*).

There is some uncertainty about the extent to which other lupins produce nectar. The white lupin (*Lupinus albus*), blue lupin (*Lupinus angustifolius*) and yellow lupin (*Lupinus luteus*) are all now grown commercially across the British Isles, either for forage or to produce a high-protein seed. Lupin provides a substitute for expensive, imported soya and the area grown has been increasing. The crop is self-fertile and self-pollinates; any extra seed yield from bee pollination is considered minimal by growers in the British Isles. However, bees may still benefit commercial crops that are combined for seed and can do no harm. The exception is where a crop is grown for seed for sowing, in which case cross-pollination from another variety nearby could contaminate it. The main use on farms is white lupin grown as a forage mixture with triticale (a hybrid of wheat and rye). The whole crop is harvested after the lupin has flowered and turned into silage for cattle. Bees get the full benefit of the long flowering period of 4–6 weeks and all three of these lupin species are attractive to honeybees, bumblebees and solitary bees.

Family:	**Fabaceae**
Flowering:	**May to July**
Cultivation:	**annual or perennial herb**
Honey:	**no**
Honeybees:	||||| |||||
ST Bumblebees:	||||| |||||
LT Bumblebees:	|||||
Solitary Bees:	|||||

Above:
*Leafcutter bee (*Megachile *species) visiting garden lupin (*Lupinus *species)*
(photo: T. C. Ings)
Left:
*Flowers of yellow lupin (*Lupinus luteus*)*
(photo: W. D. J. Kirk)

L

Lungwort — Lupin

Mahonia — *Mahonia* species

This evergreen shrub, with its holly-like leaves, is much cultivated on account of its ability to withstand shade and is naturalised in some parts of the British Isles. Its grape-like fruits, which may be used for jelly, although bitter, account for its other common name – Oregon grape. It is in flower for many weeks and its bright yellow fragrant blossoms are worked moderately by honeybees for nectar when the weather is warm enough for them to forage. Several species and varieties are available, but *Mahonia aquifolium* is planted widely and has also naturalised. The variety *Mahonia* x *media* 'Winter Sun' flowers particularly early, in the middle of winter, from November to March. Winter-flowering plants are usually of no value to bees, but in recent years, the buff-tailed bumblebee (*Bombus terrestris*) has been observed foraging on flowers during the winter in southern England. They visit mahonias that are in flower in November and December. Milder winters appear to be allowing this bumblebee to establish a second generation. Plants that flower in autumn and winter may become more important to bumblebees in the future.

Family:	Berberidaceae
Flowering:	November to April
Cultivation:	evergreen small to medium shrub
Honey:	no
Honeybees:	|||||
ST Bumblebees:	|||||
LT Bumblebees:	—
Solitary Bees:	|||||

Above:
*Pollen grain of mahonia (*Mahonia aquifolium*) (41 μm)*

Top right:
*Buff-tailed bumblebee (*Bombus terrestris*) on mahonia (*Mahonia x media*)*
Bottom right:
*Male mining bee (*Andrena nitida*) on mahonia (*Mahonia aquifolium*)*
Far right:
*Honeybee on mahonia (*Mahonia x media*)*
(photos: T. C. Ings)

Maize — *Zea mays*

The amount of maize grown in the British Isles has increased enormously in the last few decades. It is now grown widely for silage to provide a high-energy forage for cows. Maize is also grown as a cover crop for game birds and varieties that produce sweetcorn are cultivated more extensively than formerly. The male flower-heads or tassels produce an abundance of pollen which is sometimes collected by honeybees. In parts of southern Europe, maize pollen is considered to be one of the major pollen sources for honeybees. However, in the British Isles it flowers and matures later in the season and is not harvested until September or October. This means that when pollen is available the weather is cooler and so less suitable for

Family:	Poaceae
Flowering:	July to September
Cultivation:	annual herb
Honey:	no
Honeybees:	|||||
ST Bumblebees:	—
LT Bumblebees:	—
Solitary Bees:	—

foraging. There may also be other more palatable sources of pollen available. Since the plant is wind-pollinated, no nectar is produced. There have been cases of honeybees collecting insect honeydew from the plants and there is also some evidence from the USA that under conditions of rapid growth the leaf sheaths may split exposing a certain amount of sweet sap or juice, which honeybees collect.

Far left:
Pollen grain of maize (Zea mays) (85 μm)
Left:
Male tassel of maize (Zea mays)
(photo: W. D. J. Kirk)

Mallow — *Malva sylvestris*

Although usually considered a weed, the common mallow is a handsome plant with its large pale mauve flowers. These are to be seen at their best from June to August when they always find favour with honeybees and bumblebees, not only for pollen but for nectar also. The pollen is white or very pale mauve in colour. Bees often get themselves covered in it and the top of the thorax can be quite white as if daubed with white paint. A range of bumblebee species visit, particularly the red-tailed bumblebee (*Bombus lapidarius*). The flowers are visited by solitary bees, such as mining bees (*Andrena* species).

The pollen grain under the microscope is spherical, rough and exceptionally large, as is common in members of this family (see hollyhock). Its diameter may be as much as 144 μm, as against as little as 3–4 μm in forget-me-not, which has some of the smallest pollen grains. It is just possible to see the individual pollen grains in the hair of bees on the flower. The musk mallow (*Malva moschata*) and dwarf mallow (*Malva neglecta*) are other wild species that are useful to bees and are in flower until frosts arrive. The former is a particularly handsome plant with rosy-pink flowers.

Family:	Malvaceae
Flowering:	June to September
Cultivation:	perennial herb
Honey:	no
Honeybees:	|||||
ST Bumblebees:	||||| |||||
LT Bumblebees:	||||| |||||
Solitary Bees:	||||| |||||

Above:
Mallow flower (Malva sylvestris)
(photo: W. D. J. Kirk)

Malope — *Malope trifida*

This showy annual that originated in the western Mediterranean attracts bees. It grows to a height of about one metre and is best sown where it is intended to flower. The varieties generally cultivated have white, pink and crimson flowers about 7 cm across. The bee visitors are similar to those for the related species of lavatera and mallow (see separate entries).

Family:	Malvaceae
Flowering:	July to September
Cultivation:	annual herb
Honey:	no
Honeybees:	|||||
ST Bumblebees:	||||| |||||
LT Bumblebees:	||||| |||||
Solitary Bees:	|||||

Maple — *Acer* species

Family:	**Sapindaceae**
Flowering:	**March to May**
Cultivation:	**deciduous medium to large tree**
Honey:	**no**
Honeybees:	||||| |||||
ST Bumblebees:	|||||
LT Bumblebees:	|||||
Solitary Bees:	|||||

Above:
Field maple flowers (Acer campestre)
(photo: W. D. J. Kirk)

There are well over a hundred different species of maple distributed more or less throughout the northern hemisphere. As a group they are good bee plants, producing nectar freely and supplying early pollen. The open nature of the flower enables the honeybee and other short-tongued bees to have easy access to the nectar, but as most maples flower very early (March–April) they are only of use to species of bee that are active very early. The extent to which bees are able to make use of them is dependent upon suitable weather at the time. Early bumblebees visit the flowers as well as a few early solitary bees, such as the tawny mining bee (*Andrena fulva*). This species is widespread in England and Wales, but is rarely recorded from Scotland or Ireland. The females are about 8–10 mm long and their upper surface is covered in bright reddish brown hairs, which makes them easy to recognise on the flowers.

The only maple native to the British Isles is the field maple (*Acer campestre*), often to be seen as a small tree on calcareous soils and common in hedges, where it may be coppiced. When allowed free growth it often reaches 15–18 m in height. Its bunches of upright, delicate green blossoms appear in April or May and produce nectar freely. This is secreted by a thick, fleshy central disc and is freely exposed as in other maples. If the tree were more common it would doubtless be as valuable to the beekeeper as the closely related sycamore (*Acer pseudoplatanus*) (see separate entry).

A number of different maples are frequently to be seen in cultivation as ornamental trees, usually for their foliage, which may be attractively shaped or give yellow or reddish tints in autumn. Among the maples that are worked for nectar, the following are among the better known: the Italian maple (*Acer opalus*), which is very free flowering; Norway maple (*Acer platanoides*); Montpellier maple (*Acer monspessulanum*); Oregon maple (*Acer macrophyllum*); ashleaf maple or box elder (*Acer negundo*); and sugar maple (*Acer saccharum*).

Marrow, see vegetable marrow

Marsh marigold — *Caltha palustris*

Family:	**Ranunculaceae**
Flowering:	**February to June**
Cultivation:	**perennial herb**
Honey:	**no**
Honeybees:	|||||
ST Bumblebees:	|||||
LT Bumblebees:	|||||
Solitary Bees:	|||||

The marsh marigold or kingcup is common in moist pastures and by the sides of streams. It always prefers damp situations as the name implies. The flowers, which might be those of a giant buttercup, are among the first of the wild flowers and sometimes appear as early as February, continuing until June. Bees are frequent visitors for pollen and nectar, the latter being half-concealed and secreted, sometimes quite abundantly, in two shallow depressions at the base of the flower. There are garden forms of the plant, some with double flowers that should be avoided.

Left:
*Honeybee on marsh marigold (*Caltha
palustris*)*
(photo: T. C. Ings)

Masterwort — *Astrantia* species

Although masterwort often has rather insignificant whitish green flowers, a number of varieties are available with attractive pink to red flowers, such as *Astrantia major* 'Claret'. Another species available for gardens, *Astrantia maxima*, has larger flowers (up to 30 mm across). A big advantage of this plant for bees is the long flowering season, particularly if they are cut back after first flowering, which produces a second crop of flowers. Honeybees visit the flowers particularly for the pollen, which is apparent from the dark brown pollen loads on their hind legs. A range of bumblebee species, including the buff-tailed bumblebee (*Bombus terrestris*), and several species of solitary bee also visit.

Family:	**Apiaceae**
Flowering:	**June to August**
Cultivation:	**perennial herb**
Honey:	**no**
Honeybees:	‖‖
ST Bumblebees:	‖‖
LT Bumblebees:	‖‖
Solitary Bees:	‖‖

Left:
*Male white-tailed bumblebee (*Bombus
lucorum*) on masterwort (*Astrantia major
'Claret'*)*
(photo: W. D. J. Kirk)

Meadow-foam — *Limnanthes douglasii*

Meadow-foam or poached egg plant, with its distinctive yellow and white flowers, is a Californian annual that has long been grown in British Isles gardens. The yellow and white flowers are sweet-scented and varieties differing in size and colour exist. Under favourable conditions they produce nectar freely and are well liked by bees. It is attractive to honeybees when grown in the mass, but if only a few odd plants are grown in the flower border they often prove disappointing and bees do

Family:	**Limnanthaceae**
Flowering:	**April to September**
Cultivation:	**annual herb**
Honey:	**no**
Honeybees:	‖‖ ‖‖
ST Bumblebees:	‖‖ ‖‖
LT Bumblebees:	‖‖
Solitary Bees:	‖‖

Above:
Pollen grain of meadow-foam (Limnanthes douglasii) (21 μm)

Right:
Female ashy mining bee (Andrena cineraria) on meadow-foam (Limnanthes douglasii)
(photo: L. A. Hislop)
Far right:
Honeybee on meadow-foam (Limnanthes douglasii)
(photo: M. A. Kirk)

not visit them. The plant has a somewhat straggling habit but is quite suitable for edgings, beds and rockeries. Any soil suits it but a moist situation is preferable. Sow seed in September for early spring flowering and in March for summer flowering. A combination of sowing times can maintain a long flowering season, which will be valuable to bees. The plant is likely to be of most benefit when it flowers early as this will provide pollen and nectar when few other sources are available.

A variety of bumblebee species visit the flowers, including the early bumblebee (*Bombus pratorum*). The flowers are also visited by early solitary bees, such as the ashy mining bee (*Andrena cineraria*).

Meadow saffron — *Colchicum autumnale*

Family:	**Colchicaceae**
Flowering:	**August to September**
Cultivation:	**perennial herb, grown from corms**
Honey:	**no**
Honeybees:	‖‖‖
ST Bumblebees:	—
LT Bumblebees:	---
Solitary Bees:	—

This uncommon wild plant of damp meadows is also known as naked ladies or autumn crocus, although it is not a true crocus (see crocus). It should not be confused with a different species, also called autumn crocus (*Crocus nudiflorus*), which is a true crocus and flowers at the same time. The large pale pink or purple flowers of meadow saffron are unmistakable and provide a useful late-season source of pollen for honeybees. The flowers are probably too late to be of much benefit to other bees. Other closely related plants, which also flower around September, are available for gardens and are good for honeybees, such as *Colchicum speciosum* and *Colchicum bivonae*.

Right:
Meadow saffron flower (Colchicum autumnale)
(photo: W. D. J. Kirk)

Meadowsweet — *Filipendula ulmaria*

The dainty, sweet-scented flowers of this very common meadow and fenland plant are often visited by honeybees for pollen. There is doubt as to whether the flowers are also a source of nectar in the British Isles, but in other parts of Europe honeybees have been observed working them for this. The masses of small flowers provide easy access to short-tongued bumblebees, such as the buff-tailed bumblebee (*Bombus terrestris*) and the white-tailed bumblebee (*Bombus lucorum*).

Family:	**Rosaceae**
Flowering:	**June to August**
Cultivation:	**perennial herb**
Honey:	**no**
Honeybees:	|||||
ST Bumblebees:	|||||
LT Bumblebees:	|||||
Solitary Bees:	|||||

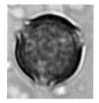

Far left:
*Pollen grain of meadowsweet (*Filipendula ulmaria*) (18 μm)*
Left:
*Buff-tailed bumblebee (*Bombus terrestris*) on meadowsweet (*Filipendula ulmaria*)*
(photo: T. C. Ings)

Medlar — *Mespilus germanica*

Although the medlar was a much-prized fruit in the 19th century, room is seldom found for the tree in present-day orchards and gardens. Some fine old trees, picturesque with their crooked branches, may often be seen in old gardens. The large white flowers that appear in May are not unlike those of the apple and attract bees for nectar and pollen. The nectar is secreted by a fleshy yellow ring at the base of the flower. The cultivated tree is nowhere near sufficiently common to be of any consequence to the beekeeper in the British Isles but is of more account in other countries, such as Spain.

Family:	**Rosaceae**
Flowering:	**May to June**
Cultivation:	**deciduous large shrub or small tree**
Honey:	**no**
Honeybees:	||||| |||||
ST Bumblebees:	||||| |||||
LT Bumblebees:	||||| |||||
Solitary Bees:	||||| |||||

Far left:
*Medlar flower (*Mespilus germanica*)*
Left:
*The centre of a medlar flower (*Mespilus germanica*)*
(photos: W. D. J. Kirk)

M

Meadow saffron — Medlar

Family:	**Fabaceae**
Flowering:	**June to September**
Cultivation:	**annual, biennial or perennial herb**
Honey:	**no**
Honeybees:	‖‖‖ ‖‖‖ ‖‖‖
ST Bumblebees:	‖‖‖ ‖‖‖ ‖‖‖
LT Bumblebees:	‖‖‖ ‖‖‖ ‖‖‖
Solitary Bees:	‖‖‖ ‖‖

Above:
Pollen grain of ribbed melilot (Melilotus officinalis) (27 µm)

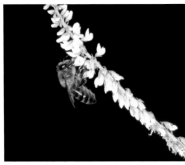

Top:
Honeybee visiting white melilot (Melilotus albus)
Above:
Honeybee on white melilot (Melilotus albus)
(photos: W. D. J. Kirk)

Melilot — *Melilotus* species

Melilot, sweet clover or honey clover is well known to many beekeepers. The very name of course suggests honey (from the Greek: *meli* = honey; *lotus* = clover flower). This is appropriate for it is always attractive to bees and an important honey-producing plant in many parts of the world, renowned as a honeybee plant from classical times.

There are two kinds of melilot commonly seen, the white-flowered white melilot (*Melilotus albus*) and the yellow-flowered ribbed melilot (*Melilotus officinalis*). They are considered to be of equal value as bee plants. Both occur wild or as occasional weeds throughout the British Isles. They may also be grown as decorative plants in gardens or for fodder or hay. Unfortunately for beekeepers, melilot has never been extensively grown as a farm crop in the British Isles, objections to it being that it has a somewhat fibrous or woody nature and that stock do not take to it easily owing to its bitterness, although they soon get used to its taste and then consume it readily. However, these objections must apply in other countries and have not prevented its being grown more widely. Melilot has been used as a green manure on thin, sandy soils, the decay of its large fleshy roots contributing to soil fertility in addition to the stems and leafage.

Both white and yellow melilot are biennials and do not flower until the second year. They then have a long flowering season. This commences in June or July, when numerous flowers appear on the tall, much-branched stems. These are rich in nectar and invariably attract many bees. The white-flowered species (*Melilotus albus*) is the one usually grown for agricultural purposes. It is the taller and more vigorous plant, producing more leafage. It flowers about a fortnight later than the yellow but does not stand cutting back so well. Both grow readily in all types of soil, except the very acid, and often thrive where few other plants will grow, such as railway embankments and the banks of quarries. White melilot usually grows 1.5–2 m high but may reach 3 m under good conditions.

Honey can be obtained when melilot is grown as a crop, but this is not very frequent. It is sometimes grown in mixtures, including as a cover for game birds. The honey from melilot is of good quality, being light in colour although often greenish. It is of medium density, with a pleasant mild flavour that is slightly vanilla-like. Granulation takes place more readily than with ordinary white clover (*Trifolium repens*). The honey is known to vary from different districts and has been accused of causing mild headache in some individuals owing to the presence of coumarin. The pollen is very like that of ordinary clover.

The history of white melilot in the USA is of interest. It first appeared as a weed and was actually scheduled as a noxious weed in some states. Later it began to be grown to a small extent as a pasture and hay crop. Beekeepers are alleged to have scattered seeds on the edges of fields and along roadsides, surreptitiously and by night. Eventually it was cultivated on an intensive scale in the mid-West region and became the source of vast quantities of honey, regions with hot dry summers being best suited for honey production. It was even the cause of derelict farms and land being restored to prosperity. However, its cultivation has declined owing to pests and diseases, particularly the sweet clover weevil. Other crops have taken its place over wide areas to the detriment of bees and beekeeping.

Melilot flowers are visited by many bumblebee species, especially for pollen. They are particularly favoured by queens and workers of the broken-belted bumblebee (*Bombus soroeensis*). This species occurs in scattered localities across Britain, but not Ireland. Several species of solitary bee collect pollen mainly from melilots, clovers and vetches, which are all members of the pea family (Fabaceae).

Many varieties of melilot have been developed, including ones that are low in coumarin and thus less bitter, which makes them more palatable to animals. Tall melilot (*Melilotus altissimus*) is often found in grassy areas, mainly in southern and central England. Another melilot sometimes found in waste places is small melilot (*Melilotus indicus*). It is an annual cultivated in some countries as an agricultural crop or orchard cover and is a good nectar plant.

Above:
*Ribbed melilot flowers (*Melilotus officinalis*)*
(photo: W. D. J. Kirk)

Michaelmas daisy, see aster

Mignonette — *Reseda odorata*

Few garden plants can compare with mignonette for fragrance and few can excel it for attracting bees when in full bloom on a fine morning in a good-sized bed. For continuous blooming, seed should be sown at intervals in the spring and summer. Besides the common garden mignonette, there are dwarf forms and varieties with red or yellow flowers. Nectar is the main attraction, but pollen is collected also. Honeybees visit the flowers all day long. Some claim that mignonette is capable of giving more blossom and more nectar for a given area than any other plant.

The wild mignonette (*Reseda lutea*), which is a common plant on chalk hills and in flower from June to August is also a good source of nectar and pollen for the honeybee, but is probably nowhere sufficiently abundant for surplus honey. Unlike its garden counterpart, which originated in the southeast Mediterranean, the flowers have little fragrance.

Family:	**Resedaceae**
Flowering:	**May to September**
Cultivation:	**annual to biennial herb**
Honey:	**no**
Honeybees:	‖‖‖ ‖‖‖ ‖‖‖
ST Bumblebees:	‖‖‖ ‖‖
LT Bumblebees:	‖‖
Solitary Bees:	‖‖‖ ‖‖‖ ‖‖‖

Far left:
*Pollen grain of mignonette (*Reseda odorata*) (22 μm)*
Left:
*Mining bee (Lasioglossum species) on wild mignonette (*Reseda lutea*)*
(photo: T. C. Ings)

Bumblebees visit flowers of mignonette, particularly the red-tailed bumblebee (*Bombus lapidarius*). Several solitary bees make use of mignonette and its close relatives, including the coast leafcutter bee (*Megachile maritima*) and a small, black stem-nesting bee (*Hylaeus signatus*). Weld (*Reseda luteola*) is visited for nectar by a mining bee (*Colletes halophilus*), which occurs along southern and eastern coasts of England.

Right:
*Male red-tailed bumblebee (*Bombus lapidarius*) on wild mignonette*
(photo: L. Hebdon)
Far right:
*A mating pair of stem-nesting bees (*Hylaeus signatus*) on weld (*Reseda luteola*)*
(photo: N. P. Jones)

Mint — *Mentha* species

Family:	**Lamiaceae**
Flowering:	**May to October**
Cultivation:	**perennial herb**
Honey:	**no**
Honeybees:	‖‖‖ ‖‖‖
ST Bumblebees:	‖‖‖
LT Bumblebees:	‖‖‖
Solitary Bees:	‖‖‖

The various mints, wild and cultivated, are all good honeybee plants and yield nectar freely, although they are rarely sufficiently abundant to yield surplus honey. The fields of mint that are grown for culinary purposes are normally harvested before they flower, which is unfortunate for bees and beekeepers. Many different kinds of mint are grown commercially in the British Isles, many of them hybrid forms. Spearmint (*Mentha spicata*) and peppermint (*Mentha x piperita*) are sometimes cultivated on a field scale and surplus honey has been obtained from them. It is amber in colour with a minty flavour when fresh but this becomes less noticeable in time.

Among the wild mints, two of the most common are water mint (*Mentha aquatica*) and corn mint (*Mentha arvensis*). Both flower late in the season, from August onwards, and are a useful source of late nectar for bees in districts where they grow freely. The former sometimes occurs in masses near streams, as in parts of East Anglia, and the latter occurs in field margins and damp places. Pennyroyal (*Mentha pulegium*) with its more straggling habit may occur freely in and around bogs. It is often to be seen in gardens, especially rock gardens, in one or other of its many forms. Pennyroyal has become naturalised in other countries and is a source of honey in New Zealand where it has spread to the extent of becoming a weed. The honey from it is pale in colour and rather thin. Mints are visited by both short-tongued and long-tongued bumblebees.

Right:
*Flowers of peppermint (*Mentha x piperita*)*
(photo: W. D. J. Kirk)
Far right:
*Brown-banded carder bee (*Bombus humilis*) on mint (*Mentha species*)*
(photo: T. C. Ings)

Mock orange — *Philadelphus* species

The highly-scented flowers of the mock orange are known to attract honeybees for nectar and pollen, but not in large numbers. Short-tongued bumblebees, such as the buff-tailed bumblebee (*Bombus terrestris*), are frequent visitors. There are many different hybrids and varieties in cultivation, some with double flowers that will not benefit bees.

Family:	**Hydrangeaceae**
Flowering:	**June**
Cultivation:	**deciduous medium shrub**
Honey:	**no**
Honeybees:	|||||
ST Bumblebees:	||||| |||||
LT Bumblebees:	|||||
Solitary Bees:	—

Left:
*Tree bumblebee (*Bombus hypnorum*) on mock orange (*Philadelphus *species)*
(photo: T. C. Ings)

Monk's hood — *Aconitum napellus*

The flowers of the monk's hood or aconite are a rich blue-violet colour with a distinctive hood. Native plants still survive in damp, shady places in parts of England and Wales, but it also occurs widely as a garden escape. The garden varieties are quite variable in terms of flowering time, so that early and late ones can be grown to extend the flowering season for bees. It is an excellent plant for bumblebees, particularly long-tongued species, which are considered to be the main pollinators. The garden bumblebee (*Bombus hortorum*) is likely to be the most frequent visitor in gardens. The plant and nectar are highly toxic to humans, but bumblebees are not affected. The aconite is occasionally mentioned as a honeybee plant, but this is probably a result of confusion with the winter aconite (*Eranthis hyemalis*) (see separate entry).

Family:	**Ranunculaceae**
Flowering:	**May to September**
Cultivation:	**perennial herb**
Honey:	**no**
Honeybees:	—
ST Bumblebees:	|||||
LT Bumblebees:	||||| |||||
Solitary Bees:	—

Left:
*Worker garden bumblebee (*Bombus hortorum*) on monk's hood (*Aconitum napellus*)*
(photo: L. Hebdon)

M

Mint — Monk's hood

Motherwort — *Leonurus cardiaca*

Family:	**Lamiaceae**
Flowering:	**July to September**
Cultivation:	**perennial herb**
Honey:	**no**
Honeybees:	|||||
ST Bumblebees:	|||||
LT Bumblebees:	|||||
Solitary Bees:	|||||

The plant is sometimes to be seen, apparently wild, in Britain but not in Ireland. It is neither common nor indigenous and so is not well known. However, it is more prevalent in other parts of Europe and is regarded there as a good honey plant. One writer referred to its long flowering season, from July onwards, and considered it better than phacelia, borage and melilot as a nectar plant in Germany. It reaches a metre in height, has characteristic, lobed, lower leaves and white or purplish-pink flowers, which are distinctively hairy. The flower-tube is only 4 mm long and the pollen is white. Motherwort is now extensively naturalised as a weed in other countries, especially Canada and the USA, where it is also very attractive to bees. Nectar may be secreted very freely.

Right:
*Honeybee on motherwort (*Leonurus cardiaca*)*
(photo: W. D. J. Kirk)

Mountain ash — *Sorbus aucuparia*

Family:	**Rosaceae**
Flowering:	**May to June**
Cultivation:	**deciduous medium tree**
Honey:	**no**
Honeybees:	|||||
ST Bumblebees:	|||||
LT Bumblebees:	—
Solitary Bees:	—

The rowan or mountain ash is a characteristic wild tree of the north and west of the British Isles. It is also much planted throughout the British Isles as an ornamental tree on account of its feathery foliage. The bunches of greenish-white flowers, which have a strong sweet scent, generally appear in May and June and are visited by honeybees and bumblebees for nectar and pollen, but not in large numbers. The small, open flowers are also much visited by flies.

Right:
*Pollen grain of mountain ash (*Sorbus aucuparia*) (27 µm)*

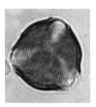

Mullein — *Verbascum* species

The mulleins or verbascums are visited by honeybees and bumblebees at times, mainly for pollen. The majority, wild and cultivated, are in flower late in the summer and so furnish pollen when many other sources are over. When nectar is secreted it appears to be done sparingly and on the inner sides of the petals. The great mullein (*Verbascum thapsus*), which grows 2 m high and has light yellow flowers, is often to be seen on waste ground, especially on chalk or light soils, and is not uncommon as a wild plant.

The wool-carder bee (*Anthidium manicatum*) lines its nest with plant hairs gathered from plants with hairy leaves and stems and the hairy leaves and stems of mullein are often visited for this purpose. The females can be observed collecting their little balls of wool before flying off to the nest. The bees can be recognised by the rows of distinctive yellow spots down the body.

Family:	**Scrophulariaceae**
Flowering:	**June to August**
Cultivation:	**biennial herb**
Honey:	**no**
Honeybees:	|||||
ST Bumblebees:	|||||
LT Bumblebees:	|||||
Solitary Bees:	||||| |||||

Left:
*Centre of a mullein flower (*Verbascum *'Primrose')*
(photo: M. A. Kirk)

Mustard — *Sinapis alba* and *Brassica juncea*

Mustard is closely related to several other crops, such as oilseed rape and turnip, and to a weed, charlock (see separate entries). They are of similar value to bees and yield a similar, characteristic type of honey. Two distinct kinds of mustard are now grown for seed in the British Isles for the preparation of the condiment. These are white mustard (*Sinapis alba*) and Chinese or brown mustard (*Brassica juncea*), the former with a larger and paler-coloured seed. Black mustard (*Brassica nigra*) used to be grown, but it has now been replaced by brown mustard, which is easier to harvest. Fields in flower yield a copious supply of nectar as well as pollen. They are mainly grown in the rich fenlands and marshlands of East Anglia, where they sometimes produce good crops of honey. White mustard is also cultivated as a forage crop, as a green manure and as a cover crop. A modern use is to sow selected varieties of mustard before

Family:	**Brassicaceae**
Flowering:	**May to September**
Cultivation:	**annual herb**
Honey:	**yes**
Honeybees:	||||| ||||| |||||
ST Bumblebees:	||||| ||||| |||||
LT Bumblebees:	||||| ||||| |||||
Solitary Bees:	||||| |||||

M

Motherwort — Mustard

sowing a different crop, such as sugar beet, to reduce weeds, pests and diseases. The plant has a biofumigant action in the soil. In the case of both brown and white mustard, the plants from a single sowing are usually in flower for about a month, but the timing depends on the purpose of the crop. The honey from mustard is whitish in colour and has a mild flavour, but it can have a strong aroma and flavour when fresh which is inclined to leave a slight burning sensation in the mouth. Granulation takes place more rapidly than in most other honeys.

The flowers are popular with bumblebees such as the buff-tailed bumblebee (*Bombus terrestris*), the red-tailed bumblebee (*Bombus lapidarius*) and the common carder bee (*Bombus pascuorum*), as well as many solitary bees, including mining bees (*Andrena* and *Lasioglossum* species) and small, black stem-nesting bees (*Hylaeus* species).

Right:
Flowers of white mustard (Sinapis alba)
(photo: W. D. J. Kirk)

Myrtle — *Myrtus communis*

Although well known for its fragrance and use in bridal bouquets this plant is only hardy in the milder parts of the British Isles. It is often grown in gardens in Devon and Cornwall and produces white lowers in late summer. These yield pollen and perhaps a little nectar for honeybees and bumblebees, particularly the buff-tailed bumblebee (*Bombus terrestris*). Double flowered varieties will be of little or no benefit to bees.

Family:	**Myrtaceae**
Flowering:	**July to August**
Cultivation:	**evergreen medium to large shrub**
Honey:	**no**
Honeybees:	‖‖
ST Bumblebees:	‖‖
LT Bumblebees:	‖‖
Solitary Bees:	‖‖

M

Myrtle — Nemophila

Nasturtium — *Tropaeolum majus*

There are many dwarf and climbing forms of this popular garden annual, which originates from Central and South America. The orange, red or yellow flowers normally have a long spur (about 20–30 mm) that secretes and collects the nectar, but some varieties lack the spur and so are nectarless. Typically, only the garden bumblebee (*Bombus hortorum*), which has a very long tongue will be able to reach the nectar within the spur, although other bumblebee species may be able to reach some when the spur has accumulated a lot of nectar. This restricted access means that most bee visitors are usually foraging for pollen.

Family:	Tropaeolaceae
Flowering:	July to September
Cultivation:	annual herb
Honey:	no
Honeybees:	|||||
ST Bumblebees:	|||||
LT Bumblebees:	|||||
Solitary Bees:	|||||

Far left:
*Pollen grain of nasturtium (*Tropaeolum majus*) (31 μm)*
Left:
*Nasturtium flower (*Tropaeolum majus*)*
(photo: W. D. J. Kirk)

Nemophila — *Nemophila* species

Among the most easily grown of annuals, the nemophilas thrive in any soil. They are well suited for edging and small beds, being of compact growth, and several species and varieties are available with various patterns of blue, purple and white flowers. The best displays are probably obtained in the north and the cooler parts of the British Isles. The flowers are particularly popular with bees for nectar, but pollen is also collected. Autumn and successional spring sowings give a longer flowering period.

Family:	Boraginaceae
Flowering:	June to October
Cultivation:	annual herb
Honey:	no
Honeybees:	|||||
ST Bumblebees:	|||||
LT Bumblebees:	|||||
Solitary Bees:	|||||

Left:
*Honeybee on baby blue eyes (*Nemophila menziesii*)*
(photo: W. D. J. Kirk)

N

Myrtle — Nemophila

Nipplewort — *Lapsana communis*

Family:	**Asteraceae**
Flowering:	**July to October**
Cultivation:	**annual to perennial herb**
Honey:	**no**
Honeybees:	‖‖
ST Bumblebees:	‖‖
LT Bumblebees:	‖‖
Solitary Bees:	‖‖ ‖‖

This is a common plant in some areas, found by hedges and roadsides, producing its pale yellow flower-heads, rather like small dandelion flowers on long, branched stems, from July onwards. Honeybees and bumblebees sometimes visit them, particularly late in the season when other bee forage becomes scarce. The flowers, together with other yellow-flowered members of the daisy family (Asteraceae), are visited by many solitary bees, including mining bees (*Andrena*, *Colletes* and *Lasioglossum* species). Many hoverflies also visit and are easily mistaken for bees.

Right:
*Flower-head of nipplewort (*Lapsana communis*)*
(photo: W. D. J. Kirk)

Oak — *Quercus* species

The dominant wild oak species are the pedunculate oak (*Quercus robur*) and the sessile oak (*Quercus petraea*). Both the wild and the many cultivated oaks produce pollen that is sometimes collected by honeybees and bumblebees. This is produced in April or May, when many other sources are available. There are reports of nectar from the oak, but this has probably been insect honeydew, which honeybees collect and use for honey in the same way as nectar. Honeydew can sometimes make a useful contribution to honey stores. The oak is the host plant of a very large number of different kinds of insect, including many gall wasps. Solitary bees occasionally collect pollen from oak flowers. A very rare mining bee (*Andrena ferox*), which is found in a very few sites in southern England, appears to collect pollen almost exclusively from oak flowers and so is dependent on it. It may be more widespread, but it is hard to see it in the tops of oak trees. It is a darkish bee with a disproportionately large head in the male. They may also collect nectar from flowers of hawthorn (*Crataegus* species) and field maple (*Acer campestre*).

It should be noted that the Turkey oak (*Quercus cerris*) and the evergreen oak (*Quercus ilex*) have the potential to be invasive species in the UK and should not be planted in the wild.

Family:	**Fagaceae**
Flowering:	**April to May**
Cultivation:	**deciduous or evergreen medium to large tree**
Honey:	**no**
Honeybees:	|||||
ST Bumblebees:	|||||
LT Bumblebees:	|||||
Solitary Bees:	||||| |||||

Oilseed rape — *Brassica napus*

The name 'oilseed rape' is used for both swede rape (*Brassica napus*) and turnip rape (*Brassica rapa*), but it is predominantly swede rape that is grown in the British Isles, mainly for the oil that is extracted from the seeds. The name 'rape' is from the Latin word for a turnip. In the 1970s there was a large increase in the area that was grown in the British Isles, mainly in England, and this has stayed high ever since and is still increasing. Most is now winter rape, which is sown in August or September, flowers the following April to June and then is harvested in July or August. When the crop is sown as spring rape, it flowers later from June to July. When both winter and spring rape occurs in the same area, there can be a four-month season of forage available for bees.

The flowers are very attractive to honeybees, which collect nectar and often pollen as well. Beekeepers often move their hives to the rape to obtain more honey and strengthen their colonies. The flowers are also much visited by bumblebees such as the buff-tailed bumblebee (*Bombus terrestris*), the red-tailed bumblebee (*Bombus lapidarius*) and the common carder bee (*Bombus pascuorum*). Solitary bees, such as mining bees (*Andrena* and *Lasioglossum* species), are also frequent.

At the base of the bright yellow flowers are dark green nectaries, which are clearly visible. Honeybees find it hard to reach the nectar from the front of the flower, so they often feed on the nectar from the side of the flower by poking the tongue between the bases of the petals. This behaviour is known as 'base working'.

The honey contains a high concentration of glucose sugar, which

Family:	**Brassicaceae**
Flowering:	**April to June**
Cultivation:	**annual or biennial herb**
Honey:	**yes**
Honeybees:	||||| ||||| |||||
ST Bumblebees:	||||| ||||| |||||
LT Bumblebees:	||||| ||||| |||||
Solitary Bees:	||||| |||||

Above:
*Pollen grain of oilseed rape (*Brassica napus*) (27 μm)*

Top:
Oilseed rape flower (Brassica napus)
viewed from the front
Above:
Oilseed rape flower (Brassica napus)
viewed from the side, with a green nectary
visible at the base
Right:
Honeybee on oilseed rape (Brassica napus)
(photos: W. D. J. Kirk)

causes it to granulate and set hard within a few weeks of being taken from the hive. This set honey is white and mild with a delicate flavour. It is popular, partly because children create less mess when eating it than they do with runny honey. In the 1970s, some beekeepers noted a cabbage taste in the honey, but this no longer occurs with modern varieties. The rapid granulation causes problems for beekeepers because the honey must be harvested quickly and not left on the hive. For beekeepers with plenty of time to check their hives regularly and collect and harvest honey during May and June, oilseed rape strengthens colonies and provides a large honey harvest. However, if beekeepers do not have time to do this, they can find the honey has set solid in the comb which makes it very difficult to extract and also means that the bees have difficulty feeding on it.

In the past, there have been cases of honeybee colonies being killed as a result of insecticides that were sprayed on the crop during flowering. Legislation is now much stricter about the use of insecticides and there are restrictions on use that are intended to protect bees. If a farmer needs to spray a crop, a beekeeper can move bees away temporarily or a farmer can spray early or late when honeybees are not flying. However, care should also be taken to protect bumblebees, which start flying earlier in the day and finish later than honeybees.

Oleaster — *Elaeagnus* species

Family:	**Elaeagnaceae**
Flowering:	**May to June**
Cultivation:	**evergreen or deciduous medium to large shrub**
Honey:	**no**
Honeybees:	|||||
ST Bumblebees:	|||||
LT Bumblebees:	|||||
Solitary Bees:	—

The sweet-scented blossoms of several different species of oleaster or silverberry are much frequented by honeybees and bumblebees in June. However, it is doubtful whether honeybees are able to obtain much nectar from the flowers of these shrubs owing to the length of the flower-tube. Some of the evergreen species and varieties, such as Ebbinge's silverberry (*Elaeagnus* x *ebbingei*) which is much used for hedging, flower much later from September to November, but can still attract some bees in good weather.

Onion, see allium

Oregon grape, see mahonia

Osoberry — *Oemleria cerasiformis*

Although not generally cultivated, this deciduous shrub (formerly *Osmaronia cerasiformis*) is of interest for its early flowering and the zeal with which honeybees work its white, almond-scented blossoms for pollen when opportunity arises. These are produced in great profusion. The shrub eventually forms a thicket 2–3 m high with numerous stems from the base. It is quite hardy in the British Isles although a native of western North America. Male and female flowers are on different plants, the latter producing plum-like fruits which are purple when ripe. Bees visit the flowers for nectar as well as pollen.

Family:	**Rosaceae**
Flowering:	**February to March**
Cultivation:	**deciduous medium shrub**
Honey:	**no**
Honeybees:	‖‖
ST Bumblebees:	—
LT Bumblebees:	—
Solitary Bees:	—

Oxeye daisy — *Leucanthemum vulgare*

The oxeye daisy with its flower-heads up to 7 cm across and common on roadside verges and in grassy places is visited by a wide range of insects, including butterflies, beetles, hoverflies and thrips. The open flower makes the nectar accessible to a wide range of bees, including short-tongued bumblebees and a variety of solitary bees, such as mining bees (*Andrena*, *Colletes* and *Halictus* species) and some small, black stem-nesting bees (*Hylaeus* species).

Family:	**Asteraceae**
Flowering:	**June to August**
Cultivation:	**perennial herb**
Honey:	**no**
Honeybees:	‖‖
ST Bumblebees:	‖‖
LT Bumblebees:	‖‖
Solitary Bees:	‖‖ ‖‖

Above:
Pollen grain of oxeye daisy (Leucanthemum vulgare) *(27 μm)*
Left:
Stem-nesting bee (Hylaeus *species) on oxeye daisy* (Leucanthemum vulgare)
(photo: T. C. Ings)

O

Oleaster — Oxeye daisy

Parsnip — *Pastinaca sativa*

Family:	**Apiaceae**
Flowering:	**July to September**
Cultivation:	**biennial herb**
Honey:	**no**
Honeybees:	|||||
ST Bumblebees:	|||||
LT Bumblebees:	||||
Solitary Bees:	||||| |||||

Both the wild and the cultivated parsnip of the vegetable garden are sources of nectar and pollen for bees. The wild plant has a tough fibrous root quite unlike the large fleshy root of its cultivated relative, but the leaves and flowers are similar. It is abundant in many parts of the British Isles and is to be seen around fields, in hedgerows and meadows, and on sea cliffs. Its bunches of yellow flowers are present from July to September, and are visited by many kinds of insect. It would appear that nectar is not usually present in abundance, and it is unusual for it to be of any consequence as a nectar source for honeybees.

Early last century, one beekeeper in Surrey related how a large fallow field at the back of his house, which was covered with the plant, gave a good crop of honey in one year, but in the four previous years he had hardly seen any honeybees on it. Where the garden parsnip has been grown on an extensive scale for seed purposes in the USA, crops of honey have been obtained. This has been described as light amber in colour and of medium quality.

Many solitary bees have a preference for the flat-headed flowers of parsnip and other members of the carrot family (Apiaceae). These include mining bees (*Andrena, Colletes* and *Lasioglossum* species) and small, black stem-nesting bees (*Hylaeus* species). A mining bee (*Andrena nitidiuscula*) depends on flowers of this type, such as wild parsnip and wild carrot, for pollen and occurs in scattered locations across southern England. It is a small, blackish bee with about four thin, white stripes across the hind part of the body. The cuckoo bee *Nomada errans*, a brownish bee with yellow markings, lays eggs in its nest, but has not been sighted for many years and may now be extinct in the British Isles.

Right:
Parsnip flowers (Pastinaca sativa)
(photo: M. A. Kirk)

Pea, see vetchling

Peach — *Prunus persica*

Like its near relative the almond, this fruit tree flowers early and is a source of nectar and pollen. It is of some importance to beekeepers in warmer climates, but in the British Isles is only to be seen occasionally on walls or in glasshouses. Decorative flowering peaches are also grown in gardens and open 2–3 weeks later than the almond. Some of these have double flowers and will be of little benefit to bees. Honeybees have in the past been used successfully as pollinators in peach houses by some growers, thereby effecting a big saving in labour as compared with hand-pollinating.

Family:	Rosaceae
Flowering:	February to May
Cultivation:	deciduous small tree
Honey:	no
Honeybees:	‖‖‖
ST Bumblebees:	‖‖‖
LT Bumblebees:	‖‖‖
Solitary Bees:	‖‖‖

Left:
*White-tailed bumblebee (*Bombus lucorum*) on nectarine (*Prunus persica*), a form of peach*
(*photo: D. R. Skingsley*)

Pear — *Pyrus communis*

The pear is one of the four important tree fruits of the British Isles, and ranks with the apple, plum and cherry. With them it is of value to the beekeeper as a source of nectar and pollen early in the season for strengthening and building up stocks for the main honey flow. The pear is in general less hardy than the apple and is often grown on walls. It is not grown on the extensive scale that is sometimes the case with the apple. Generally it is to be found in mixed orchards with other fruits. For this reason pear honey is more or less unknown in the British Isles.

Family:	Rosaceae
Flowering:	April to May
Cultivation:	deciduous small tree
Honey:	no
Honeybees:	‖‖‖ ‖‖‖
ST Bumblebees:	‖‖‖
LT Bumblebees:	‖‖‖
Solitary Bees:	‖‖‖ ‖‖‖ ‖‖‖

As a nectar or honey producer the pear has always been regarded as inferior to the apple, even in the early days of beekeeping with skeps. The sugar concentration of pear nectar has often been found to be considerably lower than that of apples in flower at the same time in the same area. Some varieties of pear in fact have a very low concentration and there are times when bees visit the blossoms only for pollen, while other fruit trees in the same area are being visited for nectar.

Pear blossoms have a distinctive odour, not unlike hawthorn, and vary in size and shape in different varieties of pear. In some they are more or less bell-shaped, and in others spread out flat with little protection from rain. It usually takes from five to seven days for all the anthers in a flower to open and liberate their pollen. The pollen is collected by bees and is pale or greenish yellow in colour, almost identical with that of the apple,

Above:
*Flower of Williams pear (*Pyrus communis* 'Williams Bon Chrétien')*
(*photo: W. D. J. Kirk*)

and is not the same colour as the unopened reddish-brown anthers.

Most varieties of pear commence blooming ahead of the apple, but like the apple the date of the appearance of the first blossoms varies from year to year according to the earliness or lateness of the season. In most years in the southeastern districts flowering is at its zenith between the middle and the end of April. The total period of blossoming with pears is not so long as with apples. Some varieties like Vicar of Winkfield and Louis Bonne of Jersey flower early. Others, such as Comice, Glou Morceau and Catillac, are late flowering. The same order of flowering with different varieties is maintained whatever the season. Individual pear trees remain in blossom from 10–21 days, according to variety and weather during flowering. Low temperatures extend the flowering period.

The flowers are visited by solitary bees, such as the red mason bee (*Osmia rufa*), the tawny mining bee (*Andrena fulva*) and the ashy mining bee (*Andrena cineraria*).

Penstemon — *Penstemon* species

Family:	**Plantaginaceae**
Flowering:	**July to October**
Cultivation:	**perennial herb**
Honey:	**no**
Honeybees:	‖‖
ST Bumblebees:	‖‖
LT Bumblebees:	‖‖ ‖‖
Solitary Bees:	‖‖

These garden plants are mostly of hybrid origin and have attractive flowers of a wide range of colours and sizes. The long flower-tube makes the flowers particularly useful to long-tongued bumblebees, such as the common carder bee (*Bombus pascuorum*). Honeybees visit garden penstemons to a lesser extent, usually for pollen. Several of the wild penstemons of North America are known to be good honeybee plants. The closely related snapdragon penstemon (*Keckiella antirrhinoides*), which is generally grown against a warm wall because it is not altogether hardy, has been a source of surplus honey in California.

Right:
Penstemon flower (Penstemon *species*)
(photo: W. D. J. Kirk)
Far right:
Pollen grain of penstemon (Penstemon '*June Tune*') (25 µm)

Peony — *Paeonia* species

Family:	**Paeoniaceae**
Flowering:	**June to July**
Cultivation:	**perennial herb**
Honey:	**no**
Honeybees:	‖‖
ST Bumblebees:	‖‖
LT Bumblebees:	‖‖
Solitary Bees:	‖‖

Many of the peonies seen in gardens have double flowers and are of little interest or use to bees. The single-flowered sorts, however, produce an abundance of pollen and honeybees and bumblebees may often be seen collecting it, sometimes three or four on a flower together. It has been estimated that as many as three million pollen grains may be produced by a single peony flower.

The flowers are also visited by solitary bees, such as the hairy-footed flower bee (*Anthophora plumipes*). These large, furry bees look rather like bumblebees, but they have a darting flight. The females are black and the males are brown. They are absent from Scotland and Ireland.

Far left:
Worker white-tailed bumblebee (Bombus lucorum) *collecting pollen on peony* (Paeonia *'Pink Dawn'*)
Left:
Honeybee collecting pollen on peony (Paeonia delavayi*)
(photos: M. A. Kirk)

Perezia — *Perezia multiflora*

This plant, from the slopes of the Andes, is little known in cultivation but is very attractive to honeybees. It is an annual or biennial, reaching about 1 m in height with masses of china-blue flowers with yellow centres, rather like a Michaelmas daisy. As many as 100 flower-heads may be carried by a single stalk. The flowering period lasts for several weeks, usually from early June onwards. Seeds are produced in abundance and seedlings come up freely round the old plants by the time autumn arrives. These generally survive the winter and only need thinning in the spring. Honeybees work the flowers for nectar all day in fine weather and the masses of pollen in their pollen baskets are conspicuous on account of their pure white colour. The plant is a useful and easily grown addition to the bee garden.

Family:	Asteraceae
Flowering:	June
Cultivation:	annual or biennial herb
Honey:	no
Honeybees:	||||| |||||
ST Bumblebees:	|||||
LT Bumblebees:	|||||
Solitary Bees:	|||||

Persicary — *Persicaria* and *Fallopia* species

Several wild plants and weeds closely related to buckwheat (see separate entry) and belonging to the genera *Persicaria* or *Fallopia* are good bee plants. These include black bindweed (*Fallopia convolvulus*), which is a troublesome weed, and common bistort (*Persicaria bistorta*) with its pretty spikes of small, flesh-coloured flowers. The latter is usually to be found in moist, grassy places. Redshank or persicary (*Persicaria maculosa*), a ubiquitous weed across the British Isles is reputed to be a good nectar plant in some other countries. The honey is described as spicy, very dark, and granulating rapidly. In the British Isles, this plant does not seem to be very freely worked by honeybees. Other wild species visited for nectar are water pepper (*Persicaria hydropiper*), frequent in ditches, and the amphibious persicary (*Persicaria amphibia*), a showy aquatic plant. The latter may be a useful plant for establishing on or around ponds or waste stretches of water to increase the bee pasturage of a district. Nectar secretion in a water plant is probably less liable to be affected by dry spells than are terrestrial

Family:	Polygonaceae
Flowering:	June to October
Cultivation:	annual to perennial herb
Honey:	no
Honeybees:	||||| |||||
ST Bumblebees:	||||| |||||
LT Bumblebees:	||||| |||||
Solitary Bees:	|||||

Above:
*Male white-tailed bumblebee (*Bombus
lucorum*) on garden persicary (*Persicaria
species*)*
(photo: W. D. J. Kirk)

Family:	**Boraginaceae**
Flowering:	**April to December**
Cultivation:	**annual herb**
Honey:	**no**
Honeybees:	||||| ||||| |||||
ST Bumblebees:	||||| |||||
LT Bumblebees:	|||||
Solitary Bees:	|||||

Top:
*Flowers of phacelia (*Phacelia tanacetifolia*)*
Above:
*Red-tailed bumblebee (*Bombus lapidarius*)
on phacelia (*Phacelia tanacetifolia*)*
(photos: W. D. J. Kirk)

plants, provided always of course the drought is not severe enough to dry up the pool or pond.

Some members of this group that are cultivated in gardens are good bee plants. The most spectacular is perhaps the giant knotweed (*Fallopia sachalinensis*), introduced from the Sakhalin Islands off the coast of Siberia in 1869, an imposing giant perennial with stems 3–4 m high and leaves up to 40 cm in length. It is a good nectar plant with its clusters of greenish-white flowers in late summer. Unfortunately, it has also proved to be a highly invasive weed.

Phacelia — *Phacelia tanacetifolia*

This fast-growing, hairy annual is of considerable value to honeybees and the seed forms a major proportion of seed mixtures, such as the 'Tübingen mixture', that have been developed to provide a succession of food sources for honeybees and other beneficial insects on set-aside land. The bluish-pink flowers produce large amounts of nectar and pollen and can be covered with honeybees at all hours of the day. Phacelia was introduced into Europe from North America in the early 19th century. It can be planted as a cover crop or grown as a green manure.

The flowers are particularly popular with honeybees and short-tongued bumblebees, such as the buff-tailed bumblebee (*Bombus terrestris*) and the white-tailed bumblebee (*Bombus lucorum*). They are less frequently visited by long-tongued bumblebees and solitary bees, such as mining bees (*Halictus* and *Lasioglossum* species). The pollen is on the end of the stamens, which project beyond the flower and so are hard to reach for a bee that has landed on the petals. Some honeybees hover above the flower and use their legs to dislodge pollen from the anthers onto the underside of the body.

When seed is sown in the spring or early summer, flowering commences after about eight weeks, and lasts for 4–6 weeks: a long period for an annual. Large numbers of flowers are produced by each plant, which succeeds in almost any soil and grows to about 70 cm in height. It lacks the showiness associated with the best garden plants, but is not out of place as an edging. Grown in quantity by itself it is inclined to fall over unless supported. Sown mixed with melilot (see separate entry), it provides good honeybee forage in the first season when the melilot does not flower. In most areas, two crops of flowers may be obtained from the same plot of ground by sowing in late September or early October to stand the winter, and again in early June. The autumn sowing will flower at the end of April and May, while the June sowing provides welcome bee forage in August. A very long flowering period can be obtained by sowing at successive times.

In the phacelia flower, the nectar is secreted freely by a disc at the base of the ovary and is protected by special appendages at the base of the stamens. These do not hinder the honeybee. The pollen is a very distinctive dark blue in the bees' pollen baskets. Phacelia is one of the top plants for potential honey yield. The honey is amber or light green with a delicate flavour and granulates to a pale beige or near-white colour. Honey has also been obtained from other wild species of phacelia in the southern USA. At Kew Gardens, honeybees have been observed working the following species for nectar: sticky phacelia (*Phacelia viscida*), blue curls (*Phacelia congesta*) and desert bluebell (*Phacelia minor*, formerly *Phacelia campanularia*). The last mentioned has large bell-shaped blue flowers, and is sometimes grown in gardens.

Pheasant's eye — *Adonis* species

The vivid flowers of this old favourite annual are sometimes visited by bees for pollen. The annual pheasant's eye (*Adonis annua*) with deep scarlet flowers used to occur wild as a naturalised cornfield weed in southern England. Perennial species are also available, which flower instead in the spring.

Family:	**Ranunculaceae**
Flowering:	**June to August**
Cultivation:	**annual or perennial herb**
Honey:	**no**
Honeybees:	|||||
ST Bumblebees:	|||||
LT Bumblebees:	|||||
Solitary Bees:	|||||

Pieris — *Pieris* species

Pieris or lily-of-the-valley bush is an evergreen shrub with white pitcher-shaped pendent flowers that bloom early in the year. It provides a useful source of early nectar for bumblebees. Honeybees visit the blossoms, but as the flower-tube is about 7 mm or more in length, with a constricted opening, it is doubtful whether the honeybee obtains much nectar unless secretion is very heavy. Many varieties of Japanese andromeda (*Pieris japonica*) and Chinese pieris (*Pieris formosa*) are available for gardens. Conditions for successful cultivation are the same as for rhododendrons.

Family:	**Ericaceae**
Flowering:	**March to May**
Cultivation:	**evergreen medium to large shrub**
Honey:	**no**
Honeybees:	|||||
ST Bumblebees:	||||| |||||
LT Bumblebees:	||||| |||||
Solitary Bees:	—

Left:
*Queen red-tailed bumblebee (*Bombus lapidarius*) on Japanese andromeda (*Pieris japonica*)*
(photo: M. A. Kirk)

P

Phacelia — Pieris

Plum — *Prunus domestica*

Family:	**Rosaceae**
Flowering:	**April to May**
Cultivation:	**deciduous small tree**
Honey:	**yes**
Honeybees:	||||| |||||
ST Bumblebees:	||||| |||||
LT Bumblebees:	||||| |||||
Solitary Bees:	||||| |||||

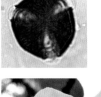

Top:
Pollen grain of plum (Prunus domestica)
(40 μm)
Above:
Plum flower (Prunus domestica)
(photo: M. A. Kirk)

Plums are the hardiest and the most heavy yielding of stone fruits. They are cultivated throughout the British Isles, but far less than they used to be. The number of varieties runs into hundreds, but few of these are easily available. Some plum varieties are self-sterile and the question of cross-pollination and the insect agents responsible becomes of great importance. Bumblebees and honeybees are normally the most numerous visitors to the blossoms and are believed to account for most of the pollination. The flowers are also visited by solitary bees, such as mining bees (*Andrena* species) and the red mason bee (*Osmia rufa*). Whether bumblebees predominate or not depends upon the surroundings. If these consist mainly of arable land, which is unsuited for the nesting of wild bees, honeybees may be the more frequent visitors, but if rough land, such as commons, numerous hedgerows or woods prevail, providing good breeding conditions for bumblebees, they are liable to outnumber the honeybee visitors.

Like the fruits themselves, the blossoms of plums exhibit a good deal of variation in size among different varieties. Some varieties also flower much earlier than others. The cherry plum or myrobalan (*Prunus cerasifera*) (see cherry plum), not really a plum in the strict sense, is the first to flower and is generally ahead of the others by many weeks. The domestic plum, wild plum and damson are closely related and are all members of the same species. Among the domestic plums, 'Angelina Burdett', 'Jefferson' and 'Warwickshire Drooper' flower early. Late flowering kinds include 'Belle de Louvain' and 'Marjorie's Seedling'. Intermediate in flowering are 'Victoria', 'Czar', 'Pershore', and many of the gages. There is generally a difference of about three weeks between the blossoming of the earliest and the late varieties. The duration of flowering is usually 2–3 weeks or rather more, depending on weather conditions, but varieties vary in this respect also.

In most years, early to mid April finds most varieties in flower. Blossoms appear with the leaves and the life of each individual flower, from the opening of the bud until the petals fall, is about a week. The blossoms of some varieties of plum have more scent than others. Honeybees generally show a preference for plum blossom over that of pear and currant when able to exercise a choice.

Poached egg, see meadow-foam

Poplar — *Populus* species

Family:	**Salicaceae**
Flowering:	**March to April**
Cultivation:	**deciduous large tree**
Honey:	**no**
Honeybees:	|||||
ST Bumblebees:	—
LT Bumblebees:	—
Solitary Bees:	—

Poplars are sometimes useful for early pollen. The half dozen or so different kinds that are commonly to be seen produce their catkins in March or April. These may be conspicuous on account of their red or purple anthers. In the balsam poplars, such as the western balsam poplar (*Populus trichocarpa*) from western North America, the buds are covered with a fragrant balsamic gum. Honeybees have been observed buzzing round the trees and collecting it, presumably for use as propolis, which is a resinous mixture that honeybees use to seal small gaps in a hive and for various other purposes.

Poppy — *Papaver* species

Both wild and garden poppies produce pollen in abundance. This is generally very dark coloured and seems to be much to the liking of honeybees and bumblebees, for they visit the red flowers in large numbers, even when many other sources of pollen are available. After visiting poppies, the pollen loads on the bees' hind legs are almost black. In the large single flowers of the Oriental poppy (*Papaver orientale*), it is not unusual to see three or four honeybees together, all revelling in the rich store of pollen. The flowers are visited for pollen also by mining bees (*Andrena* and *Halictus* species). The poppy mason bee (*Hoplitis papaveris*) lines its nest with pieces of poppy petals. It occurs across much of Europe, but not in the British Isles. Pollen is the main reward in the non-red poppies as well and these can be at least as valuable to bees (see Californian poppy). The Welsh poppy (*Meconopsis cambrica*) produces large amounts of pollen over a particularly long flowering period and is particularly useful to solitary bees.

There seems to be some evidence that a certain amount of nectar may also be available from poppies at times, particularly the common poppy (*Papaver rhoeas*). Various reports have suggested that the poppy may have a narcotising or stupefying effect on bees. Last century, one German observer noticed that 90% of his honeybees returning with pollen loads from the common poppy had difficulty in finding the entrance of their hive. As the poppy is the source of opium and various narcotic principles this may not be surprising, but further investigation is needed to confirm this.

Family:	**Papaveraceae**
Flowering:	**May to October**
Cultivation:	**annual or perennial herb**
Honey:	**no**
Honeybees:	||||| |||||
ST Bumblebees:	||||| |||||
LT Bumblebees:	|||||
Solitary Bees:	||||| |||||

Above:
Pollen grain of common poppy (Papaver rhoeas) (25 µm)

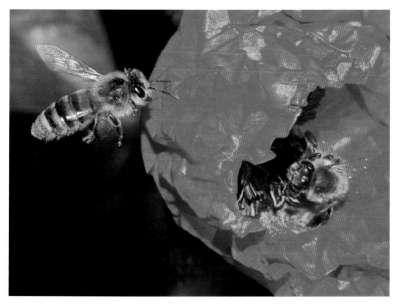

Above:
A bee dusted thickly with pollen on a poppy (Papaver species)
(photo: J. Craig)
Left:
Honeybees on common poppy (Papaver rhoeas)
(photo: N. W. Owens)

P

Plum — Poppy

Portugal laurel, see cherry laurel

Potentilla — *Potentilla* species

Family:	Rosaceae
Flowering:	June to September
Cultivation:	perennial herb or deciduous small shrub
Honey:	no
Honeybees:	‖‖‖
ST Bumblebees:	‖‖‖
LT Bumblebees:	—
Solitary Bees:	‖‖‖

Above:
Pollen grain of shrubby cinquefoil
(Potentilla fruticosa) *(19 μm)*
Right:
Shrubby cinquefoil flower (Potentilla
fruticosa)
(photo: M. A. Kirk)
Far right:
Ashy mining bee (Andrena cineraria) *on*
potentilla (Potentilla *species)*
(photo: T. C. Ings)

Some of the potentillas or cinquefoils, both wild and cultivated, are visited by bees for nectar. There are more than a dozen in the British Isles flora. One of the best known is the silverweed (*Potentilla anserina*), a creeping plant with silvery leaves and yellow flowers that occurs more or less everywhere. Bees visit the flowers at times, but not in large numbers. The same applies to the shrubby cinquefoil (*Potentilla fruticosa*), a rare plant in the wild, but grown in gardens.

A small darkish mining bee (*Andrena tarsata*) collects pollen only from tormentil (*Potentilla erecta*) and so is dependent on it. It inhabits heaths and moors in scattered locations across the British Isles. It is scarce, but not as scarce as a cuckoo bee (*Nomada roberjeotiana*) that lays eggs in its nest and also visits flowers of tormentil. This bee is now mainly restricted to a few sites in southern England. The hind part of its body is reddish brown with yellow markings.

Pride of India — *Koelreuteria paniculata*

Family:	Sapindaceae
Flowering:	July to August
Cultivation:	deciduous medium tree
Honey:	no
Honeybees:	‖‖‖ ‖‖‖
ST Bumblebees:	‖‖‖
LT Bumblebees:	—
Solitary Bees:	—

This tree from China is not often seen in cultivation. It produces panicles or loose bunches of yellow flowers at the ends of the branches in July and August and these may be heavily worked for nectar by honeybees.

Primrose — *Primula vulgaris*

Right:
Primrose flower (Primula vulgaris)
(photo: M. A. Kirk)
Far right:
Mining bee (Andrena bicolor) *on primrose*
(Primula vulgaris)
(photo T. C. Ings)

The primrose is in flower early in the season and can provide a useful nectar source, particularly for early emerging queen bumblebees. It is a favourite of the common carder bee (*Bombus pascuorum*). The flowers are visited by solitary bees, such as the hairy-footed flower bee (*Anthophora plumipes*). These large, furry bees look rather like bumblebees, but they have a darting flight. The females are black and the males are brown. They are absent from Scotland and Ireland. There have been reports that honeybees visit primroses, but it is doubtful whether they are of any value, certainly not for nectar.

The large bee fly (*Bombylius major*) visits primrose flowers and is easily mistaken for a brown bumblebee or flower bee. It can be distinguished by the hovering flight and the dark band along the front edge of the wings.

Family:	Primulaceae
Flowering:	December to May
Cultivation:	perennial herb
Honey:	no
Honeybees:	—
ST Bumblebees:	‖‖‖
LT Bumblebees:	‖‖‖
Solitary Bees:	‖‖‖

Privet — *Ligustrum ovalifolium*

The flowers of privet yield nectar freely and this is readily collected by honeybees and bumblebees. Unfortunately, it produces a strong-flavoured, bitter honey, thick and dark coloured, which will spoil any other honey with which it is mixed. This is a problem for the beekeeper, but not for the honeybee. However, privet in flower is seldom sufficiently abundant for this to occur and in most districts it is more useful than not to the beekeeper. Overgrown or neglected privet hedges, bearing a profusion of blossom, are far more useful than neatly clipped ones. They are generally viewed with favour by urban beekeepers, especially as they provide food for bees at a time when limes are over and there is little else.

The wild privet (*Ligustrum vulgare*) is found across most of the British Isles in hedgerows and scrub, flowering usually in June and July. As a hedge plant it has been largely superseded by garden privet (*Ligustrum ovalifolium*), which retains its leaves better. This privet flowers later, in August and September, when allowed to do so and not regularly trimmed.

The clusters of white flowers of privet have a heavy penetrating odour that some find rather objectionable. The flower-tubes are short and honeybees and short-tongued bumblebees have no difficulty in getting at the nectar. Sometimes nectar secretion is so copious overnight as to reach half-way up the flower-tube in the morning.

Other privets are sometimes cultivated as ornamental shrubs. Of these, Chinese privet (*Ligustrum sinense*) is one of the most handsome, with its large feathery masses of bloom in June and July. These are frequently covered with honeybees. Even when the limes are in flower at Kew Gardens, honeybees have been observed continuing to work the blossoms.

Family:	Oleaceae
Flowering:	August to September
Cultivation:	evergreen large shrub
Honey:	no
Honeybees:	‖‖‖ ‖‖‖
ST Bumblebees:	‖‖‖ ‖‖‖
LT Bumblebees:	‖‖‖ ‖‖‖
Solitary Bees:	‖‖‖

Above:
Flowers of wild privet (Ligustrum vulgare)
(*photo: W. D. J. Kirk*)

Pumpkin, see gourd

P

Portugal laurel — Pumpkin

Purple loosestrife — *Lythrum salicaria*

Family:	**Lythraceae**
Flowering:	**June to August**
Cultivation:	**perennial herb**
Honey:	**no**
Honeybees:	‖‖‖ ‖‖‖
ST Bumblebees:	‖‖‖
LT Bumblebees:	‖‖‖ ‖‖‖
Solitary Bees:	‖‖‖

The purple loosestrife is one of the most handsome of British Isles wild plants and is to be seen in most parts, especially where soil conditions are moist, as on the edges of pools, streams and ditches. In such situations it often forms a vivid patch of colour on the landscape. It grows to 1.5 m in height with flowering spikes about 30 cm long bearing rich purple-red flowers from June to August. The flowers, much studied by Charles Darwin, are of interest in that the length of stamens and styles and the size of the pollen varies between plants. The pollen may be yellow or greenish with large or small individual grains.

Purple loosestrife is a good bee plant and supplies nectar and pollen in quantity. Unfortunately, it is seldom sufficiently abundant for honey surplus in the British Isles, but the honey is said to be dark with a strong flavour. Bumblebees, particularly the common carder bee (*Bombus pascuorum*), visit the flowers.

The plant is common in most parts of Europe. It has naturalised in many other countries and it is considered an invasive weed in North America and New Zealand. There are many garden forms of it with flower spikes larger and of a different shade. These are equally attractive to bees.

Yellow loosestrife (*Lysimachia vulgaris*) is an unrelated species, despite the similar name (see separate entry).

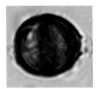

Above:
Pollen grain of purple loosestrife (Lythrum salicaria) *(28 μm)*
Right:
Purple loosestrife flower (Lythrum salicaria)
Far right:
Honeybee on purple loosestrife (Lythrum salicaria)
(photos: W. D. J. Kirk)

Purple ragwort — *Senecio elegans*

Family:	**Asteraceae**
Flowering:	**May to July**
Cultivation:	**annual herb**
Honey:	**no**
Honeybees:	‖‖‖ ‖‖‖
ST Bumblebees:	‖‖‖ ‖‖‖
LT Bumblebees:	‖‖‖ ‖‖‖
Solitary Bees:	‖‖‖ ‖‖‖

This hardy South African annual is grown from seed and looks best in a mass planting, although it can look rather weedy. The plants grow about 30 cm tall and are covered in daisy-like purple flowers with a yellow centre. They attract bees for nectar and pollen and are generally in flower from May until July if sown at intervals. It is related to ragwort (see separate entry).

Queen Anne's thimble, see gilia

Quince — *Cydonia oblonga*

The quince, like the medlar, is one of those hardy fruits that cannot claim wide popularity in the British Isles and is more extensively grown in some warmer countries where they fruit more reliably. It reached this country from southern Europe, where it is naturalised, but its real origin is in Asia. The quince has solitary flowers. These are similar in structure to those of the apple and pear, but are larger and appear later. They are a source of nectar and pollen for bees. The so-called Japanese quince or japonica (*Chaenomeles speciosa*) is a closely related plant grown for ornamental purposes (see Japanese quince).

Family:	**Rosaceae**
Flowering:	**May**
Cultivation:	**small deciduous tree**
Honey:	**no**
Honeybees:	‖‖‖
ST Bumblebees:	‖‖‖
LT Bumblebees:	‖‖‖
Solitary Bees:	‖‖‖

Radish — *Raphanus* species

When left neglected in the vegetable garden, the flowers of the garden radish (*Raphanus sativus*) attract bees for nectar and pollen. The same species, under the name 'fodder radish', can also be grown as a fodder crop, cover crop, catch crop or green manure and so will usually reach the flowering stage and be of use to bees. It is sometimes included in seed mixes designed to benefit farmland birds and insects. Where this has been done in northern Scotland, the flowers have attracted the great yellow bumblebee (*Bombus distinguendus*). This scarce species persists in coastal northern Scotland but is declining rapidly. It also visits other flowers, such as red clover (see separate entry).

Family:	**Brassicaceae**
Flowering:	**June to July**
Cultivation:	**annual to perennial herb**
Honey:	**no**
Honeybees:	‖‖‖ ‖‖‖ ‖‖‖
ST Bumblebees:	‖‖‖ ‖‖‖ ‖‖‖
LT Bumblebees:	‖‖‖ ‖‖‖ ‖‖‖
Solitary Bees:	‖‖‖ ‖‖

The wild radish or white charlock (*Raphanus raphanistrum*) is also of importance to bees. It is a weed in arable land on all types of soil throughout the British Isles. It grows about 60 cm high and the flowers are yellow or white and distinctly veined. The plant is often confused with charlock (see separate entry), which it resembles, but may be distinguished by the strong indentations of the seed pod between the seeds. The roots smell like radish but are more pungent. As a bee plant it is probably of about the same value as charlock and useful to the beekeeper when present in quantity. The honey is also believed to be similar and light in colour.

A very rare mining bee (*Andrena nigrospina*) collects pollen from wild radish and closely related species. It is found at only a few sites in central and southern England.

Above:
Pollen grain of garden radish (Raphanus sativus) *(21 μm)*
Left:
Flowers of sea radish (Raphanus raphanistrum *subspecies* maritimus)*, which is a form of wild radish*
(photo: J. P. Early)

R

Purple loosestrife — Radish

Ragged robin — *Silene flos-cuculi*

Family:	**Caryophyllaceae**
Flowering:	**May to August**
Cultivation:	**perennial herb**
Honey:	**no**
Honeybees:	‖‖
ST Bumblebees:	‖‖
LT Bumblebees:	‖‖
Solitary Bees:	—

Right:
Ragged robin flower (Silene flos-cuculi)
(photo: J. P. Early)
Far right:
Worker garden bumblebee (Bombus hortorum) *on ragged robin* (Silene flos-cuculi)
(photo: L. Hebdon)

Bees visit the ragged pink flowers of this declining wild plant. Nectar is secreted at the base of the stamens, which is at the end of a long (9 mm) flower-tube and so is only accessible to bees with long tongues. The pollen is near the mouth of the tube and so can also be reached by bees with short tongues.

Ragwort — *Senecio jacobaea*

Family:	**Asteraceae**
Flowering:	**June to October**
Cultivation:	**biennial to perennial herb**
Honey:	**no**
Honeybees:	‖‖
ST Bumblebees:	‖‖ ‖‖
LT Bumblebees:	‖‖
Solitary Bees:	‖‖ ‖‖ ‖‖

Above:
Male red-tailed bumblebee (Bombus lapidarius) *visiting ragwort* (Senecio jacobaea)
(photo: J. Craig)

Ragwort is frequently a troublesome weed in the British Isles, as well as in many other countries, so should not be encouraged. Landowners can be required to control its growth. It is common in waste places and meadows and may be anything from 0.3–1.5 m high. With its masses of yellow flowers, produced any time from June to October, it may be a striking feature of the landscape, particularly on light, medium or calcareous soils.

The plant is toxic to grazing animals, but the effects are most significant for horses, which suffer irreversible liver damage and can die. Usually animals avoid feeding on the plant, but they may turn to it when it dominates or little other food is available. The whole plant has a strong smell, which accounts for the name 'stinking Willie' applied to it in Scotland.

There has been much controversy in relation to the plant; its advantages and disadvantages have even been debated in the Houses of Parliament. In contrast to the damaging effects for grazing animals, ragwort is beneficial to many species of bee and it is a prolific source of nectar and pollen, particularly late in the season when other sources are over. Unfortunately, the honey, like the plant, is strong flavoured, almost bitter in fact, and liable to spoil other honey if present in any quantity. This does not detract in any way from its usefulness for the honeybees' own consumption and for winter stores. The honey is deep yellow in colour, the aroma and flavour being characteristic and strong, although the unpleasant odour goes after a few months when the honey has granulated. When bees work this plant the wax produced is also a deep yellow, probably stained from the oil coating the deep yellow pollen. When prolonged drought causes a shortage of nectar from other plants, ragwort honey may be stored in quantity, if the plant is prevalent, because it is fairly drought resistant and so continues to produce nectar. Ragwort is not a major source of honey, but it may make a small contribution to honey in many areas.

Ragwort probably receives more visits from bumblebees than honeybees, particularly short-tongued bumblebees such as the red-tailed bumblebee (*Bombus lapidarius*). Ragwort is one of the plants most visited by solitary bees. These include mining bees (*Andrena*, *Colletes* and *Lasioglossum* species), leafcutter bees (*Megachile* species) and cuckoo bees (*Epeolus*, *Nomada* and *Stelis* species). Some mining bees (*Colletes daviesanus* and *Colletes fodiens*) particularly visit the flowers of ragwort for pollen. They can be recognised by the pale whitish stripes across the body. The hairy-legged mining bee (*Dasypoda hirtipes*) is closely associated with ragwort. This scarce bee is found in heathland and sandy places near the coast in Wales and southern England. The female has distinctive long golden hairs on its hind legs and is thought by some to be one of the most beautiful bees in the British Isles.

Oxford ragwort (*Senecio squalidus*) is a similar but more elegant plant that originated from southern Europe and is now very common across much of the British Isles. It flowers from April to November and similarly attracts bees for nectar and pollen.

Above:
Cuckoo bee (Nomada species) on Oxford ragwort (Senecio squalidus)
(photo: T. C. Ings)

Raspberry — *Rubus idaeus*

Where raspberries are cultivated on a large scale for market they provide valuable bee forage, for the flowers give a high yield of nectar. Furthermore, flowering generally takes place at a most opportune time – in a gap between the blossoming of fruit trees and the first appearance of white clover. Raspberries have long been grown on a field scale in Scotland where they thrive and claim more attention than they do further south, where there is a wider range of fruits available for cultivation. Bees are the main pollinators of the crop and are important to raise the quantity and quality of the harvested fruit. Hives of honeybees or colonies of bumblebees (*Bombus terrestris*) can be brought to the crop during flowering and are widely used to boost yields. Studies have shown that bumblebees are more effective pollinators of raspberry than honeybees. The wild raspberry is also more common in the north than the south, and is the progenitor of the cultivated sorts, which it closely resembles. However, its fruits are smaller and more prone to be dry. The plant may often be seen thriving in places where fires have been. Many of the so-called wild raspberries are the offspring of cultivated kinds through seed being spread by birds.

Raspberry flowers are mostly pendulous and the nectar is well protected from rain. Bees are able to work them when those of other plants have been spoiled by rain and they visit them even in dull weather. The nectar is easily available to honeybees and short-tongued bumblebees and is secreted within the stamen circle at the base of the flower. It first appears as drops and if not removed by insects soon covers the base of the flower. Raspberry flowers are undoubtedly exceptionally attractive to honeybees and bumblebees. Besides nectar, masses of white pollen are sometimes collected from them. The honey from raspberry is light in colour, with a delicate flavour and granulates rapidly. Some consider it superior to any

Family:	**Rosaceae**
Flowering:	**June to August**
Cultivation:	**perennial root with biennial stems**
Honey:	**yes**
Honeybees:	||||| ||||| |||||
ST Bumblebees:	||||| ||||| |||||
LT Bumblebees:	||||| |||||
Solitary Bees:	|||||

Above:
Pollen grain of raspberry (Rubus idaeus) (26 μm)
Below:
Worker early bumblebee (Bombus pratorum) on raspberry (Rubus idaeus)
(photo: T. C. Ings)

Above:
Worker buff-tailed bumblebee (Bombus terrestris) *on raspberry* (Rubus idaeus)
(photo: T. C. Ings)

Family:	**Orobanchaceae**
Flowering:	**June to September**
Cultivation:	**annual herb**
Honey:	**no**
Honeybees:	—
ST Bumblebees:	||||| |||||
LT Bumblebees:	||||| ||||| |||||
Solitary Bees:	||||| |||||

other table honey, with an exquisite flavour and a delicious comb. The honeybee is unable to puncture the skins of fruits like plums, cherries, and grapes, for they are too tough for its jaws. This does not apply in the case of the raspberry, however, which has a very delicate skin. Not infrequently honeybees collect the sweet juice from ripe and overripe raspberries. This is considered to be the source of the so-called red honey that is reported by beekeepers from time to time.

The flowers are much visited by short-tongued bumblebees, such as the buff-tailed bumblebee (*Bombus terrestris*), the early bumblebee (*Bombus pratorum*) and the rapidly spreading tree bumblebee (*Bombus hypnorum*). Red mason bees (*Osmia rufa*) visit the flowers as well as the blossom of other fruit.

The dewberry (*Rubus caesius*), other species of *Rubus* and the hybrid berries that are often cultivated are also attractive to bees, but are not usually available in any quantity.

Red bartsia — *Odontites vernus*

This wild plant is partially parasitic on the roots of grasses. The upright leaf stems grow to a height of 50 cm and bear a series of pinkish-purple tubular flowers. The flowers are much visited by bumblebees with moderately long tongues, such as the red-shanked carder bee (*Bombus ruderarius*), the moss carder bee (*Bombus muscorum*) and the brown-banded carder bee (*Bombus humilis*). A rare species, the shrill carder bee (*Bombus sylvarum*), now restricted to just a few areas in southern England, south Wales and southern Ireland, also visits it.

A mining bee (*Melitta tricincta*) collects pollen only from red bartsia and so is dependent on it. Females collect pollen for their nests and the males fly around the flowers looking for mates. The bee is restricted to southern England, particularly areas with chalky soils.

Right:
Mining bee (Melitta tricincta) *on red bartsia* (Odontites vernus)
(photo: T. C. Ings)

Red campion — *Silene dioica*

This native plant has pink to red flowers and is common in woods and hedgerows. It is often planted in wild gardens where it grows well in shade. The flower-tube is about 13–15 mm long, which restricts access to the nectar from the front to only long-tongued bees, such as the garden bumblebee (*Bombus hortorum*). Short-tongued bumblebees poke holes in the base of the flower-tube and rob the nectar. Although honeybees rarely visit the flowers, they can secondarily rob the nectar through the holes made by short-tongued bumblebees. Red campion plants either have male flowers with pollen or female flowers without pollen, which means that bees can only collect pollen from the male flowers.

The long-horned bee (*Eucera longicornis*), which is a long-tongued solitary bee, has been seen visiting red campion. It also favours meadow vetchling (see vetchling). This large, dark brown bee has remarkably long antennae in the male. It is found in southern Britain and can be locally common, but is declining rapidly.

Family:	**Caryophyllaceae**
Flowering:	**May to June**
Cultivation:	**perennial herb**
Honey:	**no**
Honeybees:	—
ST Bumblebees:	|||||
LT Bumblebees:	||||| |||||
Solitary Bees:	|||||

Above:
Garden bumblebee (Bombus hortorum) *on red campion* (Silene dioica)
(photo: T. C. Ings)

Redcurrant, see currant

Red clover — *Trifolium pratense*

Like white clover, this species occurs very freely in the wild and is used in agriculture. The long flower-tubes and abundant production of nectar make it an excellent plant for long-tongued bumblebees, such as the common carder bee (*Bombus pascuorum*) and the garden bumblebee (*Bombus hortorum*). Some of the rarest bumblebees are long-tongued and so are helped by red clover, such as the great yellow bumblebee (*Bombus distinguendus*) in northern Scotland and the shrill carder bee (*Bombus sylvarum*) in southern England, Wales and Ireland. Red clover has been specially grown at Dungeness in Kent to aid the reintroduction of the short-haired bumblebee (*Bombus subterraneus*).

Family:	**Fabaceae**
Flowering:	**May to September**
Cultivation:	**perennial herb**
Honey:	**no**
Honeybees:	||||| |||||
ST Bumblebees:	||||| |||||
LT Bumblebees:	||||| ||||| |||||
Solitary Bees:	|||||

Above:
Pollen grain of red clover (Trifolium pratense) *(39 μm)*

The flowers are red or purplish in colour, but otherwise the flower-heads look very similar to those of white clover. The plant may be distinguished when not in flower by the white 'horse-shoe' mark on the upper surface of the leaf. There are many varieties of red clover used in agriculture. They are employed in pasture seed mixtures of various kinds and may be sown as a sole crop for cutting for silage or for grazing. They fall into three groups: (1) early or medium flowering; (2) late flowering or single-cut red clover; and (3) the wild or indigenous type. The early flowering sorts bloom from 2–4 weeks sooner than the late flowering.

It is not nearly such a good honey plant as white clover for honeybees and it is only under special or exceptional conditions that its longer flowers are able to be worked for nectar. When honey has been obtained from red clover it has usually been from the second crop, i.e. the crop arising after the first crop has been cut. The reason given for this in the past has been that the flowers of the second or third crop are smaller and have shorter

R

Red bartsia — Red clover

Top:
Red clover flowers (Trifolium pratense)
(photo: W. D. J. Kirk)
Above:
Common carder bee (Bombus pascuorum)
on red clover (Trifolium pratense)
(photo: T. C. Ings)

flower-tubes, which enables honeybees to reach the nectar. This theory has, however, been discredited as a result of careful measurements made of the flower size of first and second crop red clover. It has been shown that there is really very little difference in tube length, the small reduction being insufficient to account for the bees' ability to reach the nectar. The explanation now put forward is that the bee exploits capillary action to extract the nectar when there is enough to rise appreciably in the flower tube. The nectar forms a meniscus in the flower tube, so that it stands higher against the side of the tube formed by the stamens in the centre of the flower. Once this reaches a sufficiently high level for the honeybee to reach it with the tip of the tongue the bee is able to extract all the nectar. If, however, the nectar rises a certain amount but remains just out of reach of the bee, it is unable to obtain any of it. In other words, if the flower holds sufficient nectar for the honeybee to reach it she will be able to empty the flower, but will get nothing more from that flower until such time as the nectar again rises sufficiently high for her to reach the top of it. From this it is clear that while long-tongued bumblebees are able to get nectar from red clover, however little may be secreted, it is only when secretion is heavy that the honeybee is able to work the flowers for nectar. Since the average length of flower-tube is 9.6 mm and the average honeybee is estimated to be able to reach 7.9 mm, the nectar must rise 1.7 mm or more to become available. In many areas, conditions for nectar secretion are quite likely to be more favourable later in the year when second or third crop red clover is in flower. Even early first crops of red clover may be worked for nectar by honeybees under favourable conditions and they may also visit the flowers for pollen only.

As the actual amount of nectar secreted by the red clover flower is greater than that from either of the other two commonly cultivated clovers in the British Isles (white clover and alsike clover) (see separate entries), it is unfortunate that the honeybee cannot take full advantage of it. Nevertheless, red clover may be a more important minor source of nectar than is generally supposed by beekeepers. When honey is obtained from red clover it is of the same high quality and has the same general characteristics as that of white clover, but may granulate more quickly.

Red dead-nettle, see dead-nettle

Rhododendron — *Rhododendron ponticum*

Family:	Ericaceae
Flowering:	May to June
Cultivation:	evergreen medium shrub
Honey:	no
Honeybees:	—
ST Bumblebees:	||||| ||||| |||||
LT Bumblebees:	||||| ||||| |||||
Solitary Bees:	—

The common purple-flowered rhododendron that is naturalised and occurs so freely throughout the British Isles, often in woods, is primarily a bumblebee plant. Both short-tongued and long-tongued species visit the flowers. Queens and workers of the early bumblebee (*Bombus pratorum*) are frequently seen on rhododendrons in gardens and the white-tailed bumblebee (*Bombus lucorum*) and the bilberry bumblebee (*Bombus monticola*) are also often frequent. The same applies to many of the garden varieties of rhododendron.

Honeybees rarely visit the flowers of rhododendron in the British Isles. This cannot be due to difficulty in reaching the nectar because short-tongued bumblebees have no problems and the pollen is easily available at the front of the flower. However, the nectar and pollen of rhododendron contain a toxin called grayanotoxin and this is toxic to honeybees but not bumblebees in the British Isles. It is likely that honeybees avoid the flowers for this reason.

However, there is a different subspecies of honeybee in northeast Turkey, known as the Caucasian honeybee (*Apis mellifera caucasica*) that forages from rhododendron and does not appear to be affected. Honey from colonies that collect nectar predominantly from *Rhododendron ponticum* can contain levels of toxin high enough to affect the people that consume it. A much-quoted historical example from 401 BC (described in Xenophon's Anabasis) concerns an army of Greek mercenaries travelling near what is now Trabzon on the Black Sea coast of Turkey. They were quartered in villages that contained astonishing numbers of beehives and after eating small quantities of honey behaved as if they were mad or violently drunk for about a day. They all recovered completely without any of them dying. This is thought to have been rhododendron honey, because rhododendron honey from the Black Sea region of Turkey still has the same properties today. It is popularly known as 'mad honey' (deli bal in Turkish) and is used as an alternative medicine. The honey can be recognised easily because it produces a burning feeling in the throat when eaten. Severe intoxication can lead to heart problems, but people nearly always recover within hours. Since honeybees in the British Isles rarely visit rhododendron, they will not collect enough nectar to affect the honey and the presence of rhododendrons is not a cause for concern.

It should be noted that the common rhododendron (*Rhododendron ponticum*) and hybrids with *Rhododendrom maximum* are invasive non-native species in the UK. The Wildlife and Countryside Act 1981 (Variation of Schedule 9) (England and Wales) Order 2010 prohibits planting or causing them to grow in the wild.

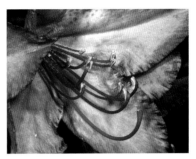

Above:
Centre of a rhododendron flower
(Rhododendron *species*)
(photo: W. D. J. Kirk)

R

Red dead-nettle — Rhododendron

Left:
*Queen red-tailed bumblebee (*Bombus lapidarius*) on rhododendron*
(Rhododendron *species*)
(photo: T. C. Ings)

Images over page
Left (p.224):
*Male red mason bee (*Osmia rufa*) on rhododendron* (Rhododendron *species*)
(photo: T. C. Ings)
Right (p.225):
*Common carder bee (*Bombus pascuorum*) on rhododendron* (Rhododendron *species*)
(photo: J. Craig)

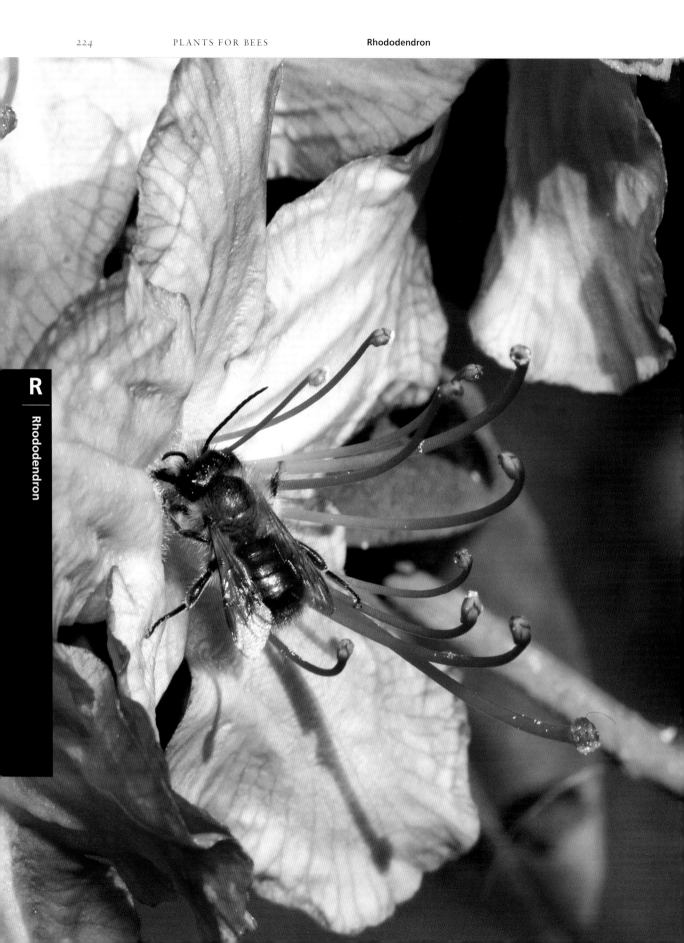

R

Rhododendron

Rock beauty — *Petrocallis pyrenaica*

Family:	**Brassicaceae**
Flowering:	**April**
Cultivation:	**perennial herb**
Honey:	**no**
Honeybees:	|||||
ST Bumblebees:	|||||
LT Bumblebees:	|||||
Solitary Bees:	|||||

This handsome little alpine plant with its cushions of leaves 5–8 cm high is rather similar to a saxifrage. It bears pale lilac, sweet-scented flowers in April, which yield nectar and pollen in spring and are occasionally visited by bees of a wide range of species.

Rock-cress, see arabis

Rock rose — *Helianthemum* species

Family:	**Cistaceae**
Flowering:	**May to July**
Cultivation:	**evergreen dwarf shrub**
Honey:	**no**
Honeybees:	||||| |||||
ST Bumblebees:	||||| |||||
LT Bumblebees:	|||||
Solitary Bees:	||||| |||||

The name rock rose is also used for species of *Cistus* (see cistus). Both the wild and the garden rock roses may attract bees in large numbers in bright sunny weather – the only time that the flowers are open in fact. The wild kinds are most common on chalk hills and on cliffs and hillsides near the sea. In these situations their yellow flowers may appear in great profusion from May until July. Each flower bears numerous stamens and is a source of much pollen, which is the main reason that bees visit the flowers. This applies also to the garden rock roses with their bright flowers of many colours, which are often favoured for rock gardens and stony slopes. The flowers may only last a morning, so the best time to see bees visiting these flowers is early on a warm, sunny day. Mining bees (*Andrena* species) and mason bees (*Osmia* species) are frequent visitors for pollen.

Right:
*Worker common carder bee (*Bombus pascuorum*) collecting pollen on rock rose (*Helianthemum nummularium* 'Georgeham')*
(photo: W. D. J. Kirk)
Far right:
*Pollen grain of common rock rose (*Helianthemum nummularium*) (38 μm)*

Rose — *Rosa* species

Family:	**Rosaceae**
Flowering:	**June to July**
Cultivation:	**deciduous small shrub**
Honey:	**no**
Honeybees:	|||||
ST Bumblebees:	||||| |||||
LT Bumblebees:	|||||
Solitary Bees:	|||||

The numerous wild roses that beautify the countryside from June onwards yield pollen in abundance and this is often collected by bees. Roses do not appear to be a useful source of nectar, at least in so far as conditions in the British Isles are concerned. The same applies to the single-flowered garden roses, which are also visited by bees. The pollen of the rose is very like that of the apple and is gathered greedily by bees at times. It should be noted that very many garden varieties of rose are double and their flowers are of no benefit to bees.

Some roses of the type that that have many yellow stamens visible in the centre, such as the shrub rose *Rosa moyesii*, are buzz pollinated. The pollen is only released from the anthers when it is vibrated. Bumblebees and some solitary bees can buzz pollinate and so can collect pollen much more efficiently than honeybees. The buzz only lasts about a second and is not the same as the hum that is produced when bumblebees fly. They only produce the special buzz on flowers that can be buzz pollinated, such as kiwifruit, tomato and borage (see tomato and borage). Worker buff-tailed bumblebees (*Bombus terrestris*) are frequent visitors, curling their bodies around the bunch of stamens.

Leafcutter bees, such as the patchwork leafcutter bee (*Megachile centuncularis*), line their nests with discs, about a centimetre across, cut from soft leaves. Rose leaves are particularly favoured and it is easy to see where the females have used their mouthparts to cut the discs neatly from the edges of the leaves. This species flies from May to the end of August and is commonest in England and Wales. The vine weevil, which is a pest beetle, sometimes eats pieces from rose leaves, but these are smaller and less regularly shaped.

It should be noted that the Japanese rose (*Rosa rugosa*) is an invasive non-native species in the UK. The Wildlife and Countryside Act 1981 (Variation of Schedule 9) (England and Wales) Order 2010 prohibits planting or causing it to grow in the wild.

Above:
Pollen grain of a shrub rose (Rosa moyesii)
(34 μm)

Far left:
Worker buff-tailed bumblebee (Bombus terrestris) *buzz pollinating a shrub rose* (Rosa moyesii)
(photo: W. D. J. Kirk)
Left:
Rose leaves (Rosa *species*) *with discs removed by a leafcutter bee* (Megachile *species*)
(photo: N. W. Owens)

Rosebay willowherb — *Chamerion angustifolium*

The rosebay willowherb is one of the best of the wild bee plants of the British Isles and not infrequently yields surplus honey to beekeepers who are fortunate enough to be in areas where extensive stands of the plant exist. The main bumblebee visitors are the buff-tailed bumblebee (*Bombus terrestris*), the white-tailed bumblebee (*Bombus lucorum*) and the common carder bee (*Bombus pascuorum*). Solitary bees also visit, including mining bees (*Lasioglossum* species).

It is one of the most conspicuous and handsome of wild plants, with its spikes of large pink flowers that appear from July onwards, and a wide expanse of it on the landscape is always a pretty sight. It is frequently among the first plants to appear where fires have been, hence the name fireweed that is often applied to it. Where heath or woodland fires have taken place it often grows in great profusion. After the Second World War, it was one of the first plants to appear on bombed sites in the heart of London, the seeds being extremely light and easily carried

Family:	Onagraceae
Flowering:	July to September
Cultivation:	perennial herb
Honey:	yes
Honeybees:	||||| ||||| |||||
ST Bumblebees:	||||| ||||| |||||
LT Bumblebees:	||||| ||||| |||||
Solitary Bees:	|||||

R

Rock beauty — Rosebay willowherb

Top:
Pollen grain of rosebay willowherb
(Chamerion angustifolium) (72 μm)
Above:
Rosebay willowherb flower (Chamerion
angustifolium)
(photos: M. A. Kirk)

Family:	**Lamiaceae**
Flowering:	**April to June**
Cultivation:	**evergreen dwarf to medium shrub**
Honey:	**no**
Honeybees:	||||| |||||
ST Bumblebees:	||||| |||||
LT Bumblebees:	||||| |||||
Solitary Bees:	||||| |||||

many kilometres by the wind. Where woodland has been cut down it may also be very common for a year or two.

Unfortunately, the willowherb does not remain a dominant plant but is ousted by other plants in time. It is therefore only of passing value in most localities. The name willowherb is due to the resemblance of the plant, before flowering, to a young willow shoot, the leaves being very similar. In parts of Canada, where willowherb has covered extensive tracts of country in the past, honey yields of 45 kg (100 lb) per hive have been obtained.

In the British Isles, the willowherb is widespread and patches of it are a common sight along roadsides, on waste ground and in woodland clearings. As well as spreading by seed, its creeping underground stems, which may ramify up to 10 m, enable it to increase rapidly and it can become a troublesome weed in gardens. The first flowers to open are at the bottom of the flowering spike. By the time those at the top are ready to open, seed pods will have ripened at the bottom and other subsidiary flowering shoots have been formed, so it has a long flowering season and is capable of giving a prolonged supply of nectar and pollen where sufficiently abundant. When it occurs on burned-over heathland it is sometimes looked upon as a nuisance by beekeepers who have taken hives to the heather, as its presence is likely to result in a blended rather than a true heather honey, and it is pure heather honey that always commands the highest price. The honey from willowherb is very pale in colour, sometimes water white and of good density but without any very distinctive flavour. Some consider it almost flavourless although very sweet. It is valuable for blending with dark and strong-flavoured honeys. Granulation takes place with a fine grain. Wax or comb built while bees are working willowherb is very pale in colour.

Pollen is produced abundantly by willowherb and is always distinctive when collected by bees, owing to its blue-green colour. The pollen grains are well above average in size and are usually bound together by sticky threads of viscin.

Other wild species attract bees, but are not usually sufficiently common to interest the beekeeper. The great willowherb (*Epilobium hirsutum*) is sometimes prevalent in patches by streams and ditches and may be visited for nectar and pollen.

Rosemary — *Rosmarinus officinalis*

The pale mauve flowers of this popular garden plant are much loved by honeybees, which crowd over them. Bumblebees also visit, particularly the common carder bee (*Bombus pascuorum*). The shrub is a native of the Mediterranean region and is not hardy everywhere in the British Isles. It succeeds best in warm situations on light, dry soils. On chalk, the bush grows smaller but is more fragrant. The shrub is well suited as a low evergreen hedge, particularly when one is required for the bee garden, for it never fails to attract.

In the south of France, the renowned Narbonne honey is derived largely from this plant. Rosemary is also an important source of honey in many parts of Spain and imparts something of its own fragrance to the honey gathered from it.

The solitary bees that visit tend to be the larger species, such as the hairy-footed flower bee (*Anthophora plumipes*). These large, furry bees look rather like bumblebees, but they have a darting flight. The females are black and the males are brown. They are absent from Scotland and Ireland.

The violet carpenter bee (*Xylocopa violacea*) is the largest solitary bee in Europe. In the last few years it has been sighted in scattered location across England and Wales and it appears to have established itself. Although it is a generalist feeder, some of the sightings have been on rosemary. The bee is large (about 20 mm) and is black with a violet sheen on the wings.

Above:
Common carder bee *(Bombus pascuorum)* on rosemary *(Rosmarinus officinalis)*
(photo: L. A. Hislop)
Far left:
Female red mason bee *(Osmia rufa)* on rosemary *(Rosmarinus officinalis)*
(photo: L. A. Hislop)
Left:
Male hairy-footed flower bee *(Anthophora plumipes) visiting rosemary (Rosmarinus officinalis)*
(photo: T. C. Ings)

Rue — *Ruta graveolens*

Bees sometimes visit the small greenish-yellow flowers for nectar. The nectar is well exposed and so attracts numerous short-tongued insects. Rue was more generally grown for medicinal purposes in bygone days. Several species and varieties of meadow rue (*Thalictrum* species) are grown in gardens for their attractive foliage as well as for their flowers. Honeybees work the flowers assiduously for pollen.

Family:	**Rutaceae**
Flowering:	**June to August**
Cultivation:	**evergreen small shrub**
Honey:	**no**
Honeybees:	‖‖‖
ST Bumblebees:	‖‖‖
LT Bumblebees:	----
Solitary Bees:	—

Above:
Pollen grain of rue *(Ruta graveolens) (25 μm)*
Left:
Rue flowers *(Ruta graveolens)*
(photo: W. D. J. Kirk)

Russian sage — *Perovskia atriplicifolia*

Family:	**Lamiaceae**
Flowering:	**July to October**
Cultivation:	**deciduous small shrub**
Honey:	**no**
Honeybees:	||||| |||||
ST Bumblebees:	||||| |||||
LT Bumblebees:	||||| |||||
Solitary Bees:	|||||

It is surprising that this exceedingly handsome Himalayan shrub is not more generally grown in gardens, although it is increasing in popularity. It is quite hardy, often dying back in winter and sending up fresh flowering shoots the following season. Flowering takes place in late summer at a time when there are few other sources for bees. The masses of purple lavender-like blossoms are covered with bees probing for nectar. The blossoms contrast well with the silver grey foliage of the plant. It generally reaches about 1.5 metres in height, needs full sun and thrives best on light well-drained soils. It is drought-resistant. The extent of flowering is dependent a good deal on the season, fine hot summers giving the best results. There are a few named cultivars and related species, such as *Perovskia scrophulariifolia*, which are also very popular with bees.

Above:
Pollen grain of Russian sage (Perovskia scrophulariifolia) (37 µm)
Top right:
Honeybee on Russian sage (Perovskia atriplicifolia)
Bottom right:
Worker buff-tailed bumblebee (Bombus terrestris) on Russian sage (Perovskia atriplicifolia)
(photos: M. A. Kirk)

R

Russian sage — Sage

Safflower — *Carthamus tinctorius*

Safflower or false saffron has long been an important oil seed crop in India and the East and has been used as an alternative crop to the sunflower in other countries. There are many varieties ranging in height up to 1.5 m and plants sometimes appear from birdseed. The reddish-orange thistle-like flowers are sometimes used as an edible yellow dye. They secrete nectar very freely and are much visited by bees. The plant will grow and flower in the south of England, but for profitable seed production doubtless needs a warmer climate.

Family:	**Asteraceae**
Flowering:	**August to September**
Cultivation:	**annual herb**
Honey:	**no**
Honeybees:	||||| |||||
ST Bumblebees:	||||| |||||
LT Bumblebees:	||||| |||||
Solitary Bees:	||||| |||||

Sage — *Salvia officinalis*

This culinary herb, much used for flavouring, has been cultivated in the British Isles for many centuries and originated in the Mediterranean region. In its native haunts it is sometimes the most common plant of the low shrubby vegetation so typical of the hillsides in that area, and there it is the source of much fine honey, light in colour, of good flavour and slow to granulate.

Family:	**Lamiaceae**
Flowering:	**June to August**
Cultivation:	**dwarf evergreen shrub**
Honey:	**no**
Honeybees:	||||| |||||
ST Bumblebees:	||||| |||||
LT Bumblebees:	||||| ||||| |||||
Solitary Bees:	||||| |||||

Sage does not grow quite so luxuriantly in the cool, moist British Isles climate, nevertheless it is grown in gardens for home use and is cultivated commercially year-round in open fields or in glasshouses or polytunnels. It is not fastidious in regard to soil. It may be harvested periodically throughout the summer or at the end of the season and dried, which is more desirable from the beekeeper's point of view as the flowers afford first-class honeybee forage. Many related species of salvia with colourful flowers are grown in gardens (see salvia).

Two wild sages, the meadow clary or meadow sage (*Salvia pratensis*) and the wild clary or wild sage (*Salvia verbenaca*) are good bee plants but probably nowhere sufficiently abundant to be a source of honey. Many varieties of meadow clary are grown in flower gardens. In California, some of the wild sages are first-class nectar plants and yield a high-grade honey in some years, which is very slow to granulate.

Sage flowers are popular with long-tongued bumblebees, such as the common carder bee (*Bombus pascuorum*) and the garden bumblebee (*Bombus hortorum*) and are also visited by the blue mason bee (*Osmia caerulescens*), which occurs mainly in England and Wales and which in the female has a slight hint of metallic blue on the hind part of the body.

Far left:
*Worker common carder bee (*Bombus pascuorum*) on sage (*Salvia officinalis*)
(photo: N. W. Owens)
Left:
*Sage flowers (*Salvia officinalis*)
(photo: W. D. J. Kirk)

Sainfoin — *Onobrychis viciifolia*

Family:	**Fabaceae**
Flowering:	**May to September**
Cultivation:	**perennial herb**
Honey:	**yes**
Honeybees:	||||| ||||| |||||
ST Bumblebees:	||||| ||||| |||||
LT Bumblebees:	||||| ||||| |||||
Solitary Bees:	||||| ||||| |||||

Top:
*Sainfoin flowers (*Onobrychis viciifolia*)*
Above:
*Bumblebee on sainfoin (*Onobrychis viciifolia*)*
(photos: W. D. J. Kirk)

Sainfoin was introduced to the British Isles as a fodder plant in about the middle of the 17th century from the Continent. It used to be much grown in the British Isles as well as in France and most other parts of Europe, particularly on chalk soils. However, it has been a victim of the intensification of agriculture and has more or less disappeared from modern farming.

It has a deep penetrating tap-root and so is not very dependent upon surface moisture and is able to withstand drought well. As a nectar plant it is reliable and used to be a good source of honey wherever it was grown. In England the cultivation of sainfoin was largely confined to chalk districts of the south, the three main centres were the Cotswold Hills, Hampshire and adjoining counties, and East Anglia. Although the crop is best suited for chalk and will thrive there where there is only a thin soil layer, it will grow in other soils provided they are not acid and drainage is good.

Two main sorts of sainfoin are cultivated, common or single-cut sainfoin and giant or double-cut sainfoin. Common sainfoin is the longer-lived plant but usually only flowers once in the season and provides only one harvest or 'cut', whereas giant sainfoin, a larger plant, gives two or three 'cuts' and will flower two or three times. Giant sainfoin is the better plant for bees. The best time to cut the plant for hay is about halfway through the flowering period, but often there is delay for one reason or another, which is to the bees' advantage if not the farmer's. When grown for seed of course flowering runs its full course. The first flowering of sainfoin usually takes place in the last week in May, the nectar flow lasting about 10 days or a fortnight. This is a good time of year, for it provides nectar after fruit blossom has finished.

The flowers of sainfoin are a rosy pink colour and a field in full bloom is a pleasing sight. As soon as the first sign of colour appears in a field, which is when the first flower at the bottom of the flower head has opened, bees will be found at work collecting nectar and pollen. Many bumblebee species visit sainfoin and it is included in seed mixtures designed to support bumblebees through the season. The late flowering allows queen bumblebees to build up reserves in preparation for winter. Honeybees will neglect other nectar sources as soon as sainfoin becomes available. The flowers secrete nectar freely, being considered one of the highest yielding honey plants, and will continue to secrete down to a temperature of about 14°C. The mechanism of the flower and the secretion of nectar is the same as in field bean and lucerne (see separate entries).

Sainfoin honey is one of the few honeys that have been obtained in the British Isles in anything like a pure or unmixed state. It is also a very distinctive type of honey, being deep yellow in colour, bright, and with a characteristic flavour and aroma. When freshly gathered in the hive the aroma is not pleasant but this unpleasantness soon disappears. The density is not so good as that of white clover as a rule. Many consider the honey superior to any other British Isles honey, but a few do not care for the flavour.

The wax of combs built during a sainfoin flow is a beautiful pale yellow in colour. The woodwork of hives and the frames themselves are also prone to become stained yellow. This is attributed to oil in the pollen clinging to particles of propolis on the bees' feet and so getting onto the woodwork, the brownish yellow pollen of sainfoin being of an exceptionally oily nature.

A mining bee (*Melitta dimidiata*) occurs at a few sites in Wiltshire, which is one of the few places where large expanses of sainfoin can still be seen, and it appears to feed only on pollen collected from sainfoin. It is large dark bee with pale hairs and is an endangered species.

Sallow, see willow

Salvia — *Salvia* species

Species of salvia vary in the length of the flower-tube. In some the nectar can be reached by honeybees and short-tongued bumblebees, whereas in others it can be reached only by long-tongued bumblebees. The scarlet salvia (*Salvia splendens*), which is much used for bedding in gardens, but is not hardy, has a flower-tube that is too long for the tongue of any British Isles bumblebee. Short-tongued bumblebees often poke a hole through the petals at the base of the flower and rob the nectar. The hole can then be used by honeybees to secondarily rob the nectar.

One of the best salvias for honeybees is violet salvia or violet sage (*Salvia* x *sylvestris*), which is a hybrid and originated from eastern Europe. A popular form is 'May Night' or 'Mainacht'. It is a perennial and perfectly hardy, reaching 60–90 cm in height, with erect growth, requiring no staking. Flowering commences in June, when the numerous spikes of purple-blue flowers are a pretty sight. It is in full bloom for a month to six weeks and continues to flower until September. During the whole of this time the flowers are alive with honeybees working for nectar, which they have no difficulty in reaching. A large circular bed of this plant at Kew Gardens has been so covered with honeybees in June that it almost looks as though a swarm were alighting. Besides being a good bee plant, violet salvia is also a first-class garden plant with its handsome flowers, long flowering season, and ease of cultivation. It needs full sun like most salvias, and is propagated by division of the roots or cuttings, not seeds. It does not form viable seed and the pollen also is abortive which is not unusual in hybrid plants. No honeybee garden should be without this plant.

Family:	**Lamiaceae**
Flowering:	**June to September**
Cultivation:	**perennial herb**
Honey:	**no**
Honeybees:	||||| |||||
ST Bumblebees:	||||| |||||
LT Bumblebees:	||||| |||||
Solitary Bees:	|||||

Above:
Pollen grain of scarlet salvia (Salvia splendens) *(58 μm)*

Far left:
Honeybee visiting a scarlet salvia flower (Salvia splendens) *from the front*
Left:
Honeybee robbing nectar from the base of a scarlet salvia flower (Salvia splendens)
(photos: W. D. J. Kirk)

S

Sainfoin — Salvia

Saponaria — *Vaccaria hispanica*

Family:	**Caryophyllaceae**
Flowering:	**July to September**
Cultivation:	**annual herb**
Honey:	**no**
Honeybees:	‖‖
ST Bumblebees:	‖‖
LT Bumblebees:	‖‖
Solitary Bees:	—

These garden annuals used to be grown much more than they are now. They can be raised easily from seed and may be listed for sale under the older name of *Saponaria vaccaria*. Two common varieties are 'Pink Beauty' and 'White Beauty'. They produce sprays of pink or white flowers, each less than a centimetre across. They are sometimes visited by bees, probably mainly for pollen, and those sown in the autumn for early spring blooming are the most useful in this respect. Single-flowered varieties of the perennial soapwort (*Saponaria officinalis*) are also sometimes visited by bees, although the flower-tube is too long for nearly all bees to reach the nectar from the front. They can sometimes reach the nectar by poking the tongue between the petals from the side of the flower and short-tongued bumblebees can poke a hole at the base to rob the nectar. The double-flowered varieties are of little value, as they have virtually no nectar.

Right:
*Flowers of saponaria (*Saponaria *'Bressingham Pink')*
(photo: W. D. J. Kirk)

Sassafras — *Sassafras albidum*

Family:	**Lauraceae**
Flowering:	**May**
Cultivation:	**deciduous medium tree**
Honey:	**no**
Honeybees:	‖‖
ST Bumblebees:	‖‖
LT Bumblebees:	—
Solitary Bees:	—

This North American tree is occasionally seen in cultivation in the warmer parts of the British Isles, and is of interest because of the fragrant leaves and bark. It is the original source of 'oil of sassafras', which used to be used as a fragrance and flavouring, but is no longer used in the natural form because of the toxic effects of safrole in the oil. Its small greenish-yellow flowers, which appear in May for about two weeks, are visited by bees for nectar. Male and female flowers are borne on different plants.

Savory — *Satureja montana*

Family:	**Lamiaceae**
Flowering:	**June to July**
Cultivation:	**perennial herb**
Honey:	**no**
Honeybees:	‖‖ ‖‖
ST Bumblebees:	‖‖
LT Bumblebees:	—
Solitary Bees:	—

Savory is one of the less common of the culinary herbs in British Isles gardens. With its strong flavour it is sometimes used for seasoning, like thyme, and in France is traditionally cooked with broad beans in the same way as mint is cooked with peas. There are two sorts, summer savory (*Satureja hortensis*) an annual, and winter savory (*Satureja montana*) a perennial. Both are good honeybee plants and well worked for nectar, especially the latter. They flower in June and July and have pale white to lilac, rather insignificant flowers. Bee stings have been traditionally treated by rubbing them with a sprig of summer savory to bring quick relief.

Left:
*Honeybee on savory (*Satureja montana*)*
(photo: W. D. J. Kirk)

Saxifrage — *Saxifraga* species

The saxifrages, wild or cultivated, are not among the best of bee plants, but honeybees frequently visit the flowers. The nectar is very exposed and only secreted in sunny weather when flies and other short-tongued insects have ready access to it. Such flowers are not usually great favourites with honeybees, perhaps because there are too many competitors for the nectar or they are too often disturbed. The same applies in the carrot family (Apiaceae) (see carrot). Among garden saxifrages, London pride (*Saxifraga* x *urbium*) is probably best known.

Family:	**Saxifragaceae**
Flowering:	**March to June**
Cultivation:	**perennial herb**
Honey:	**no**
Honeybees:	‖‖‖
ST Bumblebees:	—
LT Bumblebees:	—
Solitary Bees:	‖‖‖

Left:
*Flower of saxifrage (*Saxifraga *'Southside Seedling')*
(photo: M. A. Kirk)

Scabious — *Scabiosa, Knautia* and *Succisa* species

The common name scabious is applied to several groups of closely related species (*Scabiosa, Knautia* and *Succisa* species). Wild and garden scabious are good nectar plants. The wild species are all freely visited by bees, especially the field scabious (*Knautia arvensis*) and devil's bit scabious (*Succisa pratensis*), which occur in most parts of the British Isles. All have handsome blue or lilac flowers and are in bloom mainly later in the season. The secretion of nectar in the flower is of interest for it takes place on the upper surface of the ovary and is protected from rain by hairs in the flower-

Family:	**Dipsacaceae**
Flowering:	**July to August**
Cultivation:	**perennial herb**
Honey:	**no**
Honeybees:	‖‖‖ ‖‖‖
ST Bumblebees:	‖‖‖ ‖‖‖ ‖‖‖
LT Bumblebees:	‖‖‖ ‖‖‖ ‖‖‖
Solitary Bees:	‖‖‖ ‖‖‖ ‖‖‖

S

Saponaria — Scabious

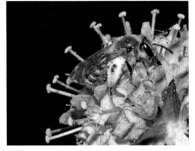

Top:
Common carder bee (Bombus pascuorum)
on Macedonian scabious (Knautia
macedonica)
(photo: W. D. J. Kirk)

Above:
Mining bee (Andrena marginata) on
devil's bit scabious (Succisa pratensis)
(photo: J. P. Early)

Right:
Scabious bee (Andrena hattorfiana) on
field scabious (Knautia arvensis)
(photo: T. C. Ings)

Far right:
Leafcutter bee (Megachile ligniseca) on
common knapweed (Centaurea nigra)
(photo: N. W. Owens)

Family:	**Apiaceae**
Flowering:	**July to August**
Cultivation:	**perennial herb**
Honey:	**no**
Honeybees:	‖‖‖‖ ‖‖‖
ST Bumblebees:	‖‖‖‖ ‖‖‖‖ ‖‖‖
LT Bumblebees:	‖‖‖‖ ‖‖‖‖ ‖‖‖
Solitary Bees:	‖‖‖‖ ‖‖‖

tube. In the field scabious, this varies from 4–9 mm in depth, according to the position of the flower in the flower-head, and the nectar is usually easily reached by short-tongued bees, including the honeybee. The pollen is also collected. Over a dozen of the wild scabious species from other countries in cultivation at Kew Gardens have been observed being freely worked for nectar by honeybees. Popularity with honeybees applies also to garden kinds with their flowers of many different shades.

The moderately long flower-tubes suit longer tongued bumblebees, such as the common carder bee (*Bombus pascuorum*). A mining bee (*Andrena marginata*) particularly visits field scabious (*Knautia arvensis*), devil's bit scabious (*Succisa pratensis*) and common knapweed (*Centaurea nigra*) (see centaurea). It is uncommon, with most records from southern England and Wales, although there are a few scattered records from Scotland and Ireland. It sometimes occurs together with the scabious bee (*Andrena hattorfiana*), which collects pollen from field scabious and sometimes small scabious (*Scabiosa columbaria*). This bee is scarce in southern Britain and declining rapidly. A cuckoo bee (*Nomada armata*) lays its eggs only in the nest of the scabious bee and so is inevitably declining with it.

Sheep's bit scabious, despite its name, is not closely related to the other scabious species, but is in the same family as the bellflower (see separate entry).

Sea aster, see aster

Sea-holly — *Eryngium* species

The sea-hollies or eryngiums are often mistaken for thistles, which they closely resemble with their prickly leaves. Besides the wild sea-holly (*Eryngium maritimum*) and field eryngo (*Eryngium campestre*), a rare plant, the flowers of several cultivated or garden kinds are much visited by honeybees and bumblebees for nectar. One of the most interesting for its potential for bees is perhaps the tall eryngo (*Eryngium giganteum*), from the Caucasus, which grows to about 1.2 m and has particularly large flower-heads.

The flowers are visited by mining bees (*Andrena* and *Colletes* species). In coastal areas, wild sea-holly is a particularly good source of nectar and is visited by several rare coastal species of bee. The coast leafcutter bee

(*Megachile maritima*) is a large brown bee that occurs mainly in coastal areas, particularly in southern England, but also in a few places in Wales and southeast Ireland. It visits sea-holly and other flowers that occur in coastal habitats. A cuckoo bee (*Coelioxys conoidea*) lays eggs in its nest and so is dependent on it.

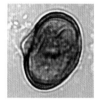

Far left:
Pollen grain of amethyst sea-holly (Eryngium amethystinum*) (30 µm)*
Left:
Male buff-tailed bumblebee (Bombus terrestris) *on sea-holly* (Eryngium *species*)
(photo: T. C. Ings)

Sea-kale — *Crambe maritima*

Sea-kale only grows wild near the seashore, as the name suggests. Its white flowers appear in June and are similar to those of the sea-kale of the vegetable garden when this is allowed to run to seed. They belong to the same species and bees visit them both for nectar. Within the flowers it is easy to see the four roundish green nectaries with a drop of nectar secreted by each. Small, black pollen beetles (*Meligethes* species) can often be abundant in the flowers. The greater sea-kale (*Crambe cordifolia*) is a spectacular plant for the back of a border, growing to a height of about 2 m and is also popular with bees.

Family:	**Brassicaceae**
Flowering:	**June to August**
Cultivation:	**perennial herb**
Honey:	**no**
Honeybees:	‖‖‖
ST Bumblebees:	‖‖‖
LT Bumblebees:	‖‖‖
Solitary Bees:	‖‖‖

Left:
Sea-kale flowers (Crambe maritima) *with a pollen beetle*
(photo: W. D. J. Kirk)

Sea-lavender — *Limonium* species

Sea-lavender is a well-known plant of the muddy shores and salt marshes of England, Wales and southern Scotland, but not Ireland. The common sea-lavender (*Limonium vulgare*) sometimes covers wide expanses, producing its flowering stalks, 30–60 cm high, from July to September. The flat-topped clusters of small blossoms (like lavender in colour, but not in scent for they are odourless) make it conspicuous from a distance. Honeybees work the blossoms well for nectar and the honey

Family:	**Plumbaginaceae**
Flowering:	**July to September**
Cultivation:	**perennial herb**
Honey:	**yes**
Honeybees:	‖‖‖ ‖‖‖
ST Bumblebees:	‖‖‖
LT Bumblebees:	‖‖‖
Solitary Bees:	‖‖‖

S

Sea aster — Sea-lavender

is light and of good quality. The plant is often prevalent in remote places, but where honeybees have access to it in quantity it is a useful late source of nectar, for it is available when most other sources, except heather, are over. Several species and varieties are grown in gardens and are also known by the name statice.

Right:
Flowers of wavyleaf sea-lavender
(Limonium sinuatum)
(photo: W. D. J. Kirk)

Senecio — *Senecio* species

Many species of senecio attract bees for nectar, for example the chamois ragwort (*Senecio doronicum*). A particularly impressive species is the broad-leaved ragwort (*Senecio sarracenicus*). This is not a native plant, but it is naturalised in some areas. It is 1–1.5 m high and best suited for the semi-wild garden, being rather coarse. The yellow flowers appear from June onwards. Interestingly, the plant is reputed to have been introduced to the British Isles by the Crusaders. See separate entries for ragwort (*Senecio jacobaea*) and purple ragwort (*Senecio elegans*).

Family:	**Asteraceae**
Flowering:	**June to September**
Cultivation:	**annual to perennial herb**
Honey:	**no**
Honeybees:	||||| |||||
ST Bumblebees:	||||| |||||
LT Bumblebees:	||||| |||||
Solitary Bees:	||||| |||||

Right:
*Flowers of chamois ragwort (*Senecio doronicum*)
(photo: M. A. Kirk)

Serradella — *Ornithopus sativus*

Family:	**Fabaceae**
Flowering:	**May to August**
Cultivation:	**annual herb**
Honey:	**no**
Honeybees:	||||| |||||
ST Bumblebees:	||||| |||||
LT Bumblebees:	||||| |||||
Solitary Bees:	|||||

Serradella, which is also known as French serradella or pink serradella, has been cultivated in some southern and central European countries as a fodder plant, but seldom in the British Isles and only in the south. It is an annual, clover-like plant, 30–60 cm high and well suited for poor, sandy soils. The small pinkish flowers may be available for as long as three months and are a good source of nectar. The plant does not ripen its seeds evenly or well in the British Isles and is really happier in a Mediterranean climate.

Shallon — *Gaultheria shallon*

This vigorous evergreen shrub of the heath family prefers moist shady spots, but will grow in any ordinary garden soil and in a wide range of conditions. It forms a dense low thicket and spreads by underground suckers. On account of its density, it has been cultivated as cover and food for game birds and so exists apparently wild throughout the British Isles. The pinkish-white pendent urn-shaped flowers appear in May and June in small racemes or bunches. They are a good source of nectar and are visited particularly by bumblebees. In its native land, western North America, the plant was regarded, in the early 20th century, as one of the best honey plants.

Family:	**Ericaceae**
Flowering:	**May to June**
Cultivation:	**evergreen medium shrub**
Honey:	**no**
Honeybees:	‖‖‖
ST Bumblebees:	‖‖‖
LT Bumblebees:	‖‖‖
Solitary Bees:	‖‖‖

Sheep's bit, see bellflower

Siberian pea-tree — *Caragana arborescens*

The Siberian pea-tree grows to about 4 m in height. It is often cultivated and there are many garden varieties. In May or June it bears yellow pea-like flowers singly on the stems. The flowers are attractive to bumblebees and, to a lesser extent, honeybees. It is a minor honey plant in parts of Canada, where it is often grown as a windbreak.

Family:	**Fabaceae**
Flowering:	**May to June**
Cultivation:	**deciduous large shrub or small tree**
Honey:	**no**
Honeybees:	‖‖‖
ST Bumblebees:	‖‖‖ ‖‖‖
LT Bumblebees:	‖‖‖ ‖‖‖
Solitary Bees:	—

Left:
Siberian pea-tree flowers (Caragana arborescens)
(photo: M. A. Kirk)

Sidalcea — *Sidalcea malviflora*

Family:	**Malvaceae**
Flowering:	**June to August**
Cultivation:	**perennial herb**
Honey:	**no**
Honeybees:	|||||
ST Bumblebees:	|||||
LT Bumblebees:	|||||
Solitary Bees:	|||||

The sidalceas of the flower border are visited for nectar and pollen, but mainly the latter. These mallow-like plants with their rose-purple or white flowers, thrive in almost any soil. In the USA, the plant is known as checkerbloom or tree hollyhock and is common enough in the wild in California to be a useful source of nectar for honeybees.

Right:
*Male buff-tailed bumblebee (*Bombus terrestris*) on sidalcea (*Sidalcea *species)*
(photo: W. D. J. Kirk)

Snapdragon — *Antirrhinum majus*

Family:	**Veronicaceae**
Flowering:	**July to September**
Cultivation:	**perennial herb**
Honey:	**no**
Honeybees:	|||||
ST Bumblebees:	|||||
LT Bumblebees:	||||| |||||
Solitary Bees:	|||||

The common snapdragon or antirrhinum of the flower garden is a bumblebee flower. Only bumblebees are sufficiently powerful to open the mouth of the flower and reach the nectar. However, honeybees and solitary bees are sometimes able to enter faded flowers and probably secure a certain amount of nectar in this way. Short-tongued bumblebees poke holes at the base of the flower tube to rob nectar and honeybees can obtain nectar through these holes. Larger solitary bees, such as the blue mason bee (*Osmia caerulescens*), which occurs in Britain but not Ireland, may also visit the flowers.

Right:
*Queen garden bumblebee (*Bombus hortorum*) on snapdragon (*Antirrhinum majus*)*
(photo: T. C. Ings)

Sneezeweed — *Helenium* species

The yellow or bronze flowers of this popular garden perennial attract bees in large numbers for nectar and pollen. Their value in the herbaceous border is mainly for autumn flowering, when they keep company with goldenrod and Michaelmas daisy. Some of the dwarf kinds, such as 'Crimson Beauty' and 'Moerheim Beauty' flower earlier and for a longer period than the others, from June to October. A bed of these plants will be covered with bees all day in good weather. Bees stand on a flower and work their way round it probing for nectar from each floret in turn, which makes it easy to observe them. Common sneezeweed (*Helenium autumnale*) has escaped from gardens and naturalised in parts of southeast England.

The main value of sneezeweed to the beekeeper in the British Isles is the same as that of other autumn garden flowers – helping to build up stores for the winter. It is interesting to note that in their native land, North America, some sneezeweeds have a reputation for yielding bitter honey, a small quantity of which can spoil other honey, although as a winter food for bees it is perfectly wholesome. The red-tailed bumblebee (*Bombus lapidarius*) is a frequent visitor. This species particularly visits the flowers of plants in the daisy family that provide a platform for it to stand on while foraging from many florets.

Family:	Asteraceae
Flowering:	June to October
Cultivation:	perennial herb
Honey:	no
Honeybees:	||||| |||||
ST Bumblebees:	||||| |||||
LT Bumblebees:	||||| |||||
Solitary Bees:	|||||

Above:
Pollen grain of sneezeweed (Helenium autumnale) *(25 μm)*

Far left:
Honeybee and male buff-tailed bumblebee (Bombus terrestris) *on sneezeweed* (Helenium *species*)
Left:
Honeybee on sneezeweed (Helenium *species*)
(photos: W. D. J. Kirk)

Snowberry — *Symphoricarpos albus*

This hardy North American shrub is common throughout the British Isles and is often seen in shrubberies, as a rough hedge plant, or apparently wild, for it is extensively naturalised. As it suckers freely it often forms dense thickets. It is easily distinguished from all other shrubs by its pure white fruits, which give it its name. The small, bell-shaped, pinkish-white flowers appear from June to August. They are not conspicuous, but must yield plenty of nectar judging by the way they attract honeybees, bumblebees and wasps. Only a few flowers are out at any one time, but the flowering period is a long one and the flowers may be worked all day. On warm summer evenings honeybees have been observed on the flowers at quite a late hour. In parts of the northern USA and southern Canada honey is

Family:	Caprifoliaceae
Flowering:	June to August
Cultivation:	deciduous medium shrub
Honey:	no
Honeybees:	||||| |||||
ST Bumblebees:	||||| |||||
LT Bumblebees:	|||||
Solitary Bees:	|||||

S

Sidalcea — Snowberry

obtained from it and this is described as light-coloured with a distinctive butterscotch flavour. Some related species that are grown for their ornamental fruits are also known to be excellent nectar plants, such as wolfberry (*Symphoricarpos occidentalis*) and coralberry (*Symphoricarpos orbiculatus*).

Right:
Honeybee on snowberry (Symphoricarpos albus)
(photo: T. C. Ings)
Far right:
Pollen grain of snowberry (Symphoricarpos albus) *(41 μm)*

Snowdrop — *Galanthus nivalis*

Family:	**Alliaceae**
Flowering:	**February to March**
Cultivation:	**perennial herb, grown from bulbs**
Honey:	**no**
Honeybees:	|||||
ST Bumblebees:	—
LT Bumblebees:	—
Solitary Bees:	—

Always one of the best loved of early spring flowers, the snowdrop is often to be found in bloom in woods and fields as early as February. It remains in bloom for several weeks. When weather is suitable, honeybees seek the flowers with zest and make good use of the bright yellowish orange pollen that it furnishes. Where the plants grow abundantly, honeybees are sometimes numerous over the flowers on bright sunny days. It flowers too early for most other bees to make use of it. Besides yielding pollen, the flowers secrete a certain amount of nectar. This is formed in depressions on the inner sides of the petals and at the base of the flowers. It is not always easily seen except when flowers have been kept in a warm room overnight. In collecting pollen from the snowdrop the honeybee inserts its head, front and middle legs into the flower, clinging with its hind legs to a petal. It then brushes the anthers with the fore and middle legs and deposits the pollen obtained in the pollen baskets of the hind legs. Garden varieties that have double flowers or flowers that are highly modified compared with the wild type of flower are unsuitable for bees.

Right:
Snowdrop flower (Galanthus nivalis)
Far right:
Centre of a snowdrop flower (Galanthus nivalis)
(photos: W. D. J. Kirk)

Snowdrop tree — *Halesia tetraptera*

The snowdrop or Carolina silverbell tree, a native of the southeastern USA, is sometimes seen in British gardens. The alternative name of *Halesia carolina* is sometimes used. It produces clusters of pendulous white flowers, not unlike snowdrops, in May. These are worked fairly freely by honeybees and bumblebees in some seasons.

Family:	**Styracaceae**
Flowering:	**May**
Cultivation:	**deciduous small tree**
Honey:	**no**
Honeybees:	|||||
ST Bumblebees:	|||||
LT Bumblebees:	|||||
Solitary Bees:	—

Left:
Flowers of snowdrop tree (Halesia tetraptera)
(photo M. A. Kirk)

Snowflake — *Leucojum vernum*

The spring snowflake (*Leucojum vernum*), like its close relative the snowdrop, is a useful early source of pollen for the honeybee and may also yield a little nectar given favourable weather. It is usually in flower from February, the fragrant drooping flowers resembling large snowdrops. The plant is very local in its distribution. The summer snowflake (*Leucojum aestivum*) is similar, but is a larger plant and flowers later from April to May.

Family:	**Alliaceae**
Flowering:	**February to April**
Cultivation:	**perennial herb, grown from bulbs**
Honey:	**no**
Honeybees:	|||||
ST Bumblebees:	—
LT Bumblebees:	—
Solitary Bees:	—

Left:
Snowflake flowers (Leucojum vernum)
(photo: L. Hebdon)

Solomon's seal — *Polygonatum* species

There are three species of Solomon's seal native to the British Isles, but all are rare or local in distribution. One of these, the angular Solomon's seal (*Polygonatum odoratum*), which flowers in May and June, was considered to be an important nectar plant for honeybees in parts of Holland early last century. The garden Solomon's seal (*Polygonatum* x *hybridum*) is a hybrid between angular Solomon's seal and common Solomon's seal (*Polygonatum multiflorum*) and is now naturalised in many areas across the British Isles.

Family:	**Asparagaceae**
Flowering:	**May to July**
Cultivation:	**perennial herb, grown from rhizomes**
Honey:	**no**
Honeybees:	|||||
ST Bumblebees:	|||||
LT Bumblebees:	||||| |||||
Solitary Bees:	|||||

The flowers are visited by honeybees, bumblebees, such as the buff-tailed bumblebee (*Bombus terrestris*), and solitary bees, such as flower bees (*Anthophora* species). Long-tongued bumblebees sometimes vibrate the flowers to extract pollen more efficiently. They do this with a special kind of buzz which only lasts about a second and is not the same as the hum that is produced while bumblebees fly. Species that have been observed to do this on flowers of the garden Solomon's seal include the garden bumblebee (*Bombus hortorum*), the common carder bee (*Bombus pascuorum*) and the early bumblebee (*Bombus pratorum*).

Right:
Flowers of common Solomon's seal (Polygonatum multiflorum)
(photo: W. D. J. Kirk)
Far right:
Queen garden bumblebee (Bombus hortorum) *on common Solomon's seal* (Polygonatum multiflorum)
(photo: N. W. Owens)

Family:	**Ericaceae**
Flowering:	**July to August**
Cultivation:	**deciduous large shrub or small tree**
Honey:	**no**
Honeybees:	‖‖‖
ST Bumblebees:	‖‖‖
LT Bumblebees:	‖‖‖
Solitary Bees:	‖‖‖

Sorrel tree — *Oxydendrum arboreum*

For those situated in heathy or peaty areas this small tree from the eastern USA may be of interest for it thrives under the same conditions as azaleas and rhododendrons. Bunches of fragrant, white, dangling, urn-shaped flowers are produced in July and August. These are a source of a high-quality and distinctive aromatic honey in its native home. The plant is often known as sourwood, owing to the acidity of the leaves. It is visited by many different species of bee.

Sowthistle — *Sonchus* species

Right:
Mining bee (Lasioglossum *species) on sowthistle* (Sonchus *species)*
(photo: L. Hebdon)
Far right:
Solitary bee (family Megachilidae) on sowthistle (Sonchus *species)*
(photo: T. C. Ings)

The flowers of the perennial sowthistle (*Sonchus arvensis*) and the smooth sowthistle (*Sonchus oleraceus*) are visited by bees. Both are weeds across much of the British Isles, the former mainly in farmland and the latter in waste places and along roadsides. The perennial sowthistle is in flower from August onwards and its yellow flower-heads, which are 40–50 mm across, attract bees for nectar and pollen. The flower tube of the smooth sowthistle is 8–12 mm long and so honeybees visit mainly for pollen. A wide range of species of solitary bee visit the flowers of sowthistle and other yellow-flowered species in the daisy family (Asteraceae).

Family:	**Asteraceae**
Flowering:	**June to October**
Cultivation:	**annual or perennial herb**
Honey:	**no**
Honeybees:	|||||
ST Bumblebees:	|||||
LT Bumblebees:	|||||
Solitary Bees:	||||| |||||

Speedwell, see veronica

Stachys — *Stachys* species

There are over 300 species of stachys. About half a dozen of them are commonly called woundworts and are native to the British Isles. Others are sometimes cultivated as ornamental plants. Most species have long flower-tubes and are particularly visited by long-tongued bumblebees. Hedge woundwort (*Stachys sylvatica*), which is common across the British Isles, is visited by many bumblebee species, but particularly the common carder bee (*Bombus pascuorum*) and the garden bumblebee (*Bombus hortorum*), both of which have long tongues. Marsh woundwort (*Stachys palustris*) is one of the plants that is visited by the great yellow bumblebee (*Bombus distinguendus*). This scarce, long-tongued species persists in coastal northern Scotland but is declining rapidly. As with many plants that have long flower-tubes, short-tongued bumblebees sometimes rob them of nectar by poking a hole at the base of the flower. In those plants where the flower-tube is not too long, the honeybee may be a frequent visitor for nectar. In the early 20th century, the perennial yellow woundwort (*Stachys recta*), with yellow flowers, was claimed to be an important source of honey in Czechoslovakia. The honey was said to be water white, dense and slow to granulate. The plant has naturalised in a few places in the British Isles.

The wool-carder bee (*Anthidium manicatum*) lines its nest with plant hairs gathered from plants with hairy leaves and stems. The hairy leaves of lamb's ears (*Stachys byzantina*) are often visited for this purpose. The females can be observed collecting their little balls of wool before flying off to their nest. The bees can be recognised by the rows of distinctive yellow spots down the body. They also visit the flowers of hedge woundwort and marsh woundwort for nectar and the males sometimes patrol the flowers territorially keeping bumblebees away.

Family:	**Lamiaceae**
Flowering:	**July to September**
Cultivation:	**annual or perennial herb**
Honey:	**no**
Honeybees:	||||| |||||
ST Bumblebees:	||||| |||||
LT Bumblebees:	||||| ||||| |||||
Solitary Bees:	||||| |||||

Above:
*Queen moss carder bee (*Bombus muscorum*) on marsh woundwort (*Stachys palustris*)
(photo: N. W. Owens)
Far left:
*Female wool-carder bee (*Anthidium manicatum*) collecting 'wool' from a lamb's ears leaf (*Stachys byzantina*) for her nest*
(photo: J. V. Adams)
Left:
*Worker buff-tailed bumblebee (*Bombus terrestris*) on lamb's ears (*Stachys byzantina*)
(photo: T. C. Ings)

St John's wort — *Hypericum* species

Family:	**Hypericaceae**
Flowering:	**May to August**
Cultivation:	**perennial herb or deciduous to evergreen small shrub**
Honey:	**no**
Honeybees:	|||||
ST Bumblebees:	||||| |||||
LT Bumblebees:	|||||
Solitary Bees:	|||||

The St John's wort of the flower garden, as well as the many wild kinds, yield pollen in abundance, each flower possessing numerous stamens. This is frequently collected by bees, and when packed in their pollen baskets is orange in colour. Short-tongued bumblebees, such as the buff-tailed bumblebee (*Bombus terrestris*) and the white-tailed bumblebee (*Bombus lucorum*), are frequent visitors. The flowers appear to yield no nectar whatsoever.

Right:
Honeybee collecting pollen on St John's wort (Hypericum hircinum)
(photo: W. D. J. Kirk)
Far right:
Pollen grain of St John's wort (Hypericum hircinum) *(12 μm)*

Stonecrop — *Sedum* species

Family:	**Crassulaceae**
Flowering:	**July to September**
Cultivation:	**perennial herb**
Honey:	**no**
Honeybees:	||||| |||||
ST Bumblebees:	||||| |||||
LT Bumblebees:	||||| |||||
Solitary Bees:	||||| |||||

The stonecrops closely resemble the saxifrages and occur in similar situations in the wild, being often seen on old walls and rocky banks. The flowers attract bees, especially those of the large purple-flowered wild sedum or orpine (*Sedum telephium*), of which there are many garden forms or varieties. The showy, rose-purple flowers of the much-grown butterfly stonecrop (*Sedum spectabile*), which generally appear in mid-August, are very attractive to honeybees and many species of bumblebee and solitary bee. The flowers form a convenient platform with easily accessible nectar and bees can spend a long time walking across them and feeding. This accommodating plant will grow in any soil or in shade and withstands great extremes of heat or cold well. Other members of the same family can also be rich in nectar, such as species of *Echeveria*.

Right:
Honeybee on butterfly stonecrop (Sedum spectabile)
(photo: W. D. J. Kirk)
Far right:
Pollen grain of reflexed stonecrop (Sedum rupestre) *(21 μm)*

Stork's bill, see erodium

Strawberry — *Fragaria* species

The garden strawberry (*Fragaria ananassa*) is one of the crops that needs bees. Cross-pollination is important for fruit development and bees can do this effectively and in sufficient numbers. This pollination service used to be provided almost exclusively by beekeepers, who moved colonies to the crop, but most growers now use commercially supplied colonies of the buff-tailed bumblebee (*Bombus terrestris*), which can fly at lower temperatures.

Strawberry has often been overrated as a honeybee plant. Bees do visit the blossoms, sometimes very freely, but mainly for pollen. Crops are grown extensively for market and on a field scale in many parts of the British Isles, but never does one hear of a beekeeper obtaining surplus from this source. Nectar is secreted at times but not in large amounts. Crops that are grown under glass or plastic provide less nectar than when grown in the open. In these circumstances, bumblebee colonies that are used for strawberry crop pollination are provided with sugar water as a nectar substitute to help colony development. Strawberry flowers are also visited by solitary bees, such as the red mason bee (*Osmia rufa*).

The flowers of wild strawberry (*Fragaria vesca*) are similar in structure but smaller and probably of about equal value to bees. Wild strawberries are usually to be seen in flower in May and June, but are not so prevalent in the British Isles as in some other parts of Europe.

Family:	Rosaceae
Flowering:	April to July
Cultivation:	perennial herb
Honey:	no
Honeybees:	|||||
ST Bumblebees:	|||||
LT Bumblebees:	|||||
Solitary Bees:	|||||

Above:
Pollen grain of garden strawberry (Fragaria ananassa) *(23 μm)*

Far left:
Wild strawberry flower (Fragaria vesca)
(photo: M. A. Kirk)
Left:
Mining bee (Lasioglossum *species) on garden strawberry* (Fragaria ananassa)
(photo: T. C. Ings)

Strawberry tree — *Arbutus unedo*

This rather unusual evergreen tree is sometimes to be seen in cultivation, but in the British Isles occurs wild only in southern Ireland. The pinkish-white, pitcher-shaped flowers are produced at an unusual time, from October to December, and develop into ripe fruits the following autumn. Honeybees have been observed visiting the flowers for nectar and pollen on fine autumn days. Honey is obtained from the strawberry tree in some parts of the Mediterranean region, for example Sardinia and Greece, and is described as lemon yellow in colour with an aromatic odour and bitter to the taste.

Bumblebee colonies have usually deteriorated before the strawberry tree

Family:	Ericaceae
Flowering:	October to December
Cultivation:	evergreen small tree
Honey:	no
Honeybees:	|||||
ST Bumblebees:	|||||
LT Bumblebees:	—
Solitary Bees:	—

S

St John's wort — Strawberry tree

comes into flower, but in recent years, the buff-tailed bumblebee (*Bombus terrestris*) has been observed foraging on flowers of the strawberry tree and the hybrid strawberry tree (*Arbutus* x *andrachnoides*) during the winter in southern England. Milder winters appear to be allowing this bumblebee to establish a second generation. Plants flowering in autumn and winter may become more important to bumblebees in the future.

A similar tree, Pacific madrone (*Arbutus menziesii*) from North America, is also sometimes cultivated. In its native land it is a source of good-quality honey.

Right:
*Queen buff-tailed bumblebee (*Bombus terrestris*) on strawberry tree (*Arbutus unedo*)*
(photo: T. C. Ings)

S

Sumach — Sunflower

Sumach — *Rhus* species

Family:	**Anacardiaceae**
Flowering:	**May to July**
Cultivation:	**deciduous medium shrub to small tree**
Honey:	**no**
Honeybees:	‖‖‖
ST Bumblebees:	—
LT Bumblebees:	—
Solitary Bees:	—

There are about 250 sumachs or species of *Rhus* distributed throughout the world. None is native to the British Isles but a few are sometimes cultivated for their ornamental foliage. The flowers are generally small, inconspicuous and dull in colour, but often very rich in nectar and several species are considered to be sources of honey in the USA. One species is often grown in British Isles gardens, the stag's-horn sumach (*Rhus typhina*). It is a shrub or small flat-topped tree with hairy stems and red-coloured autumn foliage. The clusters of fruits can be dried and used as a fuel for beekeepers' smokers. At Kew Gardens, a Chinese varnish tree (*Rhus potaninii*) has been covered with blossom in late May or June and has attracted large numbers of honeybees. Male and female flowers occur on separate plants in these species. Female flowers produce more nectar than the male flowers, but only the male flowers produce pollen.

Summer hyacinth — *Galtonia candicans*

This tall, bulbous South African plant, which is also known as Cape hyacinth, is sometimes to be seen in gardens in the British Isles. The white bell-like flowers attract bees. It is hardy in light soils and easy to grow. Flowering takes place in August and September when other sources are becoming less frequent. The nectar collects at the base of the flower from six fairly deep nectar passages that lead to it.

Family:	**Asparagaceae**
Flowering:	**August to September**
Cultivation:	**perennial herb, grown from bulbs**
Honey:	**no**
Honeybees:	|||||
ST Bumblebees:	|||||
LT Bumblebees:	|||||
Solitary Bees:	—

Left:
Honeybee visiting summer hyacinth
(Galtonia candicans)
(photo: W. D. J. Kirk)

Sunflower — *Helianthus* species

The many different kinds of garden sunflower, whether annual or perennial, tall or dwarf, are all more or less good bee plants – double forms excepted. The tall perennial kinds, such as the willow-leaved sunflower (*Helianthus salicifolius*), are mostly autumn flowering and may be numbered among the useful, although minor, late sources of nectar and pollen available to urban beekeepers. Some are very late in flowering and provided the flowers are not damaged by frost, are very freely worked, especially for pollen, on fine autumn days. This is a time when there is little else available.

The well-known, annual, giant sunflower (*Helianthus annuus*) is grown commercially for the seed for oil or as food for birds, but is also widely grown in gardens. Bees visit the flower-heads for nectar or pollen, along with numerous other insects. Sunflowers in gardens will also attract birds to feed on the seeds in autumn and so have a double benefit for wildlife. The sunflower is an important and widespread field crop in warmer countries and honey is obtained from it there, particularly in France and Spain. The honey is yellow with a delicate flavour, but crystallises rapidly.

Family:	**Asteraceae**
Flowering:	**August to October**
Cultivation:	**annual to perennial herb**
Honey:	**no**
Honeybees:	||||| |||||
ST Bumblebees:	||||| |||||
LT Bumblebees:	||||| |||||
Solitary Bees:	||||| |||||

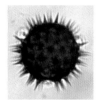

Far left:
Pollen grain of sunflower (Helianthus annuus) *(35 μm)*
Left:
Honeybees on sunflower (Helianthus annuus)
(photo: W. D. J. Kirk)

S

Sumach — Sunflower

Swedish whitebeam — *Sorbus intermedia*

Family:	**Rosaceae**
Flowering:	**May to June**
Cultivation:	**deciduous large tree**
Honey:	**no**
Honeybees:	|||||
ST Bumblebees:	|||||
LT Bumblebees:	|||||
Solitary Bees:	|||||

This large tree resembles the common whitebeam (*Sorbus aria*) and is often planted in parks and gardens across the British Isles. It has naturalised in many areas of Britain and Ireland and is common across northern and central Europe. It produces masses of white flowers and these are very freely worked for nectar.

Right:
*Flowers of Swedish whitebeam (*Sorbus intermedia*)
(photo: M. Kucharczyk)*

Sweet Alison — *Lobularia maritima*

Family:	**Brassicaceae**
Flowering:	**July to August**
Cultivation:	**annual to perennial herb**
Honey:	**no**
Honeybees:	||||| |||||
ST Bumblebees:	|||||
LT Bumblebees:	|||||
Solitary Bees:	|||||

Sweet Alison is also known by the confusingly similar names of alyssum and sweet alyssum. The scientific name of the species was formerly *Alyssum maritimum*, which led to the common name of alyssum. The species is both a wild and a garden plant in the British Isles and is much favoured by bees, as well as many other beneficial insects. The white honey-scented flowers appear in July and August. Along the southern coasts of Britain it is often to be seen on the tops of walls and in dry sandy places, where it grows as a perennial. The many garden forms with flowers of various colours are grown as annuals. A closely related species that is often grown in gardens is golden Alison (*Aurinia saxatilis*, formerly *Alyssum saxatile*), particularly the compact form known as 'Gold Dust'. It is one of the most popular of yellow spring flowers, flowering from April to May. Bees visit the flowers, although not zealously, and probably mainly for pollen.

Right:
*Flowers of sweet Alison (*Lobularia maritima*)
(photo: M. A. Kirk)*

Sweet chestnut — *Castanea sativa*

The sweet or Spanish chestnut is regarded as having been introduced to Britain by the Romans and is now common throughout most of the British Isles, except on chalk soils which it avoids. Flowering usually takes place in July and the flowers are of two kinds, the tassels of male flowers being more conspicuous than the female flowers. Honeybees are frequently to be observed assiduously working the male flowers for pollen, but little nectar seems to be obtained, at least under the average conditions prevailing in the British Isles, perhaps because the climate is not warm enough. However, in parts of continental Europe where the tree is often grown extensively for the sake of the nuts, it seems to be of some importance as a nectar plant and honey is obtained from it. The honey is variable in colour from yellowish brown to nearly black and has a strong flavour.

Family:	**Fagaceae**
Flowering:	**July**
Cultivation:	**deciduous large tree**
Honey:	**no**
Honeybees:	|||||
ST Bumblebees:	|||||
LT Bumblebees:	|||||
Solitary Bees:	|||||

Above:
*Pollen grain of sweet chestnut (*Castanea sativa*) (17 μm)*

Sweet clover, see melilot

Sweet rocket — *Hesperis matronalis*

This favourite old garden plant, with its sweet-scented mauve or white flowers, is sometimes popular with bees for pollen. Many other names are used for the same plant, including dame's violet, dame's rocket, night-scented gilliflower and mother-of-the-evening. The single form is easily naturalised in shrubberies and the many escapes from gardens have naturalised frequently across the British Isles.

Family:	**Brassicaceae**
Flowering:	**May to July**
Cultivation:	**biennial to perennial herb**
Honey:	**no**
Honeybees:	|||||
ST Bumblebees:	|||||
LT Bumblebees:	|||||
Solitary Bees:	|||||

Left:
*Flowers of sweet rocket (*Hesperis matronalis*)*
(photo: M. A. Kirk)

Sycamore — *Acer pseudoplatanus*

Family:	**Sapindaceae**
Flowering:	**April to June**
Cultivation:	**deciduous large tree**
Honey:	**yes**
Honeybees:	||||| ||||| |||||
ST Bumblebees:	||||| |||||
LT Bumblebees:	||||| |||||
Solitary Bees:	||||| |||||

Above:
*Pollen grain of sycamore (*Acer pseudoplatanus*) (39 μm)*

S

Sycamore

Although not really a native of the British Isles the sycamore is now so widespread, thanks to its wind-borne seeds and the ease with which it propagates itself, as to be considered a wild tree. In some of the beech woods of the South Downs it is almost as common as the beech itself. The hanging bunches of greenish yellow flowers appear in April or May and only last for 2–3 weeks, the flowering period being a short one.

Despite that, the flowers are a good source of nectar and pollen. They are visited by honeybees, bumblebees and solitary bees, such as a mining bee (*Andrena bucephala*), which is rare in southern England and Wales. Sycamore is valued by beekeepers for stimulating and building up stocks for the main honey flow later in the year.

The sycamore flowers later than its relatives the maples. Usually it follows close on the heels of the apple in flowering, but in some years the two flower more or less together, which is then unfortunate from the beekeeper's point of view for they are probably of greater value for stimulative purposes when they flower separately. Surplus honey is obtained from sycamore in some areas in favourable seasons. It is usually amber in colour with a greenish tinge, the green colour being possibly due to honeydew, which is common on the leaves of this tree and is sometimes collected by honeybees. When fresh the flavour of the honey is not of the best, even rank in the estimation of some, but this mellows down with age. Doubtless the flavour as well as the colour is often adversely affected by honeydew. Density is generally fair and granulation slow with a coarse grain.

The flowers of the sycamore, which are about the size of currant blossoms, are arranged in groups of three in long pendent racemes. Usually the centre flower develops into the seed while the two lateral ones are male and only produce pollen. They have longer stamens and abortive ovaries. The winged seeds germinate with great facility and seedlings may be seen coming up in all manner of unexpected places.

The sycamore is well suited for cultivation near the sea where it withstands salt sea breezes and maintains an erect position better than almost any other tree. In favourable situations it may attain large dimensions, trees over 30 m high and 6 m in girth having been recorded in Britain. There are many garden forms with coloured or variegated leaves.

The sycamore has long been a favourite tree in Scotland, probably on account of its hardiness and rapid growth, and has been much planted around country mansions as well as around farmhouses and cottages on bleak hillsides. In Scotland it is generally known as the plane tree. Great maple is another name for it. In the south the tree grows just as well and is often planted in windy and exposed situations. Its numerous branches and its large leaves render it a suitable subject where shade is required. It may be seen on farms affording shade for livestock. As an ornamental tree it is grown either singly or in groups of two or three. It is also effective in avenues, given sufficient room. The litter from its large leaves in autumn is one of its drawbacks, especially in built-up areas. Almost any soil is suitable for the sycamore provided drainage is adequate but the tree prefers a dry, free soil to one that is stiff and moist. In spite of its rapid growth it requires several years before it commences to flower and to ripen its seeds. In many of the wooded mountainous parts of Europe the sycamore is truly wild or indigenous. This includes areas covered by the Pyrenees, Alps, Carpathians, and the hilly districts that radiate from them.

Left:
*Sycamore flowers (*Acer pseudoplatanus*)*
(photo: M. A. Kirk)

S

Sycamore

Tamarisk — *Tamarix* species

Family:	**Tamaricaceae**
Flowering:	**May to August**
Cultivation:	**deciduous large shrub or small tree**
Honey:	**no**
Honeybees:	|||||
ST Bumblebees:	—
LT Bumblebees:	—
Solitary Bees:	—

These are favourite shrubs for gardens near the sea, being very well suited for exposed seaside conditions. They are either grown for ornament on account of their feathery foliage and pretty flowers or as hedges and windbreaks. The common tamarisk (*Tamarix gallica*) is much used in this way, being easily grown from cuttings planted directly in the soil. It has become freely naturalised in some seaside districts. Flowering takes place in July and August and the bunches of small pink flowers attract honeybees for nectar. Tamarisk occurs in several other countries, such as France and the southwestern USA, where it is sometimes a source of surplus honey, as well as being useful for pollen. The honey is dark with a strong and distinctive flavour. Some of the other species of tamarisk available for gardens, such as *Tamarix tetrandra*, are in flower earlier and also attract honeybees.

Right:
*Tamarisk flowers (*Tamarix *species)*
(photo: W. D. J. Kirk)

Tansy — *Tanacetum vulgare*

Family:	**Asteraceae**
Flowering:	**July to September**
Cultivation:	**perennial herb**
Honey:	**no**
Honeybees:	|||||
ST Bumblebees:	|||||
LT Bumblebees:	|||||
Solitary Bees:	||||| |||||

Honeybees and bumblebees visit the yellow flower-heads of this common wild plant and garden herb to probe for nectar and gather pollen. However, they do not often visit it in large numbers. Possibly the strong smell does not appeal to them. The dried flower-heads, leaves and stalks are said to make good smoker fuel for beekeepers, burning slowly and with a pleasant aroma. Mining bees (*Colletes* species) particularly visit the flowers of tansy and other daisy-like flowers to collect pollen. They can be recognised by the pale whitish stripes across the hind part of the body. One of these species (*Colletes daviesanus*) is fairly common in England and Wales and is often found in gardens. There are very few records of it from Scotland and Ireland.

Right:
*Tansy flowers (*Tanacetum vulgare*)*
(photo: W. D. J. Kirk)
Far right:
*Pollen grain of tansy (*Tanacetum vulgare*)*
(25 μm)

 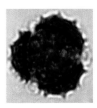

Teasel — *Dipsacus* species

The spiny seed-head of the fuller's teasel (*Dipsacus sativus*) was once widely used in cloth manufacture for raising the nap of woollen cloth. Commercial teasel crops were grown in Somerset until about the year 2000. The teasel is a biennial and flowers in its second season when the mauve flowers in the thistle-like flower-heads are a great attraction to honeybees and bumblebees. They yield nectar freely and bees visit them all day long. Flowering typically commences in July and as only a few flowers open at a time, starting at the bottom of the flower-head, they are available for several weeks. Honey was obtained from this plant when it was grown extensively in the USA for the cloth industry, and this was described as thin but light in colour and of good flavour. The wild teasel (*Dipsacus fullonum*), which is similar except for the spines on the seed-head being straight and not curved, is common in many areas and is often to be seen in waste places and along water courses. The flowers appear to be equally attractive to bees. The cut-leaved teasel (*Dipsacus laciniatus*) with deeply cut leaves, which is sometimes grown for ornament, and the small teasel (*Dipsacus pilosus*), which takes up less space and suits small gardens, also attract many bees.

Family:	Dipsacaceae
Flowering:	July to August
Cultivation:	biennial herb
Honey:	no
Honeybees:	||||| |||||
ST Bumblebees:	||||| |||||
LT Bumblebees:	||||| |||||
Solitary Bees:	|||||

Far left:
Garden bumblebee (Bombus hortorum) *on wild teasel* (Dipsacus fullonum)
(photo: W. D. J. Kirk)
Left:
Tree bumblebee (Bombus hypnorum) *on small teasel* (Dipsacus pilosus) *and a red-tailed bumblebee* (Bombus lapidarius) *approaching*
(photo: L. Hebdon)

Thistle— *Cirsium* and *Carduus* species

A large number of plants fall into the general category of thistles. Although many of them are troublesome weeds, they are also good bee plants and supply nectar and pollen in abundance. One of the most important thistles for bees is the ubiquitous creeping thistle (*Cirsium arvense*), which spreads by means of its creeping roots. It can do this very quickly, which accounts for the difficulty in eradicating it, for the smallest piece left in the soil is capable of forming a new plant. It also spreads by means of seeds. It is one of the worst weeds the farmer and gardener has to contend with in the British Isles. It is common in and around cultivated fields and in pastures, especially those grazed only by sheep. It sometimes takes almost complete possession of abandoned fields and wasteland.

Family:	Asteraceae
Flowering:	July to September
Cultivation:	annual to perennial herb
Honey:	no
Honeybees:	||||| |||||
ST Bumblebees:	||||| ||||| |||||
LT Bumblebees:	||||| ||||| |||||
Solitary Bees:	||||| ||||| |||||

T

Tamarisk — Thistle

Top:
Male common carder bee (Bombus pascuorum) on musk thistle (Carduus nutans)
(photo: W. D. J. Kirk)

Above:
Marmalade hoverfly (Episyrphus balteatus) and mason bee (Osmia leaiana) on spear thistle (Cirsium vulgare)
(photo: N. W. Owens)

Family:	**Plumbaginaceae**
Flowering:	**May to July**
Cultivation:	**perennial herb**
Honey:	**no**
Honeybees:	||||| |||||
ST Bumblebees:	||||| |||||
LT Bumblebees:	||||| |||||
Solitary Bees:	||||| |||||

Above:
Thrift flowers (Armeria maritima)
(photo: M. A. Kirk)

The creeping thistle grows from 30–100 cm high according to soil conditions and is in flower from July onwards, producing rose-purple flower-heads, each with 100 or more individual flowers or florets. These secrete nectar abundantly. The flower-tube is 8–12 mm long and terminates in a short bell. Nectar quite often rises in the tube as high as this bell and so is easily available to short-tongued bees, including honeybees, as well as other insects. The pollen, which is sticky, is also greedily collected by bees.

Honey has been obtained from creeping thistle in the USA and Canada and is of good quality, light in colour and of excellent flavour, comparing well with lime and clover. Honey is not obtained in the British Isles, where the main value to honeybees is assisting the build up of winter stores in the latter part of the season.

Both short-tongued and long-tongued bumblebees are very frequent visitors. The flower-head provides a platform for bees to stand on and this may be what particularly attracts the red-tailed bumblebee (*Bombus lapidarius*). Many solitary bees, particularly mining bees (*Andrena, Colletes* and *Lasioglossum* species) also visit.

Some thistles have so long a flower-tube that the nectar is out of reach or only rarely available to honeybees and other short-tongued bees. However, there are several thistles that afford useful late-season honeybee forage. Honeybees have been observed visiting the flowers of the following: spear thistle (*Cirsium vulgare*), melancholy thistle (*Cirsium heterophyllum*), marsh thistle (*Cirsium palustre*), welted thistle (*Carduus crispus*), musk thistle (*Carduus nutans*) and cotton thistle (*Onopordum acanthium*).

Thrift — *Armeria maritima*

The pink flowers of the common thrift or sea pink are a familiar sight near the seashore and start flowering in May or June, depending on location. In salt marshes, they are sometimes extremely abundant, the plants growing everywhere in dense cushion-like tufts. They often grow in association with sea-lavender (*Limonium vulgare*) (see separate entry), a closely related plant, which, however, blooms later. Thrift occurs also in mountainous areas. It is a good source of nectar when bees have access to it and useful for supplementing the nectar obtained from other sources.

Besides occurring wild, thrift is commonly grown as a garden plant, particularly in coastal districts. There are many varieties and introduced forms in cultivation which are also attractive to bees.

Several solitary bees visit thrift, mainly for nectar, including many mining bees (*Andrena, Colletes* and *Lasioglossum* species). Quite a few solitary bees are restricted to coastal areas and for these thrift can be a useful nectar source. For example, the gold-fringed mason bee (*Osmia aurulenta*) occurs mainly in coastal areas, particularly in southern England and Wales. It visits thrift and other coastal plants and has the remarkable habit of nesting in empty snail shells.

Thyme — *Thymus* species

Both wild thyme (*Thymus polytrichus*) and the garden thyme (*Thymus vulgaris*), which are used for seasoning, are excellent bee plants and are well worked for nectar. So also are lemon thyme (*Thymus* x *citriodorus*) and the many varieties with pink or mauve flowers or variegated leaves grown in the flower garden or rock garden.

Wild thyme is very abundant in some parts of the British Isles, especially in the chalk districts, on moorland, and on dry pastures. It may even impart a purplish colour to the landscape when in full flower in June and July in spite of its lowly growth. Frequently, it grows in combination with wild marjoram (*Origanum vulgare*) (see separate entry), another good bee plant, and the two form a useful combination for any nearby beekeeper. Honey is not obtained pure from wild thyme in the British Isles as there are invariably other nectar sources available at the same time. However, the honey from thyme is known to be of excellent quality and flavour and its presence in other honey is always likely to improve it. The honey from Mount Hymettus, near Athens, famous for its excellence from classical times, was derived from the wild thyme of that region. The flowers of thyme are very fragrant and have much the same structure as those of wild marjoram. Nectar is produced freely and even this has a spicy flavour.

Garden thyme is a native of the Mediterranean region, where it may cover extensive areas of stony ground and is a wonderful sight when in flower in spring. It is then valuable for honey. In the British Isles, thyme is often killed in winter, especially on heavier soils. Besides being grown for home use it is cultivated on a commercial or field scale in some areas. It is either sold as a green herb or used for drying. The field cultivation of thyme is probably not sufficiently extensive anywhere in the British Isles for surplus honey. The ornamental thymes, which are useful for covering dry banks and able to exist in poor soils, are also very attractive to bees. No bee garden should be without some of them. The flowers are visited by a range of species of solitary bee, for example the blue mason bee (*Osmia caerulescens*), which occurs in Britain but not Ireland and in which the female has a slight hint of metallic blue on the hind part of the body.

Family:	**Lamiaceae**
Flowering:	**May to August**
Cultivation:	**evergreen dwarf shrub**
Honey:	**no**
Honeybees:	||||| |||||
ST Bumblebees:	||||| |||||
LT Bumblebees:	||||| |||||
Solitary Bees:	||||| |||||

Top:
*Male fork-tailed flower bee (*Anthophora furcata*) on thyme (*Thymus polytrichus*)
Above:
*Bilberry bumblebee (*Bombus monticola*) on thyme (*Thymus polytrichus*)
(photos: L. A. Hislop)

Tickseed — *Coreopsis* species

The tickweed or coreopsis produces a show of yellow, orange, red or white daisy-like flowers in summer and many species and varieties are available for gardens. Both the annual and perennial forms receive attention from many species of bee for nectar and pollen. Although the plants may be in flower for a long period in the summer they are seldom cultivated in anything but small groups or patches. Many of the true species, such as the large-flowered tickseed (*Coreopsis grandiflora*) and the threadleaf tickseed (*Coreopsis verticillata*) are very freely worked by honeybees in the late summer. The named garden forms may also be as good. The flowers are popular with the garden bumblebee (*Bombus hortorum*).

Family:	**Asteraceae**
Flowering:	**June to September**
Cultivation:	**annual to perennial herb**
Honey:	**no**
Honeybees:	|||||
ST Bumblebees:	|||||
LT Bumblebees:	||||| |||||
Solitary Bees:	|||||

T

Thrift — Tickseed

T

Toadflax — Tomato

Right:
*Leafcutter bee (*Megachile *species) on tickseed (*Coreopsis *species)*
(photo: T. C. Ings)
Far right:
*Pollen grain of tickseed (*Coreopsis *species) (35 μm)*

Toadflax — *Linaria* species

Family:	**Veronicaceae**
Flowering:	**June to October**
Cultivation:	**annual or perennial herb**
Honey:	**no**
Honeybees:	‖‖‖
ST Bumblebees:	‖‖‖
LT Bumblebees:	‖‖‖ ‖‖‖
Solitary Bees:	‖‖‖

The common toadflax (*Linaria vulgaris*), which occurs along hedgerows and in waste places, has a remarkable flower. The long spur is 10–12 mm long and nectar collects in this, frequently to a depth of 5–6 mm or more. Only long-tongued insects are able to take all or most of the nectar from the front of the flower, but short-tongued bees are able to have their share when nectar is being produced freely. Force is needed to open the mouth of the flower, so small insects are kept out. Short-tongued bees sometimes poke a hole in the base of the flower and steal the nectar. One of the most frequent legitimate visitors, taking nectar from the front of the flower, is the common carder bee (*Bombus pascuorum*). Honeybees creep right into the flower and suck out the nectar as far as the tongue will reach, emerging covered with pollen. Some of the other wild or cultivated species, including the purple toadflax (*Linaria purpurea*) and the pale toadflax (*Linaria repens*) are also popular, mainly with long-tongued bumblebees. Toadflax flowers can be visited also by some of the larger solitary bees, such as mason bees (*Osmia* species) and the wool-carder bee (*Anthidium manicatum*), which can be recognised by the rows of distinctive yellow spots down the body.

Right:
*Common toadflax flowers (*Linaria vulgaris*)*
(photo: W. D. J. Kirk)
Far right:
*Male wool-carder bees (*Anthidium manicatum*) on purple toadflax (*Linaria purpurea*)*
(photo: T. C. Ings)

Tomato — *Solanum lycopersicum*

Family:	**Solanaceae**
Flowering:	**May to August**
Cultivation:	**annual to perennial herb**
Honey:	**no**
Honeybees:	‖‖‖
ST Bumblebees:	‖‖‖ ‖‖‖
LT Bumblebees:	‖‖‖
Solitary Bees:	—

Tomato flowers have no nectar but they produce large amounts of pollen. The pollination mechanism is unusual in that the flower needs to be vibrated to release pollen from the anther – a process called buzz pollination. In the past, this was often done artificially by touching the stem of each plant with a vibrating rod, sometimes known as an electric bee, or by shaking the flowers or spraying them with water. Of course a real bee can do this much better, but the problem was that the only bees

that could be moved easily to crops were honeybees and they are not able
to buzz pollinate. Only bumblebees and some solitary bees are capable
of buzz pollinating. The buzz only lasts about a second and is not the
same as the hum that is produced as bumblebees fly. They only produce
the special buzz on flowers that can be buzz pollinated, such as tomato,
kiwifruit and some roses. In the late 1980s, methods were developed to
allow bumblebee colonies to be produced and sold commercially on a
large scale and these soon took over the role of pollination in commercial
tomato crops. Bumblebees bite the cone of stamens in the centre of the
flower as they collect pollen and the brown bruise marks that are
produced can be used by tomato growers to indicate how often the
flowers have been visited. As there is no nectar in a tomato crop, the bees
need to be provided with sugar solution as a substitute. The buff-tailed
bumblebee (*Bombus terrestris*), which produces large colonies with many
workers, is the species used across Europe. Although the species is native
to the British Isles, the commercial variety that has been used is the
southeastern Mediterranean subspecies (*Bombus terrestris dalmatinus*)
and not the British Isles subspecies (*Bombus terrestris audax*). There is
a risk that bumblebees escaping from glasshouses could over time
displace or hybridise with the native sub-species. Fortunately, colonies
of the native sub-species have been made available commercially in the
British Isles from 2011.

In the USA, the eastern bumblebee (*Bombus impatiens*) and the
western bumblebee (*Bombus occidentalis*) were used commercially for
pollination, but following major disease problems with the western
bumblebee, the eastern bumblebee has taken over as the main species
used. The commercial use of bumblebees and consequent spread of bee
diseases is thought by some scientists to be a cause of the recent severe
declines of several species of native bumblebees in the USA.

Honeybees will visit tomato flowers for pollen, but they cannot
obtain very much and other flowers are usually more attractive if
available. The strong smell of the tomato plant seems to be offensive to
honeybees and it is said that if one manipulates a colony soon after
disbudding tomato plants and with the hands still smelling of the juice
or oil of the plant, honeybees are prone to sting.

T

Toadflax — Tomato

Left:
*Tomato flower (*Solanum lycopersicum*)*
(photo: W. D. J. Kirk)

Tree hollyhock — *Hibiscus syriacus*

Family:	**Malvaceae**
Flowering:	**July to October**
Cultivation:	**deciduous medium shrub**
Honey:	**no**
Honeybees:	|||||
ST Bumblebees:	||||| |||||
LT Bumblebees:	|||||
Solitary Bees:	—

The tree hollyhock or rose of Sharon exists in numerous cultivated varieties. Flowers may be white or any shade of red, blue, purple or striped, and vary in size up to 10 cm across. They do not appear until late in the season but may be visited for pollen. Single-flowered varieties are likely to be best for bees. Some large-flowered plants in the same family, such as flannel bush (*Fremontodendron* species) are also popular with bees, particularly bumblebees.

Right:
*Worker buff-tailed bumblebee (*Bombus terrestris*) collecting pollen from the anthers of flannel bush (*Fremontodendron 'Californian Glory')*
(photo: C. Stevens)

Tree-of-heaven — *Ailanthus altissima*

Family:	**Simaroubaceae**
Flowering:	**July to August**
Cultivation:	**deciduous large tree**
Honey:	**no**
Honeybees:	|||||
ST Bumblebees:	—
LT Bumblebees:	—
Solitary Bees:	—

This large handsome tree from China used to be often seen in cultivation in the south of England. Its high pollution tolerance makes it suitable for urban planting. Terminal bunches of small white flowers are produced in July or August and honeybees visit them for nectar. The flowers are of two kinds, male and female, the former being rather evil smelling with an odour not unlike that of elder flowers – much like cat urine.

In the 1940s, honey obtained by a London beekeeper with hives not far from Kensington Gardens was believed, from pollen analysis, to be mainly from this source, the tree-of-heaven being not uncommon in that neighbourhood as a street tree. This honey, when fresh, was described as possessing an unpleasant aftertaste recalling elder, but after being kept for some time the flavour changed to one of a pleasant muscatel flavour. The honey was of a pale greenish-brown colour and crystallised after about three months with a fine grain. In some other parts of Europe and the USA the tree-of-heaven is sufficiently abundant to be a source of surplus honey.

It should be noted that the tree-of-heaven not only has an unpleasant smell but is widely considered to be an invasive species and should not be planted in the wild. It is fast growing and it suckers and resprouts as well as spreading rapidly by seed, making it very difficult to eradicate. As a result, the tree has also acquired the names 'stink tree' and 'tree-of-hell'.

Tulip tree — *Liriodendron tulipifera*

The tulip tree, or yellow poplar, is often to be seen in cultivation in the British Isles, where it is quite hardy. Its large tulip-like flowers, that appear in June and July, serve to distinguish it readily from other trees. These attract honeybees to some extent in hot sunny weather but at other times bees pay no attention to them and no nectar is visible in the flowers.

Family:	**Magnoliaceae**
Flowering:	**June to July**
Cultivation:	**deciduous large tree**
Honey:	**no**
Honeybees:	‖‖‖
ST Bumblebees:	‖‖‖
LT Bumblebees:	‖‖‖
Solitary Bees:	—

In its homeland (eastern North America), the tulip tree is an important source of honey and equals the lime or basswood (*Tilia* species) as a nectar producer. The honey from it is of good quality, reddish amber in colour and rather strong. There it is found to give the best flow when the flowers open late and the weather is warm and dry, but in the more northerly limits of its distribution it is not much use for nectar. The climate of the British Isles probably corresponds more to these northerly limits and the tree is unable to be at its best as a source of nectar.

Flowers of the tulip-tree placed in water overnight in a warm room often show large drops of nectar on the yellow mark at the base of each of the large petals. As much as 3 g of nectar, about a teaspoonful, have been collected from a single blossom in North America. The nectar is only secreted for a short time by each flower – about a day and a half. Nevertheless, it has been calculated that a single tree may yield at one time over 4 kg of nectar, equivalent to 1 kg of honey.

Turnip — *Brassica rapa*

The turnip used to be grown extensively in the 19th century and dug up as a feed for livestock, particularly in Ireland, Scotland and the north of England, where the cooler conditions are well suited to it. The amount declined as alternative feeds became available. Stubble turnips are now often grown as a catch crop for grazing by cattle or sheep. This is a fast-growing turnip with a large top and a root that sticks out of the ground so that it can be efficiently grazed by animals as it grows without having to be dug up.

Family:	**Brassicaceae**
Flowering:	**May to August**
Cultivation:	**annual or biennial herb**
Honey:	**no**
Honeybees:	‖‖‖ ‖‖‖ ‖‖‖
ST Bumblebees:	‖‖‖ ‖‖‖ ‖‖‖
LT Bumblebees:	‖‖‖ ‖‖‖ ‖‖‖
Solitary Bees:	‖‖‖ ‖‖‖

Normally turnips are grazed or harvested before flowering takes place. Sometimes, however, a certain amount of flowering can occur due to causes such as bolting and late frosts. When grown for seed, flowering is very profuse and a field of this sort is of benefit to bees. The turnip is the equal of other well-known brassicas as a nectar yielder and produces a similar type of honey (see brassica, oilseed rape and charlock).

V

Vegetable marrow — Vetch

Vegetable marrow — *Cucurbita pepo*

Family:	**Cucurbitaceae**
Flowering:	**June to August**
Cultivation:	**annual herb**
Honey:	**no**
Honeybees:	||||| |||||
ST Bumblebees:	||||| |||||
LT Bumblebees:	||||| |||||
Solitary Bees:	|||||

Above:
Courgette flower (Cucurbita pepo)
(photo: W. D. J. Kirk)

The vegetable marrow and courgette are the only members of the large group of edible gourds that may be said to be commonly grown out of doors in the British Isles. Although differing in size, they are just varieties of the same species. Pumpkins and summer squashes are occasionally seen in private gardens or allotments, but their cultivation is not so widespread, although pumpkins are being increasingly grown commercially for sale for Halloween.

The large flowers of these plants are much visited by bees as well as by many other insects. The male flowers produce nectar and pollen and are easily distinguished from the female flowers, which produce only nectar, by the absence of a baby fruit at the base. Nectar is produced abundantly at times, being secreted at the bottom of the cup of the flower formed by the fusion of the sepals and the petals. Honey has been obtained from pumpkins, squashes and melons in other countries where they are grown on a large scale.

The pollen of the vegetable marrow, like that of other cucurbits, is very adhesive, due to the presence of a thin layer of oily or gummy matter on the grain. The individual grain is spherical, covered in spines and very large (about 150 μm in diameter), which makes it large enough to be seen with the naked eye. It is among the largest pollen grains found in honey. Both honeybees and bumblebees seem very partial to the pollen and collect it in large quantities.

Verbena — *Verbena* species

Family:	**Verbenaceae**
Flowering:	**July to November**
Cultivation:	**perennial herb**
Honey:	**no**
Honeybees:	||||| |||||
ST Bumblebees:	||||| |||||
LT Bumblebees:	||||| |||||
Solitary Bees:	|||||

Above:
Flowers of slender vervain (Verbena rigida)
(photo: M. A. Kirk)

There are over two hundred species of verbena and they are mostly natives of the New World. In many, the flower-tubes are too long for short-tongued bees, but in others this is not so. They often produce nectar freely and are good bee plants as well as good butterfly plants. This is the case with some of the blue- or purple-flowered, hardy perennial verbenas that have been introduced to cultivation in the British Isles, such as Argentinean vervain (*Verbena bonariensis*), blue vervain (*Verbena hastata*) and hoary vervain (*Verbena stricta*), which can flower for many months and are freely worked for nectar and pollen. The only wild verbena in the British Isles is the vervain (*Verbena officinalis*), which has a long history of use for medicinal purposes. It is common in England and Wales, but less so in Scotland and Ireland, and is often found on roadsides and rough ground. Its pale lilac flowers appear in slender spikes in July and August and bees are frequent visitors for nectar.

Vervain, see verbena

Veronica — *Veronica* species

Bees visit the flowers of both the wild and the garden or cultivated veronicas. Among the latter, the garden speedwell (*Veronica longifolia*), which is one of the commonest garden sorts and flowers from July to September, is an excellent bee plant. It is of sturdy and erect growth, with long flower spikes, and is in bloom a long time, hence its general popularity. Its flowers never fail to attract honeybees and bumblebees in large numbers. This applies to the various varieties with blue, white, rose or purple flowers. The nectar, which may be produced copiously, is secreted by the fleshy disc at the base of the ovary and is protected by hairs in the throat of the flower-tube. No bee garden should be without this excellent bee plant, which will thrive in any ordinary garden soil in a sunny position.

The flowers of the wild germander speedwell (*Veronica chamaedrys*), which appear from March to July, are visited by several solitary bees, for example mining bees (*Halictus* species). The girdled mining bee (*Andrena labiata*) collects pollen mainly from germander speedwell. It occurs in southern England and Wales, but not Scotland or Ireland. The front part of the body is blackish, while most of the hind part is distinctly reddish brown. A very rare cuckoo bee (*Nomada guttulata*) lives in the nest of the girdled mining bee and may also be found at flowers of germander speedwell.

Family:	Veronicaceae
Flowering:	March to September
Cultivation:	annual or perennial herb or evergreen dwarf shrub
Honey:	no
Honeybees:	||||| ||||| |||||
ST Bumblebees:	||||| ||||| |||||
LT Bumblebees:	||||| ||||| |||||
Solitary Bees:	||||| |||||

Far left:
*Girdled mining bee (*Andrena labiata*) on garden speedwell (*Veronica longifolia*)*
(photo: T. C. Ings)
Left:
*Leafcutter bee (*Megachile willughbiella*) on garden speedwell (*Veronica longifolia*)*
(photo: N. W. Owens)

Vetch — *Vicia* species

Vetches or tares used to be an important forage crop throughout the British Isles, but their use has declined considerably. The intensification of agriculture has meant that old flower-rich meadows have been replaced with selected grass varieties. Removal of hedges, drainage of marshy areas and use of herbicides on crops have also reduced populations of wild flowers. Vetches have particularly suffered from these agricultural practices. They, together with related plants such as red clover, are particularly visited for pollen by many of the long-tongued bumblebees that are declining, such as the short-haired bumblebee (*Bombus subterraneus*) and the ruderal bumblebee (*Bombus ruderatus*). In contrast, vetches are not good honeybee plants, although bees visit the flowers on occasions and seem to get a certain amount of nectar. There are even old records from other countries of surplus honey being obtained from them.

Family:	Fabaceae
Flowering:	May to September
Cultivation:	annual or perennial herb
Honey:	no
Honeybees:	|||||
ST Bumblebees:	||||| ||||| |||||
LT Bumblebees:	||||| ||||| |||||
Solitary Bees:	||||| |||||

V

Vegetable marrow — Vetch

Top:
*Flowers of common vetch (*Vicia sativa*)*
(photo: W. D. J. Kirk)

Above:
*Queen moss carder bee (*Bombus muscorum*)*
*on kidney vetch (*Anthyllis vulneraria*)*
(photo: L. A. Hislop)

This is said to resemble that of clover but to have a stronger flavour. As the flower is rather long for the honeybee it is not unusual for the nectar to be reached from the back or side. It would seem that the plant may be useful for nectar to honeybees in some seasons, but not in others and that some localities are more favourable than others. Several solitary bees visit vetch flowers. A very rare and endangered mining bee (*Andrena lathyri*), which is a large darkish bee, is associated with grassland with vetch, but is only known from a couple of sites in southern England. It appears to provision its nest with only vetch pollen and so is dependent on it.

Vetch is not being squeezed out of our agricultural landscape completely as it remains a good forage crop for animals. A modern approach is to sow selected varieties of common vetch (*Vicia sativa*) or hairy vetch (*Vicia villosa*) as a forage mixture with triticale (a hybrid of wheat and rye). The whole crop is harvested after the vetch has flowered and turned into silage for cattle.

Like its close relative the field bean (*Vicia faba*) (see separate entry), the vetch has well-developed extrafloral nectaries. These become functional about a fortnight before the flowers open.

Besides the common vetch (*Vicia sativa*), there are many wild vetches that receive visits from bees, such as the tufted vetch (*Vicia cracca*), bush vetch (*Vicia sepium*), hairy tare (*Vicia hirsuta*), horseshoe vetch (*Hippocrepis comosa*) and kidney vetch (*Anthyllis vulneraria*).

Vetchling — *Lathyrus* species

Family:	**Fabaceae**
Flowering:	**May to August**
Cultivation:	**annual or perennial herb**
Honey:	**no**
Honeybees:	‖‖
ST Bumblebees:	‖‖ ‖‖
LT Bumblebees:	‖‖ ‖‖ ‖‖
Solitary Bees:	‖‖

Vetchlings are rather similar to vetches (see vetch), scrambling or climbing by means of tendrils and having winged or flattened stems like the well-known sweet pea (*Lathyrus odoratus*), which belongs to the same genus. There are fewer leaflets per leaf than in the vetches. Although of prolific growth they are not so useful to the farmer as they are less readily eaten by stock and in some instances the seeds are poisonous.

Vetchlings are particularly useful to bumblebees. Several species visit the sweet pea, while the meadow vetchling (*Lathyrus pratensis*) is much visited by the common carder bee (*Bombus pascuorum*) and also attracts rare long-tongued bees, such as the moss carder bee (*Bombus muscorum*). The narrow-leaved everlasting pea or flat pea (*Lathyrus sylvestris*) also attracts long-tongued bumblebees. It grows wild in many parts of Britain, but not Ireland, and is particularly abundant along some of the Cornish cliffs.

The Wagner pea (*Lathyrus sylvestris* 'Wagneri') has small pea-like flowers that are worked most industriously by honeybees for nectar and are produced in great profusion. This plant is simply a cultivated form of the narrow-leaved everlasting pea.

The garden pea (*Pisum sativum*) is closely related to the vetchlings and the flowers are similar in shape, but bees usually show little interest in them. Bumblebees can occasionally be seen visiting the flowers.

Long-horned bees (*Eucera longicornis*) collect pollen from meadow

Above:
Flowers of narrow-leaved everlasting pea
*(*Lathyrus sylvestris*)*
(photo: W. D. J. Kirk)

vetchling, tuberous pea (*Lathyrus tuberosus*) and several other related plants with similar flowers This large, dark brown bee has remarkably long antennae in the male. It is found in southern Britain and can be locally common, but is declining rapidly.

Far left:
*Queen great yellow bumblebee (*Bombus distinguendus*) on meadow vetchling* (Lathyrus pratensis)
(photo: N. W. Owens)
Left:
*Female two-coloured mason bee (*Osmia bicolor*) on meadow vetchling* (Lathyrus pratensis)
(photo: J. P. Early)

Violet — *Viola odorata*

In warmer climates, violets are commonly visited by honeybees for nectar, but the wild violets of the hedgerow appear so early in the year that they are seldom likely to be a source of much nectar in the British Isles. The flowers are visited by several solitary bees, such as flower bees (*Anthophora* species) and a mason bee (*Osmia pilicornis*), which occurs in southern England. Bees also visit the flowers of the common wild pansy (*Viola tricolor*). There are many species and varieties of violet in cultivation, but not all are suitable for bees, and of those that are, the length of the nectar-containing spur is variable, which means that their suitability for bees depends on the tongue length of the bee.

Family:	Violaceae
Flowering:	March to May
Cultivation:	perennial herb
Honey:	no
Honeybees:	‖‖‖
ST Bumblebees:	‖‖‖
LT Bumblebees:	‖‖‖
Solitary Bees:	‖‖‖

Far left:
*Flower of common dog-violet (*Viola riviniana*)*
(photo: M. A. Kirk)
Left:
*Queen garden bumblebee (*Bombus hortorum*) on violet (*Viola odorata*)*
(photo: L. Hebdon)

Viper's bugloss — *Echium vulgare*

The conspicuous purple flowers of this plant are very attractive to bees. Without doubt the viper's bugloss is one of the most stately of British wild plants and one of the most beautiful. Its rough stem is speckled (like a viper) and grows up to about a metre in height. The narrow leaves are also rough or bristly.

The wild plant is most frequently seen on light or sandy soils. Unfortunately for bees, it is somewhat local in its distribution in the British Isles and is most frequent in the south and east of England. Flowering takes place mainly in June and July. The colour of the flowers is variable

Family:	Boraginaceae
Flowering:	June to July
Cultivation:	biennial herb
Honey:	no
Honeybees:	‖‖‖ ‖‖‖ ‖‖‖
ST Bumblebees:	‖‖‖ ‖‖‖ ‖‖‖
LT Bumblebees:	‖‖‖ ‖‖‖ ‖‖‖
Solitary Bees:	‖‖‖ ‖‖‖

V

Vetchling — Viper's bugloss

Above:
*Flowers of viper's bugloss (*Echium vulgare*)*
(photo: W. D. J. Kirk)
Right:
*Hairy-footed flower bee (*Anthophora
plumipes*) visiting purple viper's bugloss
(*Echium plantagineum*)*
(photo: N. W. Owens)
Far right:
*Pollen grain of viper's bugloss (*Echium
vulgare*) (16 μm)*

and in addition to purple may be pale blue, bluish pink or even white. The plant sometimes finds a place in the flower garden, although other echiums are more generally cultivated.

Nectar is produced very freely and the plant has been recommended for sowing in waste places, cuttings and roadside verges to improve the bee pasturage of a district. Viper's bugloss is regularly included in wild-flower seed mixes that are sold to help bees. The flowers are visited by honeybees and bumblebees such as the buff-tailed bumblebee (*Bombus terrestris*) and the common carder bee (*Bombus pascuorum*). When present, rare bumblebee species, such as the great yellow bumblebee (*Bombus distinguendus*) in northern Scotland, will visit the flowers. The larger solitary bees, such as species of flower bee (*Anthophora* species) and leaf-cutter bee (*Megachile* species), also visit.

A similar plant, the purple viper's bugloss (*Echium plantagineum*), which occurs in Jersey and parts of Cornwall is also an excellent bee plant. It has become a common weed in Australia, especially South Australia, where it may cover hectares of grazing land. Commonly known as salvation Jane or Paterson's curse, it is a valuable source of honey, which is sometimes sold as Australian bluebell honey.

Virginia creeper — *Parthenocissus quinquefolia*

Family:	**Vitaceae**
Flowering:	**June to August**
Cultivation:	**deciduous large woody climber**
Honey:	**no**
Honeybees:	||||| |||||
ST Bumblebees:	|||||
LT Bumblebees:	—
Solitary Bees:	—

This climber is very commonly cultivated. It is to be seen covering walls and the sides of houses everywhere and is valued for the brilliant red colour it turns in the autumn just before the leaves fall. Its flowers, each about 5 mm across, are in small bunches of three to eight and are not at all conspicuous, especially when the plant grows on walls, for then they are completely hidden from view by the overhanging leaves. Their presence, however, is usually given away by the hum of honeybees as they seek the flowers for nectar and pollen. The closely related species Boston ivy (*Parthenocissus tricuspidata*) is similarly popular with honeybees. The Virginia creeper is regarded as a useful nectar plant in its native land (eastern North America), where it frequently climbs the loftiest trees.

It should be noted that the Virginia creeper (*Parthenocissus quinquefolia*) and the false Virginia creeper (*Parthenocissus inserta*) are invasive non-native species in the UK. The Wildlife and Countryside Act 1981 (Variation of Schedule 9) (England and Wales) Order 2010 prohibits planting or causing them to grow in the wild.

Above:
Pollen grain of Boston ivy (Parthenocissus tricuspidata) *(34 μm)*
Left:
Virginia creeper flower (Parthenocissus quinquefolia)
(photo: W. D. J. Kirk)

Virginia mallow — *Sida hermaphrodita*

The small, white flowers of this vigorous, mallow-like perennial, which is not often cultivated, are visited for nectar and pollen by bees. It has been considered as a potential biomass crop for renewable energy in parts of central and eastern Europe.

Family:	**Malvaceae**
Flowering:	**July to September**
Cultivation:	**perennial herb**
Honey:	**no**
Honeybees:	||||| |||||
ST Bumblebees:	|||||
LT Bumblebees:	—
Solitary Bees:	|||||

Left:
Flowering stem of Virginia mallow (Sida hermaphrodita)
(photo: M. Kucharczyk)

Wallflower — *Erysimum* species

Family:	**Brassicaceae**
Flowering:	**April to June**
Cultivation:	**perennial herb**
Honey:	**no**
Honeybees:	||||| |||||
ST Bumblebees:	||||| |||||
LT Bumblebees:	||||| |||||
Solitary Bees:	|||||

Wallflowers are among the most useful of the early spring garden flowers for bees and are visited continuously for nectar and pollen when weather is suitable. There seems to be little if any difference between the many varieties in cultivation where attraction to bees is concerned. All are popular except of course the double-flowered varieties and these are not grown to nearly the same extent as the single forms. The nectaries take the form of two swollen ridges at the base of the two short stamens.

The wallflower is not really a native of the British Isles, being of eastern Mediterranean origin, but is to be found naturalised or apparently wild in some areas, especially on cliffs near the sea, old walls, and rocky places generally.

The main visitors are honeybees and bumblebees, but the flowers are also visited by solitary bees, such as species of flower bee (*Anthophora* species), mason bee (*Osmia* species) and stem-nesting bee (*Hylaeus* species).

Right:
*Male buff-tailed bumblebee (*Bombus terrestris*) on wallflower (*Erysimum *species)*
(photo: T. C. Ings)
Far right:
*Pollen grain of wallflower (*Erysimum cheiri*)*
(23 µm)

Watercress — *Nasturtium officinale*

Family:	**Brassicaceae**
Flowering:	**June to August**
Cultivation:	**perennial herb**
Honey:	**no**
Honeybees:	|||||
ST Bumblebees:	|||||
LT Bumblebees:	|||||
Solitary Bees:	|||||

The white flowers of watercress, like those of most plants in the cabbage family (Brassicaceae), are a source of nectar and pollen for bees and are usually available from June to August. Despite having the scientific name *Nasturtium*, watercress is not closely related to the garden nasturtium (see nasturtium). The plant is common on the margins of streams and ponds across most of the British Isles. It is also cultivated on a large scale for market in special watercress beds in southern England, sometimes several hectares in extent. However, normally it is harvested before it reaches the flowering stage. The great yellowcress (*Rorippa amphibia*) is a somewhat similar plant with yellow flowers and is also visited for nectar and pollen.

Right:
*Queen buff-tailed bumblebee (*Bombus terrestris*) on watercress (*Nasturtium officinale*)*
(photo: T. C. Ings)

Weigela — *Weigela* species

These deciduous shrubs, which are allied to the honeysuckle (see separate entry), secrete nectar very freely. They are among the most beautiful of summer-flowering shrubs with white, cream, pink, or red flowers of various shades. Bumblebees may be seen working the flowers with zest in June, particularly long-tongued species such as the common carder bee (*Bombus pascuorum*). Short-tongued bumblebees frequently bite holes at the base of the flower which they and honeybees make use of to obtain the nectar.

Family:	**Caprifoliaceae**
Flowering:	**May to June**
Cultivation:	**deciduous medium shrub**
Honey:	**no**
Honeybees:	‖‖‖
ST Bumblebees:	‖‖‖
LT Bumblebees:	‖‖‖ ‖‖‖
Solitary Bees:	—

Far left:
Weigela flower (Weigela *species*)
(photo: W. D. J. Kirk)
Left:
Worker garden bumblebee (Bombus hortorum) *approaching weigela* (Weigela *species*)
(photo: L. Hebdon)

White bryony — *Bryonia dioica*

The rather unattractive greenish-white flowers of white bryony are visited by bees. One species of mining bee (*Andrena florea*) restricts its pollen foraging to white bryony, so this plant is essential for it. The flowers may be seen in hedgerows and other places from May to September for this climbing plant has a long flowering season. Although pollen is collected, the visits of honeybees often seem to be primarily for nectar, especially in the latter part of the summer. The nectar, which is partly concealed, is secreted at the bottom of the naked fleshy cup formed by the fusion of the lower part of the sepals and petals.

Family:	**Cucurbitaceae**
Flowering:	**May to September**
Cultivation:	**perennial herb**
Honey:	**no**
Honeybees:	‖‖‖
ST Bumblebees:	‖‖‖
LT Bumblebees:	‖‖‖
Solitary Bees:	‖‖‖ ‖‖‖ ‖‖‖

Far left:
Mining bee (Andrena florea) *on white bryony* (Bryonia dioica)
(photo: T. C. Ings)
Left:
Female mining bee (Andrena florea) *on white bryony* (Bryonia dioica)
(photo: J. P. Early)

W

Wallflower — White bryony

White clover — *Trifolium repens*

Family:	**Fabaceae**
Flowering:	**June to September**
Cultivation:	**perennial herb**
Honey:	**yes**
Honeybees:	‖‖‖ ‖‖‖ ‖‖‖
ST Bumblebees:	‖‖‖ ‖‖‖ ‖‖‖
LT Bumblebees:	‖‖‖ ‖‖‖ ‖‖‖
Solitary Bees:	‖‖‖ ‖‖‖

Top:
Pollen grain of white clover (Trifolium repens) (25 μm)
Above:
Flower-head of white clover (Trifolium repens)
(photo: W. D. J. Kirk)

Although white clover is usually considered to be a weed in gardens, it is one of the best plants for bees. It produces large amounts of nectar and some pollen over a long time in summer when few other sources are available. The flower-tube is shorter than in red clover (*Trifolium pratense*) (see separate entry), which means that the nectar can be reached easily by bees with shorter tongues, such as honeybees and short-tongued bumblebees. Although long-tongued bumblebees prefer the longer flower-tubes of red clover, they are also frequent visitors to white clover. The flowers are also visited by many solitary bees, such as mining bees (*Lasioglossum* species) and leafcutter bees (*Megachile* species).

In the 19th and early 20th centuries, white clover was abundant in the British Isles because it occurred in widespread permanent pastures. Clover, which was mainly white clover, was estimated to account for about 75% of the British honey crop and clover honey was common. However, changes in agricultural practice have dramatically reduced the amount of white clover across much of the British Isles, although it remains a major honey source in some areas, such as parts of southeast Ireland. Intensification of agriculture has reduced the amount of permanent pasture and the easy availability of nitrogenous fertilisers has reduced the need for white clover to be sown. Even when clover is present, silage cutting can remove flowers before bees have had much chance to visit them. However, the tide may be changing in favour of a greening of agriculture and an increased use of white clover rather than fertilisers. White clover is still an excellent bee plant, even if it is far less widespread than a hundred years ago. Large quantities of honey are obtained from white clover in other temperate regions around the world, including Canada, the northern USA, New Zealand and Australia.

Throughout the British Isles, white clover is one of the commonest plants, except on acid soils. It is prevalent along roadsides where it often thrives in the gravel or sand swept off the road surface. This may be due largely to the good soil aeration such a habitat provides. It also occurs freely in waste places and as a weed in arable land and lawns.

There are two main types of white clover, the so-called wild white and the ordinary white or Dutch clover. The wild white is a smaller plant than the Dutch, with smaller leaves and flowers and a free running or creeping habit. It is also longer lived and is most used for permanent pasture. There is probably little difference between the two types as honey producers, but some observers have expressed the view that the wild white is more freely worked than the Dutch when they are grown side by side. There are many commercially available varieties of white clover, some of which are more attractive to bees than others.

White clover commences flowering early in June in most southern districts and continues in flower for the greater part of the summer, provided prolonged drought does not intervene. The actual nectar flow usually commences about 10 days after the first open blossoms appear. Flowers that appear towards the end of the flowering period do not produce much nectar.

Each flower-head contains from 50 to 100 individual flowers or florets. These all stand erect at first, but as they become pollinated and cease to secrete nectar they bend downwards and eventually wither. The stamens or male elements of the flowers are hidden from view and are united into a tube for the greater part, as in other clovers and most members of the pea family (Fabaceae). It is on the lower inner surface of this stamen tube that the nectar is to be found.

Under favourable conditions the flowers secrete nectar very freely and heavy honey crops are taken in good seasons. The temperature range over which white clover will secrete nectar is wide compared with that of many plants, and probably extends lower than the temperature required for honeybees to fly. Assuming there is adequate soil moisture and the plants do not wilt, it is doubtful whether the mild climate of the British Isles ever becomes too hot for the plant to secrete. Most beekeepers in clover areas hold the view that the warmer the weather the better the flow, assuming always that drought does not unduly deplete soil moisture. This probably does not apply to Continental climates where much hotter summers are the rule.

Even with the right climatic and temperature conditions the soil is all-important in determining to what extent white clover will prove to be a good honey source. Soils having an abundance of lime always yield the best results and when clover was more widespread some of the best clover honey districts were those on the chalk, such as the slopes of the Chilterns and Cotswolds. Some contend the plant yields better on hilly slopes than it does on lowlands and will continue to yield later in the year. Where there is a marked deficiency of lime in the soil, white clover may yield no nectar at all, but be visited by bees for pollen.

In the British Isles, white clover honey is the honey par excellence – the honey with which all other honeys are compared. It is light in colour, from water white to pale amber, and very bright. It has good density combined with a delicate flavour and aroma. The flavour has a more or less universal appeal. This accounts for the popularity of the honey as a trade product. It finds favour with the largest possible number of customers. The density and colour of the honey vary to some extent with the season and the soil. When the nectar flow is slow or intermittent the honey is darker than when it is obtained from a fast steady flow. The honey granulates well and is white with a fine and very smooth grain. It does not granulate quickly. This is one of the reasons why it is favoured for comb honey, in which form it can hardly be excelled.

It is worth noting that honey preferences vary with country according to what people are used to. In the British Isles, mild-flavoured light-coloured honeys predominate and are most popular, whereas dark strong-flavoured honeys do not sell well and are often considered only suitable for baking. In contrast, in regions that have large forests and so regularly produce honeydew honey, dark strong-flavoured honey is popular and mild honey is considered bland and unappealing.

The pollen of white clover is produced rather sparingly by the flowers. When packed on bees' hind legs it assumes a dark greenish brown appearance and is not usually brought back to the hive in large loads as is

W

White clover

Top:
Male white-tailed bumblebee (Bombus lucorum) *on white clover* (Trifolium repens)
(photo: J. Craig)

Middle:
Male red-tailed bumblebee (Bombus lapidarius) *on white clover* (Trifolium repens)
(photo: J. Craig)

Bottom:
Red-tailed bumblebee (Bombus lapidarius) *on white clover* (Trifolium repens)
(photo: T. C. Ings)

the case with many pollens, perhaps because they can collect a full load of nectar before they can collect much pollen. It is one of the pollens most commonly found in English honey. The individual pollen grains are somewhat variable in size, shape and colour, and may easily be confused with those of other clovers and clover-like plants.

Whitecurrant, see currant

White dead-nettle, see dead-nettle

White horehound — *Marrubium vulgare*

Family:	**Lamiaceae**
Flowering:	**June to September**
Cultivation:	**perennial herb**
Honey:	**no**
Honeybees:	||||| |||||
ST Bumblebees:	|||||
LT Bumblebees:	—
Solitary Bees:	|||||

White horehound and black horehound (see separate entry) are both good bee plants, but the former is better for honeybees. White horehound was once much esteemed as a medicinal plant and so was widely grown in herb gardens. In the wild state the plant is not common and occurs usually in waste places. It is a bushy plant with stems 30–60 cm high, the stems and leaves being covered with a white woolly down giving the plant a greyish appearance. The small white flowers appear from June in dense whorls or clusters on the stem. They are rich in nectar and much loved by honeybees. The plant is well worth a place in a honeybee garden with honeybees often preferring it to other plants.

Wild marjoram — *Origanum vulgare*

Family:	**Lamiaceae**
Flowering:	**July to September**
Cultivation:	**perennial herb**
Honey:	**no**
Honeybees:	||||| |||||
ST Bumblebees:	||||| |||||
LT Bumblebees:	||||| ||||| |||||
Solitary Bees:	||||| |||||

Wild marjoram is a much-loved wild flower with its delightful fragrance and masses of purple flowers. It favours calcareous soils and is common on chalk hills in southern England, often dominating the landscape when in flower. This takes place from July onwards. The flowers are in crowded clusters at the ends of the stalks, which are 30–60 cm in height. Bumblebees and honeybees are frequent visitors for nectar and this is yielded abundantly at times.

A pure wild marjoram honey is not usually obtained in southern England as there are generally other nectar-yielding flowers available at the same time, such as blackberry and thyme (see separate entries). However, it is considered to yield a high-quality honey of good flavour and aroma and its presence is always likely to improve rather than detract from the quality of other honey, particularly that of rosebay willowherb (see separate entry), which is naturally a honey of little flavour and is in flower at the same time.

The cultivated version of wild marjoram is also known as oregano and several varieties are available for gardens, which can be grown either decoratively or as a herb. Sweet marjoram (*Origanum majorana*) and pot marjoram (*Origanum onites*) are also generally cultivated, their aromatic leaves being used either in the fresh or dried state for flavouring. Sweet marjoram is a native of the Mediterranean, and is grown as an annual in

Above:
Pollen grain of wild marjoram (Origanum vulgare) *(32 μm)*

the British Isles as it does not withstand the winter. Plants grown from seed sown in April usually flower in July. The flowers are small and pale, with the flower tubes about 4 mm long. They are much sought after by bees for nectar. Common carder bees (*Bombus pascuorum*) are frequent visitors and the flowers are also visited by several solitary bees. One example is the blue mason bee (*Osmia caerulescens*), which occurs in Britain but not Ireland and in the female has a slight hint of metallic blue on the hind part of the body.

Far left:
Male white-tailed bumblebee (Bombus lucorum) *on wild marjoram* (Origanum vulgare)
Left:
A drone fly (Eristalis tenax) *on wild marjoram* (Origanum vulgare)*. It is easily mistaken for a honeybee, but the angled body and the very short antennae distinguish it.*
(photos: W. D. J. Kirk)

Willow — *Salix* species

The willows or sallows are valuable plants for bees in the early part of the season. There are some twenty wild species in the British Isles as well as numerous hybrid forms. Other introduced kinds, such as the weeping willow (*Salix babylonica* and hybrids), are also often cultivated. The willows vary in size from large trees, like the crack willow (*Salix fragilis*) and white willow (*Salix alba*) to small shrubs, sometimes not more than a few inches high and of a creeping nature. Some, like the grey willow (*Salix cinerea*) and goat willow (*Salix caprea*) – commonly called palm and much sought for decoration when in the silvery bud stage – and the dwarf or creeping willow (*Salix repens*) are widely distributed throughout the British Isles and very prevalent in some districts. Their presence is always appreciated by local beekeepers as a source of early pollen and nectar.

Willows are in flower from February to May according to species and district. The male and female catkins are borne on different plants in most cases. These vary much in size and shape and are generally silky, the minute flowers being devoid of petals and consisting only of a scale bearing either the male or the female parts. Small yellow glands or nectaries may also be present. Many willows are a source of nectar as well as pollen to the honeybee and bumblebee when weather conditions are favourable. Catkins generally appear on the naked shoots of the previous summer and before the leaves arrive. Both male and female flowers secrete nectar under favourable conditions, although only the male flowers produce pollen.

The willows already mentioned are visited by bees for nectar and pollen, but there are many more. Included among them are the eared willow (*Salix aurita*) found in woods, the almond willow (*Salix triandra*) which is an osier cultivated for basket making and the European violet willow (*Salix daphnoides*). The last mentioned is a central European willow, although naturalised in places, and has been recommended on the Continent for

Family:	Salicaceae
Flowering:	February to May
Cultivation:	deciduous small shrub to large tree
Honey:	yes
Honeybees:	||||| ||||| |||||
ST Bumblebees:	||||| ||||| |||||
LT Bumblebees:	||||| ||||| |||||
Solitary Bees:	||||| ||||| |||||

Top:
Pollen grain of goat willow (Salix caprea) *(18 μm)*
Above:
Willow flowers (Salix *species*)
(photo: W. D. J. Kirk)

Top:
*Male mining bee (*Colletes cunicularius*)*
(photo: N. P. Jones)
Middle:
*Mining bee (*Andrena clarkella*) at its nest
entrance with pollen collected from willow
(*Salix *species)*
(photo: N. P. Jones)
Bottom:
*Male mining bee (*Andrena flavipes*) on
willow (*Salix *species)*
(photo: J. V. Adams)

cultivation by beekeepers, for it flowers earlier than most willows and has large catkins. Furthermore, it is highly ornamental with its waxy, purple shoots. The use of willows, such as osier (*Salix viminalis*), as a short-rotation coppice (SRC) for biofuel is increasing and may become much more widespread. Large plantations of willow would be very beneficial for bees.

Willows in close proximity to an apiary are always desirable. Most willows are easily propagated by cuttings placed in the open ground any time between November and early March. In the case of the tree sorts like the crack willow and white willow, quite large sets, 2–3 m long and 2–4 cm in diameter usually root readily and are commonly used. If difficulty is experienced in obtaining rooting, as may happen in dry localities, the following is a more certain method of obtaining rooted plants. Cuttings about 30 cm long and the thickness of a pencil are taken in the winter and kept in a cool place or heeled in. In March these are placed with their ends in water (half immersed) and brought indoors or placed in a greenhouse when the warmth and moisture soon causes profuse root development. The rooted cuttings may then be planted out in April or May and kept watered for a time in the event of dry weather. The male forms of the goat willow (*Salix caprea*) with their large handsome catkins are probably as good as any for cultivation by the beekeeper. Some forms flower earlier than others and could be used to lengthen the flowering period. Honey may be obtained from willow in some areas in seasons when a fine spell of weather accompanies flowering.

The flowers provide an important early source of nectar and pollen for queen bumblebees of many species and so are particularly valuable in helping queens survive to establish nests. Pollen early in the season is also important to the many solitary bees that collect pollen for their nest. For example, creeping willow (*Salix repens*) is exclusively visited for pollen by a rare mining bee (*Colletes cunicularius*), which has been recorded from coastal areas of Wales and northwest England. Several mining bees (*Andrena* species) collect pollen almost exclusively from willow, for example *Andrena clarkella*, which occurs locally throughout the British Isles. The flowers are also visited by other solitary bees, such as flower bees (*Anthophora* species) and mason bees (*Osmia* species).

Winter aconite — *Eranthis hyemalis*

Family:	**Ranunculaceae**
Flowering:	**January to March**
Cultivation:	**perennial herb, grown from tubers**
Honey:	**no**
Honeybees:	‖‖‖ ‖‖‖
ST Bumblebees:	‖‖‖
LT Bumblebees:	—
Solitary Bees:	—

This tuberous-rooted perennial does not exceed 15 cm in height and has attractive yellow flowers early in the year before anything else. It is not native, originating from southern Europe, but it has naturalised in woods scattered across Britain. In mild winters, the flowers are out in January and are always well ahead of the crocus. With suitable weather, honeybees work them industriously, not only for pollen but for nectar as well. The flowers are probably too early to be visited by other bees, except perhaps winter-active buff-tailed bumblebees (*Bombus terrestris*) in southern England (see mahonia).

In this flower the nectar is produced and stored, as in the Christmas rose (*Helleborus niger*) (see hellebore), in vase-shaped containers arranged on the flower where the petals are usually to be found. The containers are in fact modified petals. Like the crocus, the winter aconite is well worth cultivating near beehives as an early source of pollen. Once established it requires little attention and grows well under shrubs or trees where few other plants succeed. It is usually in flower for 4–6 weeks.

Left:
*Honeybee collecting pollen on winter aconite (*Eranthis hyemalis)
(photo: T. C. Ings)

Winter cress — *Barbarea vulgaris*

Winter cress or yellow rocket is a native plant that occurs both wild and cultivated. Its yellow mustard-like flowers appear in dense terminal clusters from May to July and bees visit them mainly for nectar. Several different forms are available, including one with variegated leaves. Those with double flowers are of little benefit to bees.

Family:	Brassicaceae
Flowering:	May to July
Cultivation:	biennial or perennial herb
Honey:	no
Honeybees:	||||| |||||
ST Bumblebees:	||||| |||||
LT Bumblebees:	|||||
Solitary Bees:	|||||

Wisteria — *Wisteria sinensis*

The purple masses of pea-like flowers of this magnificent climber will attract honeybees and bumblebees in some seasons but not in others. The flowers appear in May and there is sometimes a second but much smaller crop of flowers in August. In bright or warm weather bees visit the flowers for nectar at Kew Gardens, but when conditions are cool they seem to offer little attraction. In other warmer climates, the flowers of wisteria are known to be worked for nectar and pollen.

Family:	Fabaceae
Flowering:	May to June
Cultivation:	deciduous large woody climber
Honey:	no
Honeybees:	|||||
ST Bumblebees:	|||||
LT Bumblebees:	|||||
Solitary Bees:	—

Left:
*Wisteria flowers (*Wisteria sinensis)
(photo: W. D. J. Kirk)

Wood anemone — *Anemone nemorosa*

Family:	**Ranunculaceae**
Flowering:	**March to May**
Cultivation:	**perennial herb**
Honey:	**no**
Honeybees:	||||| |||||
ST Bumblebees:	|||||
LT Bumblebees:	|||||
Solitary Bees:	|||||

The white flowers of the well-known wood anemone (*Anemone nemorosa*) appear in early spring, sometimes as early as the middle of March, and may be a useful source of pollen for bees. The flowers yield a pale-coloured pollen in abundance and honeybees are sometimes frequent visitors. The flowers are unusual in producing no nectar. A careful observer in the 19th century recorded that honeybees not only collected pollen but sometimes pushed the tongue into the base of the flower so as to obtain sap for moistening the pollen.

An early-flying solitary bee, the two-coloured mason bee (*Osmia bicolor*), visits early wild flowers, such as wood anemone and bluebell. It occurs mainly in areas with chalky soil in southern England and south Wales. The female is very distinctive, with the front part of the body black and the hind part reddish. It has the curious habit of nesting in empty snail shells.

Other anemones may be visited for pollen, such as the pasque flower (*Pulsatilla vulgaris*), which grows wild on chalk downs as well as being grown in gardens, and the autumn-flowering Japanese anemones (*Anemone hupehensis*).

Above:
Pollen grain of *Japanese anemone* (Anemone hupehensis) *(20 μm)*
Right top:
Wood *anemone flower* (Anemone nemorosa)
(photo: W. D. J. Kirk)
Right bottom:
Pasque flower (Pulsatilla vulgaris)
(photo: M. A. Kirk)

Wood sage — *Teucrium scorodonia*

Wood sage or wood germander can grow in masses, often in woods, heathy places or dunes. It is about 0.5 m high and has wrinkled leaves, very like those of ordinary sage (see sage). Its yellowish-green flowers appear in July and August. They often have a faint tinge of purple and grow in one-sided clusters at the top of the stems. The flower-tube is some 9–10 mm in length, which would normally restrict the nectar to long-tongued bees, such as the common carder bee (*Bombus pascuorum*) and long-tongued flower bees (*Anthophora* species). These visit the flowers and can reach the nectar most of the time. However, the nectar is secreted freely and may accumulate to a level of 4–5 mm up the tube, so short-tongued bees are also often able to reach it. Honeybees often work the flowers and surplus honey has been obtained in the past in places where the plant was common. Some of the other species of germander attract bees, including the shrubby germander (*Teucrium fruticans*) and the water germander (*Teucrium scordium*), which is now a rare and declining plant.

Family:	**Lamiaceae**
Flowering:	**July to August**
Cultivation:	**perennial herb**
Honey:	**no**
Honeybees:	||||| |||||
ST Bumblebees:	||||| |||||
LT Bumblebees:	||||| |||||
Solitary Bees:	|||||

Left:
*Red mason bee (*Osmia rufa*) on shrubby germander (*Teucrium fruticans*)*
(photo: T. C. Ings)

W

Wood anemone — Woundwort

Woundwort, see stachys

Y

Yarrow, see achillea

Yellow loosestrife — *Lysimachia vulgaris*

Family:	**Primulaceae**
Flowering:	**June to August**
Cultivation:	**perennial herb**
Honey:	**no**
Honeybees:	—
ST Bumblebees:	—
LT Bumblebees:	—
Solitary Bees:	||||| ||||| |||||

The plant has attractive, yellow flowers, which produce plenty of pollen, but no nectar. The feature that makes them unusual is that they secrete a fatty oil from glandular hairs on the stamens in the centre of the flower and at the base of the petals inside the flower. The oil attracts an unusual mining bee (*Macropis europaea*). Adult females visit the flowers to collect oil, which is used for nest provisions and to provide a waterproof lining to the cells of the nest. The female bee collects pollen by curling its body around the anthers so that pollen rubs off on to its underside, simultaneously pollinating. It also absorbs oil from the glandular hairs by dabbing at them with its front and mid-legs. The ends of their legs are covered with a layer of fine hairs that take up the oil by capillary action. While the bee is in the flower, it holds its hind legs up above its body in a distinctive manner. In flight, the bee transfers oil and pollen to special structures on the hind legs to form a pollen-oil mixture. About 60 visits over 10 to 15 minutes are needed to collect a full load. The oil can remain in a liquid state for a long time, but it rapidly forms a solid mass on contact with bees or pollen. The full load of the pollen-oil mixture is taken back to the nest. Adult females mark the flowers they visit with a scent that attracts passing females on foraging flights and males on mating flights. The species is uncommon and appears to be restricted to southern and eastern England, roughly south of a line from Norfolk to Somerset. The flowers are also visited for pollen by other solitary bees, such as mining bees (*Lasioglossum* species).

Above:
Female mining bee (Macropis europaea) *gathering oil on yellow loosestrife* (Lysimachia vulgaris)
(photo: J. P. Early)

Right:
Female mining bee (Macropis europaea) *approaching yellow loosestrife* (Lysimachia vulgaris)
(photo: R. Williams)

Yellow rattle — *Rhinanthus minor*

This meadow plant has unusual growing requirements because it is partially parasitic on the roots of neighbouring plants. The yellow flowers are much visited by bumblebees. The flower-tubes are, like those of its near relative the red bartsia (see separate entry), too long for the honeybee. However, they are frequently punctured near the base by short-tongued bumblebees that cannot reach the nectar from the front of the flower and the honeybee takes advantage of this. Yellow rattle gets its name from the flower colour and the way the mature seeds rattle when the plant is shaken.

Family:	**Orobanchaceae**
Flowering:	**May to August**
Cultivation:	**perennial herb**
Honey:	**no**
Honeybees:	|||||
ST Bumblebees:	||||| |||||
LT Bumblebees:	||||| |||||
Solitary Bees:	|||||

Left:
Flowers of yellow rattle (Rhinanthus minor)
(photo: J. P. Early)

Yellow suckling clover, see lesser trefoil

Yew — *Taxus baccata*

The yew is common, both growing wild and deliberately planted. Some of the largest trees are those in churchyards and these are often of great age. It is most prevalent in the chalk districts of southeast England. On the western Sussex Downs it forms extensive woods. Yew flowers early, generally in March, and produces pollen in abundance from its male flowers. This is light and powdery and will often float away in clouds when the branches are tapped. Honeybees work the flowers well for pollen in some districts. Possibly, as is the case with other dry or wind-borne pollens, bees only take it when no other source is available. The yew does not yield nectar.

Family:	**Taxaceae**
Flowering:	**March to April**
Cultivation:	**evergreen medium tree**
Honey:	**no**
Honeybees:	|||||
ST Bumblebees:	—
LT Bumblebees:	—
Solitary Bees:	—

Left:
Yew flowers (Taxus baccata)
(photo: W. D. J. Kirk)

Above:
Queen buff-tailed
bumblebee
(Bombus terrestris)
on willow (Salix
species)
See p.273.
(photo: T. C. Ings)

A QUICK REFERENCE GUIDE TO PLANTS

A quick guide to the plants that are of most value to honeybees, short-tongued (ST) bumblebees, long-tongued (LT) bumblebees and solitary bees. Look down the column for a particular type of bee to see which plants are the best for it. The very best plants are indicated by a coloured symbol. Alternatively, look for plants with several symbols to find plants of value to several types of bee. Plants in the Top 10 for a type of bee (see chapters 2, 3 and 4) are in bold.

Colour key

Honeybees	✿
ST Bumblebees	✿
LT Bumblebees	✿
Solitary bees	✿

A

Plant	Honeybees	ST Bumblebees	LT Bumblebees	Solitary bees	Page
Achillea	✿	✿		✿	60
Agrimony					60
Alder					61
Allium	✿	✿	✿		61
Almond	✿				62
Alsike clover	✿	✿	✿	✿	63
Anchusa	✿	✿	✿		63
Anise hyssop					64
Anthericum					64
Apple	✿	✿	✿	✿	65
Apricot					66
Arabis	✿	✿			66
Aralia	✿	✿			67
Arnica	✿	✿	✿		68
Ash					68
Asparagus	✿	✿	✿		68
Aster	✿	✿	✿	✿	69
Aubrieta	✿	✿	✿		69
Autumn hawkbit	✿			✿	70
Avens	✿	✿	✿		70
Azalea		✿	✿		71

B

Plant	Honeybees	ST Bumblebees	LT Bumblebees	Solitary bees	Page
Baby's breath					72
Balsam	✿	✿	✿		72
Baptisia	✿	✿	✿		73
Barberry		✿			73
Basil	✿	✿	✿	✿	73
Bearberry		✿	✿		74
Bee balm			✿		74
Begonia					75
Bellflower	✿	✿	✿	✿	75
Bilberry		✿	✿	✿	76
Birch					76
Bird's-foot trefoil	✿	✿	✿	✿	77
Blackberry	✿	✿	✿	✿	78
Black horehound			✿		79
Blackthorn	✿			✿	79
Bloodroot					80
Bluebell		✿	✿		80
Borage	✿	✿	✿	✿	81
Box	✿				82
Brassica	✿	✿	✿		83
Broom					84
Buckthorn					85
Buckwheat	✿				85
Bugle		✿	✿	✿	87
Burning bush					87
Butterbur	✿	✿	✿	✿	88
Buttercup				✿	88
Butterfly bush	✿	✿	✿		90
Buttonbush	✿	✿	✿		90

FURTHER READING AND INFORMATION
BOOKS AND PUBLICATIONS

Aston, D. & Bucknall, S. A. (2004) *Plants and Honey Bees – Their Relationships*. Northern Bee Books, Mytholmroyd.

Aston, D. & Bucknall, S. A. (2010) *Keeping Healthy Honey Bees*. Northern Bee Books, Mytholmroyd.

Baldock, D. W. (2008) *Bees of Surrey*. Surrey Wildlife Trust, Pirbright.

Benton, T. (2006) *Bumblebees. New Naturalists' Series 98*. Harper Collins, London.

Brickell, C. (2008) *The Royal Horticultural Society A-Z Encyclopedia of Garden Plants*. 3rd revised edition. Dorling Kindersley, London. [This book is a useful guide to garden plants]

Chinery, M. (1993) *Collins Field Guide – Insects of Britain and Northern Europe*. 3rd revised edition. Harper Collins, London. [This book is useful for recognition of bees]

Dicks, L. V., Showler, D. A. & Sutherland, W. J. (2010) *Bee Conservation: Evidence for the Effects of Interventions*. Pelagic Publishing, Exeter.

Edwards, M. (1995) *Site Management for Aculeate Populations*. Central Association of Bee-Keepers publications, UK.

Edwards, M. & Jenner, M. (2009) *Field Guide to the Bumblebees of Great Britain & Ireland*. Revised edition. Ocelli, Eastbourne. [This book is useful for bumblebee identification]

Edwards, R. & others (eds.) (1997–2009) *Provisional Atlas of the Aculeate Hymenoptera of Britain and Ireland*. Parts 1-7. Biological Records Centre, Wallingford.

Else, G. R. (2013, in press) *Handbook of the Bees of the British Isles. Ray Society Monograph*. The Ray Society, London.

Gibbons, R. & Brough, P. (2007) *Guide to Wild Flowers of Britain and Europe*. Philip's (Octopus). [This book is an illustrated guide for identification of wild plants]

Goodman, L. (2003) *Form and Function in the Honey Bee*. International Bee Research Association, Cardiff.

Goulson, D. (2010) *Bumblebees: Behaviour, Ecology, and Conservation*. 2nd edition. Oxford University Press, Oxford.

Hooper, T. (2010) *Guide to Bees and Honey*. Northern Bee Books, Mytholmroyd.

Hooper, T. & Taylor, M. (1988) *The Beekeeper's Garden*. Alphabooks A&C Black, London.

Howes, F. N. (1979) *Plants and Beekeeping*. 2nd edition. Faber & Faber, London & Boston.

Jones, R. & Munn, P. (eds.) (1998) *Habitat Management for Wild Bees and Wasps*. International Bee Research Association, Cardiff.

Kirk, W. D. J. (2006) *A Colour Guide to Pollen Loads of the Honey Bee*. 2nd edition. International Bee Research Association, Cardiff.

Matheson, A. (ed.) (1994) *Forage for Bees in an Agricultural Landscape*. International Bee Research Association, Cardiff.

Matheson, A., Buchmann, S. L., O'Toole, C., Westrich, P. & Williams, I. H. (eds.) (1996) *The Conservation of Bees*. International Bee Research Association / Linnean Society / Academic Press.

Neumann, P. & Carreck, N. L. (2010) Honey bee colony losses. *Journal of Apicultural Research* 49(1): 1–6.

O'Toole, C. (2000) *The Red Mason Bee*. Osmia Publications, Loughborough.

O'Toole, C. & Raw, A. (1991) *Bees of the World*. Blandford Press, London.

Owen, J. (1991) *The Ecology of a Garden: The First Fifteen Years*. Cambridge University Press, Cambridge.

Proctor, M., Lack, A. & Yeo, P. (1996) *The Natural History of Pollination. New Naturalist Series 83*. Collins, London.

Prŷs-Jones, O. E. & Corbet, S. A. (2011) *Bumblebees. Naturalists' Handbooks 6*. 3rd edition. Pelagic Publishing, Exeter. [This book is useful for bumblebee identification]

Stace, C. (2010) *New Flora of the British Isles*. 3rd edition. Cambridge University Press, Cambridge. [This book is an advanced guide for identification of wild plants]

Tautz, J. (2008) *The Buzz about Bees. Biology of a Superorganism*. Springer-Verlag, Berlin.

Willmer, P. (2011) *Pollination and Floral Ecology*. Princeton University Press, Princeton and Oxford.

Winston, M. (1991) *The Biology of the Honey Bee*. Harvard University Press, Cambridge, USA.

SOCIETIES PROVIDING INFORMATION ABOUT BEES AND BEEKEEPING IN THE BRITISH ISLES

Bees, Wasps and Ants Recording Society (BWARS). A society dedicated to studying and recording bees, wasps and ants (aculeate Hymenoptera) in Britain and Ireland.
www.bwars.com

British Beekeepers' Association (BBKA). An association that works to promote bees and beekeeping and to provide a range of member services to UK beekeepers. National Beekeeping Centre, Stoneleigh Park, Kenilworth, Warwickshire CV8 2LG, UK.
www.bbka.org.uk

Bumblebee Conservation Trust (BBCT). A trust that aims to prevent further declines, and to raise awareness of the problems bumblebees face. School of Biological & Environmental Sciences, University of Stirling, Stirling FK9 4LA, UK.
www.bumblebeeconservation.org.uk

Hymettus. A source of advice on the conservation of bees, wasps and ants within Great Britain and Ireland.
www.hymettus.org.uk

International Bee Research Association (IBRA). An international association that provides information on bee science and beekeeping. 16 North Road, Cardiff CF10 3DY, UK.
www.ibra.org.uk

Scottish Beekeepers' Association (SBA). The national body that represents Scotland's beekeepers within the UK, throughout Europe and globally.
www.scottishbeekeepers.org.uk

The Federation of Irish Beekeepers' Associations (FIBKA). An organisation that represents 53 local member beekeeping associations in Ireland.
www.irishbeekeeping.ie

Ulster Beekeepers' Association (UBKA). An association of the 10 affiliated local beekeeping associations in Northern Ireland.
www.ubka.org

Welsh Beekeepers' Association (WBKA). An association that keeps Welsh beekeepers informed and represents 19 local member beekeeping associations.
www.wbka.com

Information and artificial nests for mason, leafcutter and carder bees

CJ Wildbird Foods Ltd., The Rea, Upton Magna, Shrewsbury SY4 4UR, UK.
www.birdfood.co.uk

GLOSSARY

Terms that are used in the descriptions of plants and bees are explained below. The parts of the flower are illustrated on p.18.

Annual: A plant that lives for one year.

Anther: The flower structure that releases pollen. Anthers are at the end of stamens. Bees usually collect pollen from the anthers.

Biennial: A plant that lives for two years.

Calyx: All the sepals of the flower form the calyx.

Cultivar: An abbreviation of 'cultivated variety'. A form of a plant that has been selected for desirable characteristics that can be maintained by propagation. Many garden plants are sold as named cultivars with the cultivar name in quotation marks, e.g. *Pulmonaria* 'Blue Ensign'.

Herb: This is the botanical term for a herbaceous plant or one that dies down at the end of each year and has few or no woody stems above ground.

Nectar: A sugar-rich solution that is secreted by plants. Its usual function is to attract animals, typically bees, to the flowers and as a result bring about pollination. The high sugar content means it is an excellent source of energy for bees.

Nectary: A structure that secretes nectar. They are usually inside flowers near the base. A few plants have **extrafloral nectaries**, which are nectaries outside flowers and their usual function is to defend the plant against being eaten, because they attract predators, such as ants, that attack plant-eating insects.

Ovary: A part of the pistil. The structure at the base of the flower that eventually becomes the fruit. The ovules within the ovary develop into seeds.

Perennial: A plant that lives for more than two years.

Pistil: The 'female' flower structure at the centre of a flower. It consists of an ovary, a style and a stigma. A flower may have one or more pistils.

Petals: The visually obvious, often brightly coloured, parts of the flower that attract pollinators such as bees. They are usually enclosed by the sepals before the flower opens.

Pollen: Microscopic grains that are produced within anthers and transferred to stigmas within or between flowers as part of plant reproduction. They are rich in protein and so are highly nutritious to bees.

Pollination: The transfer of pollen from anthers to stigmas, either within a flower or between different flowers.

Proboscis: An elongate tubular mouthpart used for sucking up food. The tongue of a bee.

Sepals: Part of the flower that protects the bud before the flower opens. They are usually green and not very obvious once the flower has opened. However, in some species they are large and coloured and act like petals.

Stamens: The 'male' flower structures that produce pollen. They consist of a stalk with an anther at the tip.

Stigma: A part of the pistil. The receptive surface at the tip of the pistil where pollen grains land and germinate.

Stipules: The small leaf-like structures at the base of leaf stalks.

Style: A part of the pistil. The stalk-like structure that connects the ovary and the stigma.

INDEX

Note: page numbers in *italics* refer to photos, those in **bold** refer to tables.

Published by:
International Bee Research Association
16 North Road, Cardiff, CF10 3DY, U.K.

www.ibra.org.uk

©2012 International Bee Research Association

All rights reserved. No part of this publication may be reproduced
stored or transmitted in any form or by any means, electronically,
mechanically, by photocopying, recording, scanning or otherwise,
without the prior permission of the copyright owners.

ISBN–10: 0-86098-271-8
ISBN–13: 978-0-86098-271-5

Designed by www.stazikerjones.co.uk
Edited by Clare Christian
Printed and bound in Italy by Printer Trento Srl.

Printed on paper produced from sustainable sources.

This publication has been supported by funds from the Eva Crane Trust.